THE PATHOLOGY OF THINKING

PATOLOGIYA MYSHLENIYA

ПАТОЛОГИЯ МЫШЛЕНИЯ

The | International Behavioral Sciences | Series

Joseph Wortis, M. D.
Editor

THE PATHOLOGY
OF THINKING

by Blyuma Vul'fovna Zeigarnik

Foreword to the English edition by A. R. Luria

Authorized translation from the Russian by
Basil Haigh, M. A., M. B., B. Chir.

CONSULTANTS BUREAU
NEW YORK
1965

The translation was prepared with the support of grant #02679 to Dr. Joseph Wortis from the National Institute of Mental Health for the translation of Russian psychiatric literature.

The original text was published by the Moscow University Press in 1962.

Блюма Вульфовна Зейгарник

ПАТОЛОГИЯ МЫШЛЕНИЯ

Contents

Foreword

The pathology of thinking has always been one of the most complicated fields of psychology.

For a great many years a science of thinking hardly existed as an independent area in psychology: most frequently, a description of the logic of thought was substituted for an elucidation of its contents, while all research in this field came to nothing more than a description of associative communications. Nothing much was thus revealed about the laws governing thinking. Not until the beginning of the twentieth century did the psychology of thinking develop into a separate discipline. Even then, the content of this discipline was limited to the description of the basic forms of intellectual experience, logically derived emotions, and states of consciousness characteristic of complex intellectual activity.

Therefore, the appearance in Soviet psychology of studies which have advanced thinking as a special subject of scientific analysis may be considered an important step in the development of scientific psychology. Vygotskii has made important contributions within this field, having been the first to state the basic problems concerning the development of oral thought. Leont'ev and his co-workers have investigated the problem of the psychological structure of intellectual activity. Teplov has described definite thought formations. Finally, many more authors have studied various other aspects of intellectual activity. At present, an additional important study has been incorporated into this collection of research—the work of B. V. Zeigarnik, one of the most experienced Soviet psychologists, devoted to the pathology of thinking, a specific, yet extremely valuable, subject for research.

The deterioration of thought processes in various mental disorders has been studied extensively, and the psychiatric literature is replete with titles referring to the pathology of thinking. However, most of these investigations suffer from the following basic deficiency: the attempts at analyzing psychological categories are usually founded upon obsolete psychological theories, fundamental systems of ideas completely divorced from scientific psychology, or special ad hoc terminologies introduced by psychiatrists. Included in these psychiatric attempts at analyzing thought disturbances are the well-known descriptions by such authors as Kraepelin, Kleist, and Bleuler, among others. They have separated the study of disturbed thinking in mental patients from the psychological theory of the structure of intellectual activity and have conceived the changes which they have observed either as the result of deterioration of the flow of associations, as attention-span defects, or as memory disorders. Sometimes they regarded these changes as a direct consequence of disturbed abstractive ability. However, these attempts forced the observed facts into associationist schemes which have been out of date for a long time and proved completely incapable of reflecting all the wealth of material that is gathered in psychiatric practice. These descriptions of thought disturbance could not lend sufficiently strong support to psychopathology and did not make a valid contribution to the theoretical basis of the science of thinking. Thus, not infrequently, psychiatrists completely refused to undertake an investigation of pathological forms of thinking based upon scientific psychology. Attempting to describe specific systems of pathological thinking, they began to use terms derived from psychiatric practice, such as "depressed," "peculiar," "restrained," "evasive," and "derailed." To a certain extent these descriptions mirrored empirical facts, yet they did not lead to a really scientific study of thought disturbances, much less of their physiological mechanisms. Nonetheless, the exhaustive study of changes occurring in the thought processes in the presence of pathological brain conditions could contribute a great deal not only to the scientific study of mental disease, but also to the general advancement of psychological science itself. Pathological brain conditions can destroy some of the physiological conditions which are prerequisite for fully normal thinking. Such destruction may lead to various deteriorations in intellectual activity, and here "pathology ... shows us, by decomposing and simplifying, all that is hidden from view because it is encompassed and complicated by physiological norms," (Pavlov). In this fashion the normal structure of intellectual activity, too, becomes accessible to specialized study.

Dr. Zeigarnik's book is devoted to an attempt to present an analysis of the basic forms of thought disturbance which are encountered in mental disease. Her analysis is based upon ideas concerned with the structure of intellectual ability which have accumulated in present-day psychological research. The author's extensive experience in clinical psychological investigation over a period of almost a quarter of a century have enabled her successfully to undertake so complex a task.

The material is presented in broad and general terms and in a logical fashion.

Thought is always based on a definite system of ideas. These ideas make it possible to reflect reality in general and abstract forms. We have attained this system of abstraction and generalization through the development of the system of language. Language communicates experiences common to all human beings and permits man to penetrate beyond the boundary of immediate realistic impressions. In some forms of pathological mental activity (for instance, in mental retardation or in organic dementia) the ability to acquire this complex system or to make use of it becomes impaired. The patient finds himself incapable of performing the necessary intellectual operations with the degree of abstraction and generalization indispensable to normal thinking. Such a defect leads to inadequate abstractive processes in object-classifying operations. The ability to comprehend the system of communication of thought and to analyze logical relationships is equally inadequate. In the system of ideas, abstract (categorical) forms are replaced by concrete, situation-determined relationships, spontaneous ideas about objects and occurrences predominate over complex, abstract forms of communication, and thinking acquires a simplified, concrete, situation-determined character. Such impairment in the structure of thinking is encountered in a great many oligophrenics, as well as in numerous patients suffering from organic brain damage.

In other cases, this impairment of the normal system of abstraction and generalization may manifest itself in a contrasting manner. On the basis of some still insufficiently clarified causes, the thought-communication system becomes severed from the experience of reality. The vitally important properties of objects are no longer distinguished from the incidental and even extraneous ones. Communication becomes confused and muddled, since chance associations play as important a role as do those associations strengthened by the experience of reality; communication loses its selective features.

Such disturbance of the communication system basic to all thinking is most pronounced in schizophrenia. An analysis of both aspects in the impairment of the basic "code" system used in thought processes comprises the first section of Dr. Zeigarnik's most interesting book.

It would be quite incorrect, however, to reduce all possible aspects of pathological thinking exclusively to changes in the basic codes of which they are formed.

The process of thinking represents a type of intellectual activity consisting of a series of successive operations directed toward the solution of various tasks. Thinking is always subordinated to a specific aim and must always take into account conditions under which such an aim may be achieved. Also, it involves a number of processes which help achieve the proper aims. In order to successfully perform this intellectual activity, one must not only fix upon a given aim but also must constantly effect a complex organization of processes in order to achieve it. In order to successfully perform intellectual operations one must simultaneously and constantly regulate the entire process involved in solving a task by retaining adequate communication systems and discarding inadequate and unessential ones. Accordingly, successful completion of a complex task involves the step-by-step appraisal and, if necessary, correction of each individual intellectual operation. The peculiar nature of the performance of such structurally complex intellectual activity requires much more than the mere description of the system of ideas basic to thinking; it necessitates the structural and dynamic characterization of a concrete intellectual act.

The second part of Dr. Zeigarnik's book is therefore devoted to an analysis of the various manifestations of disturbances in the structure and dynamics of intellectual activity.

The author begins her analysis of certain singular pathological changes in intellectual activity by describing dynamic disturbances in thought processes that may occur in unstable conditions of brain activity, in particular, when nervous processes become weak, leading to changes in logical flow of thinking.

These thought disturbances may arise against the potentially hidden background of manifestations of abstraction and generalization; they emerge as a result of pathological changes in the dynamics of nervous processes and they permit further investigation of those pathophysiological conditions which lead to changes in intellectual activity. They develop most strongly when certain factors are present which facilitate the observation of derangement of normal powers, such as stability and mobility in basic nervous processes.

Dr. Zeigarnik dwells particularly on the instability of the logical flow of thinking that becomes particularly evident in pathological weakening of the control processes. She describes the "flight of ideas" which is characteristic of those violently insane patients typified by rapid shifts in communication and levels of abstraction and a slight loss of selectivity. She describes the phenomena of thought "tenacity," clearly seen especially in epileptics, which is characterized by a deficient mobility of nervous processes. She presents a detailed analysis of the following forms of disturbance: the inability to solve tasks, to grasp situations intelligently, and to classify objects. These disturbances develop as a result of "sluggish" nervous processes. Finally, the author describes at length a particular form of thought disturbance which she calls "respondency" (not a well-chosen term); its chief characteristic is that when a patient's orienting reactions are pathologically agitated, he is not able to retain firmly the entire flow of ideas within the boundaries of a previously conceived situation. Each unessential stimulus easily destroys this important communication system and the further flow of associations is subordinated to outside influences.

The best sections of the book are those which present a description of all the aspects of disturbed thought dynamics as they appear in pathologically decreased brain activity; uniting a fine psychological description of pathologically deteriorated thought manifestations with an analysis of their possible pathophysiological mechanisms, the author has clarified very intelligibly the importance which clinical psychological research carries for the study of the flow of basic thought mechanisms.

The last section of this interesting monograph is dedicated to structural and dynamic thought disturbances. These are perhaps of special interest, and their study has occupied a large number of authors during the last ten years. Here we are dealing with an aspect of the structural deterioration of intellectual activity as a whole, which the author describes as a "disturbance of goal-directed thought." Some individual elements of these pathological manifestations may be seen in cases where there is impairment in the normal tone of brain activity, as has been described above;

in special forms of brain pathology, however, as well as in cases of partial damage of the frontal lobes, it is seen even more clearly and distinctly.

As has been already pointed out, thinking is the most complex self-regulating form of mental activity. It is task-determined and involves a continuous unification of the results of individual processes according to the overall aim; the rectification of incorrect steps develops on the basis of such unification. It is this continuous process of unification that gives intellectual activity its selective, self-regulating characteristic.

Such a process thus presupposes a most complex network of communications. One of its apparatuses is the ability to organize intellectual activity; another is the "reverse afferentation" apparatus which is always in action. Without these apparatuses it would be impossible to evaluate adequately individual operations (least of all to correct them). All experimental data indicate an impairment in the communications network in psychopathological cases. Cases involving damage of the frontal lobes of the brain exemplify this fact most clearly.

Dr. Zeigarnik devotes a special section of her book to the analysis of thought disturbances which develop in these pathological cases. She most justifiably isolates two basic manifestations. The first involves the decrease of needs or intentions that develops in such cases and that leads to instability of action while the directing force of such action disappears altogether; the second peculiarity of these thought disturbances is an impairment of the critical evaluation of the results of one's own activity, leading to the disappearance of regular controls in the normal flow of thought processes. The ability to correct permissible errors also disappears at the same time.

The symptoms of impairment in goal-directed thinking are evident in all such patients' performances of tasks; this impairment impedes the normal course of all forms of intellectual activity. Here, in particular, the disturbance of the linguistic system's regulating role becomes quite clear; during recent years it has been studied extensively in Soviet psychology.

We still know very little about the physiological basis of this aspect of thought disturbance; however, the description of its occurrence is of great importance in the light of the existing interest in self-regulating biological systems, which have for a long time been intimately connected with the study of mental systems.

Dr. Zeigarnik describes in detail those changes in the thought processes due to (1) an impairment of stability of purpose controlling the subsequent flow of thoughts or (2) an impairment of critical evaluation of incorrect results of the intellectual act. In doing so she has greatly enriched the psychological study of intellectual activity itself.

The various forms of thought disturbance which are observed in a psychiatric clinic are extremely complex and do not lend themselves easily to an exact analysis. Also, on the basis of such cases it is not feasible to carry out a study of isolated factors which determine the pathological changes of thought. It would be of great help to study cases in which the changes of thought processes are produced by some specific foci forming isolated disturbances in separate sections of brain activity leading to sharply delineated forms of thought impairment. The recently published studies by Pribram* point in this direction, as do other investigations by the author of the present volume.

Nevertheless, despite all the complexity of the material, Dr. Zeigarnik was able to trace the basic forms of possible thought disturbances and to give a fine description of them; this alone is of great promise for future work. Further studies along these lines should yield a practical psychological method for the experienced investigator. There is no doubt that Dr. Zeigarnik's book will be read with the same interest and profit by specialists in the field of psychopathology and by psychologists, both of whom, by studying changes occurring in pathological mental processes, hope to find new and important data upon which to build a theory of man's mental activity.

A. R. Luria

*Pribram, Karl H., "On the Neurology of Thinking." Behavioral Science, Vol. 4, pp. 265-287 (1959).

Preface

This book is intended as a textbook for students of psychology, for prospective specialists in the field of abnormal psychology, and also for psychologists working in psychiatric clinics.

A course on the pathology of thinking was first introduced in the Psychology Department of the Faculty of Philosophy of Moscow University in connection with the training of a number of students in practical work in the field of abnormal psychology. Until now there has been no textbook for use with this course. The author's book, "Thinking Disturbances in Mental Patients," (1958) is not entirely satisfactory for use as a textbook by students in the psychological division, for it discusses the problems of the pathology of thinking on the basis of the practical experience of.the medically trained psychiatrist.

The present book includes full details of the course of lectures and practical work prepared by the author for students of the psychological division of the Faculty of Philosophy of Moscow University since 1949. At the same time it makes reference to the material of the author's doctoral dissertation, which was concerned with a similar topic.

The material forming the basis of the views expressed in this book consists of the results of experimental psychological investigations conducted by the author and her co-workers in the psychological laboratory of the State Research Institute of Psychiatry, Ministry of Health of the RSFSR, located at the Gannushkin Psychoneurological Hospital, and also in the psychological laboratory of the neurosurgical hospital in which was located, during World War II, a branch of the clinic for nervous diseases of the All-Union Institute of Experimental Medicine.

I wish to express my gratitude to the staffs of these institutions, who rendered me considerable help in the clinical analysis of the material. My sincere thanks are due to my collaborator in the psychopathology laboratory, Candidate of Pedagogical Sciences S. Ya. Rubinshtein, for her invaluable help with the psychological analysis of the material. Finally, I am grateful to F. A. Sokhin for his exceptional care in the editing of the text.

The Author

Introduction

Disturbances of thought are observed in patients with mental diseases. The pathology of thinking is a section of abnormal psychology, concerned with the study of the principles underlying the mental disturbances arising in diseases of the brain. The findings of abnormal psychology are becoming increasingly important in psychiatric practice. Soviet psychiatry, which has developed on the foundations of Pavlov's materialistic teaching, calls for objective methods of investigation, among which we include those of experimental psychology.

The need of physicians for a knowledge of the fundamentals of psychological science was originally mentioned by Sechenov. "In light of the trend of the modern schools of psychology to bring this subject more and more into line with the physiology of the brain, this science is clearly becoming the basis of psychiatry," he wrote to Bokova in 1876, marking the beginning of his creation of medical psychology, which he called his "swan song."

The use of psychological theories and of experimental data has been traditional among Russian psychiatrists. For example, Kandinskii, one of the leading Russian psychiatrists of the nineteenth century, wrote: "The general conclusions of scientific psychology are essential for psychiatrists, for the mind, even when disturbed, does not cease to be the mind. Rational psychiatry must be based on psychology." [126].

All the great Russian psychiatrists began their courses of instruction in psychiatry with the fundamentals of psychology. When beginning his first lecture in 1891 to the students of Moscow University, Korsakov stated: "Before we can recognize what is sick in a person we must study what is healthy in him; we must familiarize ourselves with the normal manifestations of mental life." [145].

1

Psychological laboratories and clinics for nervous and mental diseases have existed in Russia since the 1880's (among the earliest we may note Tokarskii's laboratory at Korsakov's clinic, Telyatnikov's, and later Osipov's, laboratory at Bekhterev's clinic, Bernshtein's laboratory at Serbskii's clinic, and others). From Bekhterev's psychiatric clinic alone, more than ten doctoral dissertations on experimental psychological themes have been published.

Korsakov, in particular, promoted the development of experimental psychology in association with clinical psychiatry. Under his direction and with his close participation, a psychological laboratory was organized in 1894, with Tokarskii at its head. Korsakov demonstrated the vital need for collaboration between psychology and psychiatry. In his condemnation of Lopatin, who rejected experimental methods in psychology, Korsakov stated that the main question was not whether experimental psychology was necessary at all, but rather why the existence of psychological laboratories in clinics had gone unnoticed until that time [48].

After the Great October Revolution the relative importance of psychopathological investigation in psychoneurological institutions rose considerably (see [117]). A complete system of experimental methods firmly established in psychiatric and neurological clinical practice was developed. Experimental psychological laboratories developed in Moscow (Vygotskii, Luria, and their co-workers), in Leningrad (Myasishchev and his co-workers), in Khar'kov (Lebedinskii), and elsewhere. Soviet psychologists, working in psychoneurological institutions, made an important contribution to our understanding of disturbances of mental activity.

A short time ago (during 1951-1955), for no good reason, the association between investigations in the field of psychiatry and psychology was temporarily severed. Attempts were even made to provide a theoretical explanation for this development. For example, it was suggested that in psychopathological analysis the use of psychological concepts—such as "perception," "memory," or "intelligence," which were declared to be fictitious—should be abandoned [21].

This rejection of psychology and the attempts to restrict the objective trend in the field of psychiatry to pathophysiological analysis arose as a result of an incorrect, antihistorical interpretation of some of Pavlov's statements. We know, of course, that

Pavlov tenaciously and rightly criticized the contemporary idealistic movement in psychology, but not psychology in general.

Psychology studies the fundamental principles of the various forms of reflection of the outside world: perception, ideas, thinking, the senses, and so on. In clinical practice distortions of this reflective activity of the brain are observed. Such distortions include false perceptions or hallucinations, intellectual disturbances, sensory defects, etc. The psychiatrist cannot identify a patient's mental disturbances without a knowledge of the principles governing perception, memory, thinking, etc., in normal conditions. The attempt to study mental disturbances in isolation from the facts of general psychology is tantamount to rejection of the dialectical-materialistic concept of the mind as a reflection of the outside world. Failure to appreciate the material character of this reflection is a distortion of the reflex principle of Sechenov and Pavlov. Experience shows that to disregard the facts of materialistic psychology leads psychiatrists unwittingly to employ the concepts of idealistic psychology.

Psychology itself suffered no less from the above-mentioned short-lived rupture between psychiatry and psychology. Since it is a field of practical application of the theoretical and experimental data of psychology, psychiatry, as is the case with any practical discipline, not only utilizes but also contributes to psychological theory. Without the use of the facts of the breakdown of mental activity, psychology is deprived of much of its essential material.

The problem of the necessity of strengthening the bonds between psychology and psychiatry has now been satisfactorily solved—at any rate, in principle. However, another problem has arisen: Must the connection between psychology and psychiatry be manifested simply by deep general awareness on the part of psychiatrists of the concepts of modern psychology; or can it perhaps be brought forth as an independent, border region of science—psychopathology—having its own objects and methods? The tendency has recently been observed in the various sciences for "border regions" to be formed, and such regions (or interdisciplinary approaches) have proved to be highly productive.

One group of psychiatrists insists upon the former solution. Recognizing that a knowledge of psychological principles is essential for the analysis of psychopathological phenomena, they claim that psychiatry must "assimilate" psychological concepts, and that it may restrict itself to them. This point of view has its adherents among the psychiatrists of the capitalist countries, especially among those who are phenomenologically oriented. Such a view of the role of psychology in clinical practice is particularly acceptable to the group of psychiatrists who regard disturbances of mental activity as disturbances of some form of "mental essence." In this respect they share the view of Spranger, the creator of idealistic, "understanding" psychology, who postulated that while nature must be explained, the mind need only be understood. Other psychologists (for example, Binswanger [371]) adhere either to the rather similar principles of existential psychology which deal with "reflex consciousness," or to the concepts of Freud.

A proportion (though admittedly small) of Soviet psychiatrists also believe that the psychiatrist may confine himself to the assimilation of modern psychological concepts.

Naturally, we can only welcome this desire for familiarization with the data of materialistic psychology, although this cannot evidently be the end of the matter. Mastery of the fundamental principles of materialistic psychology may prove adequate and fruitful in certain fields of psychiatric practice—for example, in psychotherapy. However, in the most important branch of psychiatric science, psychopathology, when the evaluation of the degree of the patient's intellectual deterioration is involved, knowledge alone is insufficient, for it does not provide the psychiatrist with the necessary tool of an objective method of investigation.

It was not by chance that the joint efforts of the psychologist and the psychiatrist over a period of many years led to the separation from the wide field of medical psychology (which includes psychotherapy and occupational therapy) of a special branch dealing with experimental psychopathology, with its own material and methods.

The material of psychopathology consists of disturbances of mental activity, or, in other words, disturbances of the reflection of the outside world as a result of disease of the brain. Whereas general psychology studies, for example, the principles of intelligence and its formation, psychopathology studies the principles of its disintegration. Whereas general psychology investigates the regulating role of speech in the formation of voluntary movements, psychopathology shows the forms of disintegration of skilled movements resulting from a weakening of the regulating role of speech.

Consequently, psychopathology is a branch of psychological science which deals with certain problems arising from psychiatric practice. Psychopathological investigations cannot be undertaken in isolation from clinical problems, and they must conform to the concrete situations confronting the clinician.

Like all applied branches of science, psychopathology lies on the borderline between two sciences and takes its material from both: it is guided by the principles of modern materialistic psychology and psychiatry and is devoted to the service of practice. The methods of psychopathology may now be briefly discussed.

Like general psychology, psychopathology utilizes experimental methodology. In clinical practice, experimentation is usually limited to work with animals; this is adequate for investigating, for example, the mechanisms of the action of certain drugs. In general psychology, on the other hand, experimental methods, using human subjects, attempt to evoke definite responses or decisions under the influence of definite conditions.

Experiment makes it possible to advance from the description of a fact to the analysis of the principles underlying its appearance. For example, if a patient shows impairment of memory, experiment will allow an analysis of the structure of his memory loss. Experiment reveals that the loss of memory arises in some cases when the conditions of work require a great concentration of effort, while in other cases the defect is caused by changes in the patient's attitude to his work.

What may be achieved by the use of psychological investigation in the field of clinical psychiatry? Some of its more important objectives may be mentioned:

(1) The results of experimental psychological investigation may be used by the clinician for the purpose of differential diagnosis. Although a diagnosis cannot be made on the basis of laboratory investigations alone, the wealth of experimental data accumulated in psychological laboratories concerning the nature of the disturbances of mental processes in various diseases, provides additional criteria upon which to base the diagnosis.

(2) The results of psychological investigation may be applied to the analysis of the structure of mental disorders.

(3) Psychological investigations may help to determine the degree of impairment of patients' mental activity. The need for this is especially clear both during the evaluation of the effectiveness of the latest methods of treatment and in the

course of disability evaluation for occupational or medico-legal purposes.

The experimental psychological investigations in the clinical field deal not only with the theoretical analysis of various mental disturbances and their comparison with normal mental processes, but also with the development of special experimental methods adapted to the needs of clinical psychiatry. These methods will be useful only when based on correct theoretical foundations. Disregard of the theoretical principles underlying experimental results is bound to lead to a primitive eclecticism or to empiricism.

Besides their applied importance, the results of psychological investigation may also contribute to the solution of general problems in psychology. A correlation of an analysis of the principles of disintegration of mental activity with our knowledge of the principles of its development will add considerably to our general understanding of the genesis of mental processes. The area of the pathology of thinking occupies a central position in the solution of these theoretical problems. The psychologist working in the clinical field must not only be familiar with the various types of intellectual disturbances, but he must be able to analyze and interpret experimental findings as well. This is no easy task, as psychopathology is to some extent still a frontier region of science.

The history of science shows that, while these frontier regions are usually highly productive, they are at the same time difficult to investigate. Each of psychopathology's contiguous sciences is based upon different conceptual systems, even though they may possess similar vocabularies. For example, the concept of "consciousness" has different meanings in philosophy, in psychology, and in psychiatry. Concepts such as the disintegration of intellectual activity, "reasoning," etc., are not used in psychology; the psychological term "criticality" has a somewhat different meaning in psychiatry.

This book will familiarize students and clinical psychologists with the different variants of intellectual disturbance, with the methods used in psychopathological laboratory practice, and with the theoretical principles of psychopathology.

PART I

THE PROBLEM AND METHODS OF INVESTIGATION

Chapter 1

The Problem of the Pathology of Thinking

1. PHENOMENOLOGY OF DISORDERS OF THINKING IN THE TRADITIONAL VIEW

Little has been written with special reference to the general problems of the psychopathology of thinking. At the same time, nearly every paper written on a clinical problem contains at least some statements relating to disturbances of thought, for clinicians usually study these disturbances only as they relate to more specific problems arising out of clinical practice: the bases for establishment of the differential diagnosis; the principle of the classification of mental diseases; the reversibility of intellectual disorders, etc. However, despite the varied and conflicting nature of the investigations to be described below and, in some cases, the spuriousness of their methodological principles, many valuable and positive facts have been obtained in the field of the phenomenonology of disorders of thinking.

The main achievement of these investigations must be considered to be the identification of types of disturbance of intellectual activity associated with different diseases. This process of differentiation and classification, which began during the earliest days of the existence of the science of psychiatry, is the "trunk road" along which scientific thinking in the field of psychiatry has progressed. Wonderful descriptions of intellectual activity in the schizophrenic, the general paretic, and the epileptic patient are to be found in the works of Geier, Gruhle, Gilyarovskii, Gurevich, Zhislin, Kerbikov, Korsakov, Kraepelin, Osipov, Sereiskii, Simson, Snezhnevskii, Sukhareva, Jaspers, and others. These descriptions, which remain valuable even today, are so typical, so complete, and reflect so vividly the principal psychopathological features of the thinking of patients in the various categories, that they have virtually provided the psychiatrist with labels for the establishment of his diagnosis.

If we turn to the description of the intellectual activity of patients with epilepsy, we find that all investigators characterize it as slow and sluggish; their spoken expressions are distinguished by a profusion of details of little or no meaning. All writers remark on the narrow circle of associations present in these patients. Sukhareva describes the intellectual activity of an epileptic child as follows: "His interests are narrow and simple. In intellectual work he is slow and helpless in problems requiring reasoning. He grasps a new problem with difficulty; he understands verbal material but forgets the essential words and replaces them with long descriptions and enumerations. His memory is poor, his attention narrow and unstable. His associations are poor and unvaried." [308; 1, 332].

Osipov [216] notes that, in patients with epilepsy, association is slow and difficult, reasoning ability is lowered, the range of interests is narrowed, and a tendency to pedantry and excessive attention to detail is present; these patients perform more accurately than do healthy persons on problems calling for perseverance and attention, but simple in nature (for example, underlining letters or the proof-reading test).

Il'in [122] points out that the range of knowledge of epileptic patients is narrowed. Bleuler [376], Samt [468], and Jung note the following additional characteristics: sluggishness of thinking, a poverty of association with a tendency toward unconscious repetition, a narrowing of interests, and a particularly enhanced affective evaluation of the surroundings. Their speech is characterized as slow and full of interjections. Speech becomes less frequent with increasing intellectual deterioration; at times the patients cannot find the word to name an object. (This is a symptom of oligophrasia, which has been described by Bernshtein, Gilyarovskii, Gurevich, Samt, Kraepelin, and others.)

Changes in intellectual activity arise in an equally clear and precise form in the diseases associated with senility. In these conditions a marked impairment of reasoning and a poverty of associations are observed. The patients lose the ability to form new mental connections, and their awareness of their surroundings becomes limited; they cease to keep in touch with more recent events. Meanwhile, these patients still remember events in their childhood. They conceive of their surroundings in terms of those in which they lived many years previously (Alzheimer, Gilyarovskii, Geier, Zhislin, Kahlbaum, Lyusternik, Pick, Snezhnevskii, and others). The disintegration of intellectual activity in patients of this type is classed by clinicians as amnestic dementia, i.e., as dementia based on memory disturbances. Gilyarovskii [68] describes in his lectures an elderly patient who, when in a hospital, imagined that she had just been washing her "old master's" clothes and was worried that somebody had stolen the things that she "had just hung out to dry."

The intellectual activity of the schizophrenic patient is very clearly described in the psychiatric literature. These accounts are so consistent that they may be taken as clichés, so that the psychiatrist who encounters similar intellectual disturbances in the course of his practice will usually assume that the diagnosis is one of schizophrenia. In every textbook it is stated that these patients show a tendency to overreason or moralize, to make sterile decisions, and to indulge in fruitless hairsplitting.

Korsakov [144] states that these patients aspire to discover a causal link between random, unconnected subjects, conditions, or events. As an example he cites the statement of a patient who was carefully considering the following problems: "Why is this object shaped like this, and that object like that? Why is this person short in stature, why is he small, why isn't he as tall as this room? Why aren't people taller than they are?"

Zalmanzon describes the intellectual activity of patients with schizophrenia as distinguished by pretentiousness and a tendency toward schematization and stylization; a fine grasp of details is interwoven with an inability to understand and express the structure of the whole [93, 94]. Patients speak about simple things in an excessively pretentious style, attaching particular significance to certain words.

In many cases patients with schizophrenia exhibit a block or interruption (Sperrung) of their thoughts; thinking is suddenly suspended. French writers point out that, besides this interruption of thought, a profusion or flood of thought is often observed (mentisme). The patient is apparently compelled, as Gurevich and Sereiskii [77] state, "to abandon himself against his will to thinking."

Most psychiatrists stress the symbolic nature of the patient's intellectual activity. He interprets his surroundings incorrectly and peculiarly, and any unimportant event or phenomenon acquires a special meaning. In a textbook of forensic psychiatry [302] the following example is given: "The patient asserts that he will soon die. Having been given four oranges, one of which was bad, he says that the meaning of this is as follows: 'There are four in our family; I shall soon be rotting in my grave,'" Korsakov cites the example of a patient who, on seeing a cloud in the sky, decided that it was a symbol of "forthcoming danger." When somebody spat on the ground, the patient felt that he had done so "to show his contempt." [144].

This tendency to symbolism is sometimes combined with an excessive concreteness of thought. Domarius cites the example of a patient who, when asked by the doctor to give him his hand, replied: "Why should I give you my hand? I should then have to walk without a hand." [394].

All the textbooks and specialized reports describe the illogicality of the patients' decisions and judgments, at times amounting to the disintegration of thought. Gilyarovskii points out in his lectures that the individual thoughts of the schizophrenic patient "not only have no logical connecting thread, but they are not joined at all and do not form the parts of a whole, directed to the particular goal of an act. The patients show a tendency to superficial associations: combinations of rhythmic words appear in their speech, and they flit from one idea to another on the basis of random stimuli. The patients slip from the main course of their reasoning into side issues. Often such patients have a tendency to form associations of contrast." [68; 58–59].

Gurevich and Sereiskii cite the following example of the disintegration of a patient's intellectual activity: "I am descended from Diogenes, for Diogenes searched with a lantern and I consider that this is rubbish." [77; 315–316]. Kerbikov also cites the case of a schizophrenic patient who said: "I have to sit on the washstand because some archimandrites have left me a legacy." [129; 143].

The following example of disintegrated intellectual activity can be found in a textbook of forensic psychiatry: "22 billion, pancakes in lemon... 65 wagons at a time in one grave... evil company... you warm the globe with an awl." Another patient declared: "If I am Napoleon, I must not love; if I am Alexander the First, the court physician is not my physician. When I was with a body, which is Schiller, I would be satisfied." [302].

Bleuler [376] uses the following words in order to illustrate the disintegrated thinking of these patients: "The impression is created that concepts of a particular category are collected in one pot, shaken up, and the first one to fall out is chosen."

The speech disturbances in schizophrenia sometimes assume a form resembling aphasia (schizophasia). Lebedinskii [161] illustrates this with a letter written by a schizophrenic patient: "You want to write one, but there is no beginning anywhere, no end, and no middle. What is there? A wheel within a wheel, a 'fedormic' (a combination of her married and maiden names) wheel, a devilish wheel, a fedormic breed, a 'fedormir' (fedor world), a 'plombir' (a fruit pudding), I am very fond of plombir."

In more malignant forms of schizophrenia, inane combinations of phrases and words are observed. As an example, we may cite the written words of a patient: "On the strength of reliable and irrefutable documentary evidence of the receipt of the vital and to the transfer of the powerful, which may be characterized as receiving with hermetically closed ears and two and one-half figs below the nose, I remain completely and much too unwilling and I dare, by screwing up my courage, arising in the right respiratory heart, to remain...." [302].

Nearly all writers note the peculiar construction of phrases and the tendency to coin words (neologisms). The tempo of speech is disturbed in many patients: in some there is a tendency to mutism and to slow, scanning speech; in others, the speech becomes much too rapid.

Many investigations of the disturbances of intellectual activity after brain injuries have been undertaken. The rapid onset of fatigue of the patients' intellectual processes has been observed (Geier, Gilyarovskii, Melekhov, Sukhareva, Povitskaya). The syndrome of rapid fatigue of the intellectual processes in brain injury has been analyzed in particular detail in investigations by clinical psychologists (Anikina, Gal'perina, Zeigarnik, Kogan, Kononova, Korobkova, Kostomarova, Shubert).

In comparing her clinical experimental findings with the results of her observations on patients in industry, Kostomarova found that fatigability leads to qualitative changes in intellectual activity. These changes may occur when the experimental task involves the ability to compare series of objects [147].

In their descriptions and evaluations of disturbances of intellectual activity in patients with traumatic lesions of the cerebral cortex, clinicians have been concerned with the problem of the reversibility or permanence of these disturbances. Whereas some writers accept the possibility that a permanent traumatic impairment of the intellect may arise (Geier, Golant, Dubinin, Osipov, Yudin), other investigators consider that, even when intellectual disturbances in brain injury are stable and permanent in character,

it should not be automatically concluded that dementia is present
(Leshchinskii, Melekhov, Povitskaya).

* * *

The comparison between general disturbances of intellectual
activity and the particular syndrome of each type of disease was the
principal, but not the only line of investigation of the intellectual
disorders in mental patients. Many authors attempted to compare
the disturbances of thought with lesions of definite regions of the
brain.

Distinct syndromes were found to be characteristic of temporal,
of parietal, and of frontal lesions of the brain. Some investigators
(Gurevich, Luria, Shmar'yan, Yudin, Khoroshko) noted the comparative integrity of the intellectual processes in lesions of the
temporal and parietal regions of the brain, with disturbances of
intellectual activity occurring in lesions of the frontal lobes.

Particular attention was paid in all these investigations to the
so-called "frontal syndrome"—the syndrome resulting from lesions
of the frontal lobes—first described by Eleonora Welt in 1896.
During the period 1910–1914, a dispute as to the general location of
mental processes took place between the supporters of Munk and
Monakow, on the one hand, and on the other, the followers of
Anton, Goldstein, and Foerster. While the former group claimed
that mental processes are the result of the activity of the entire
cerebral cortex, the latter group of workers attempted to prove the
existence of specific mental disturbances characteristic only of
lesions of the frontal lobes. In this discussion, Goldstein advanced
the hypothesis that after wounds of the frontal lobes the "categorical
nature" of the patients' intelligence is disturbed [407]. Whereas in
every-day situations the behavior of patients with frontal lesions
appears to be undisturbed, these patients experience difficulty in
decision-making when confronted with new situations. These patients, according to Goldstein, are unable to distinguish between the
"background" and the "figure" and cannot identify the essential
features of the problem.

Kleist [428], the founder of the localization principle in its
most limited sense, associated intellectual disturbances with a
lesion of the convex surfaces of the forebrain.

The frontal syndrome was described in especially great detail
by Shmar'yan [343], who distinguished several types of intellectual

disturbances within this syndrome. He noted a loss of spontaneity of thought and a disturbance of the higher integrative functions in lesions of the convex regions of the cortex. A lesion of the basal portion of the frontal cortex, on the other hand, leads to a disturbance of critical appraisal while leaving the formal intellect intact.

Similar results are described in Rozinskii's monograph [252]. On the basis of the comparison of clinical and pathological data, he concludes that the convex parts of the cortex are associated with integrative intellectual activity. Massive disturbances of the emotions and the will, arising in patients with lesions of the frontobasal divisions of the brain, lead, in this author's opinion, to a loss of spontaneity of thought.

In our earlier writings [107, 108], we discussed the various types of disturbance of intellectual activity to be found in patients with frontal lobe lesions—ranging from slight manifestations of reduced spontaneity of thought to cases of gross dementia. These disturbances were associated with personality changes and with changes in the patient's attitude toward his environment.

Abashev-Konstantinovskii [5] states that in frontal-premotor lesions of the brain, changes in intellectual performance occur as a result of "pathological relationships between the automatic, on the one hand, and the conscious and volitional, on the other." One of his series of investigations was aimed at describing the various intellectual disturbances typical of the different diagnostic categories, while another group of investigations categorized the intellectual disturbances which they described according to the different parts of the brain in which lesions were observed.

This concludes our brief account of the phenomenology of disturbances of thought. The descriptions given in the textbooks and monographs are distinguished by their richness, their detail, and their vividness. Yet in their explanations of these intellectual disturbances, the psychiatrists of the past have used the obsolete notions of the idealistic psychological schools and of their eclectic combinations. We shall now examine the psychological theories which have been used to explain intellectual disorders.

2. PSYCHOLOGICAL THEORIES USED TO EXPLAIN INTELLECTUAL DISORDERS

Psychiatrists of the past tended for the most part to explain the disturbances of thought from the standpoint of "functional psychology," which regards mental processes as isolated, inborn faculties or functions. In doing so, they wished to show which functions, or which associations between functions, are disturbed in a given disease. Attempts were made to show that the disturbance of intellectual activity was based on a disturbance of two of the elements of the intellect—memory and attention. For example, the disturbance of the intellectual activity of epileptic patients was attributed to a disturbance of the associative faculties (Kraepelin, Heilbronner, Sereiskii). According to Osipov, the intellectual activity of these patients was lowered as a result of the extremely unstable function of attention. Still other investigators attributed this intellectual disturbance to a defect in the functioning of the memory (Gilyarovskii, Bershtein).

Intellectual disturbances in senile patients were attributed to a disturbance in the retention of perceived information. The nature of the intellectual disturbance was also regarded as a disturbance of memory (Gilyarovskii, Gurevich, Zhislin, and others).

Several authors (Golant, Gurevich, Gilyarovskii, Povitskaya) tended to attribute the disturbances of intellectual processes after brain trauma to disorders of attention.

These views may be regarded as attempts to differentiate between disturbances of thinking and disturbances of other cognitive processes. However, many authoritative psychiatrists subscribed to another, no less widespread doctrine, according to which intellectual disturbances arise as a result of a defect in the emotional-volitional sphere. In these circumstances affect and will were understood to be faculties analogous to attention and memory—constituent elements of intelligence. This point of view was particularly prominent in the analysis of the nature of schizophrenia and in the analysis of the so-called "basic disturbance" (Grundstörung).

Following the principles of the "understanding" psychology of Spranger [482] and the descriptive psychology of Dielthei, according to which nature must be explained but the mind only understood, certain German psychiatrists considered that schizophrenia is based on a deficiency of the "primarily acquired mental structure." In the clearest enunciation of this theory, proffered by Berze, this primary structure is known as the "tone of consciousness" (activity of the "ego"), which is disturbed in schizophrenia ("hypotonia of consciousness"). Although this "hypotonia of consciousness" is not readily observable (its existence being perceived only intuitively), it nevertheless determines the entire psychopathological symptomatology, including the disturbance of thought [369; 69].

These characteristics are similar to the views of Gruhle [411]. He defines the disturbance of thought in schizophrenia as a disturbance of the "tone," at the basis of which lies a disturbance of the activity of the personality. Another supporter of these ideas was Beringer [367], who introduced the concept of weakness of the "intentional arc" as the cause of the intellectual disturbances of the schizophrenic patient. Yet another was Stransky [486], who conceived the notion of "intrapsychic ataxia."

Disturbances of thought in schizophrenia were for a long time interpreted as secondary symptoms, as manifestations of disturbances of the special "activity" or "intentions" of the mind. In an article on the psychology of schizophrenia (in Vol. IX of Bumke's "Handbuch" [381]), Gruhle stated in metaphorical terms the view which for a long time determined the course of research into the nature of the thought processes of schizophrenic patients: "The machine remains intact, but it is partially or completely out of control." Thus, although the schizophrenic patient still performs intellectual operations directed toward practical actions and has retained full use of his memory and attention, he is nevertheless unable to integrate his individually correct conclusions.

The view was particularly widely held that the "basic disturbance" (Grundstörung) of the schizophrenic patient was his autism, which was held to be responsible for the disintegration of his intellectual activity. The problem of autistic intelligence was raised by the Swiss psychiatrist Bleuler [32]. We shall now discuss in some detail his monograph, which is specifically concerned with autistic thinking.

Bleuler contrasted concrete thought, which reflects the outside world, with autistic thoughts, which depends neither on the outside world, nor on logical principles, but which is determined instead by "affective demands." "Affective demands" were defined as the seeking of satisfaction and the avoidance of unpleasant experience.

Bleuler expressed this contrast in the following words: "Logical thought, corresponding to reality, is the intellectual reproduction of the associations which reality presents to us." Autistic thought, however, is controlled by desires and has nothing to do with logic or with reality. He then goes on to contrast logical and autistic thought in accordance with their genesis. He writes: "The weakening of the logical thought processes leads to the predominance of the autistic; this is all the more understandable since the logical, which operates with the aid of memory images, must be acquired by means of experience, whereas the autistic thought processes operate solely by inborn mechanisms."

Bleuler proffers a succinct, clear description of the structure of autistic thought: "Autistic thinking may utilize for its own ends material lacking any form of logical association. Associations based upon consonance, the random coincidence of any chance perceptions or ideas: these may take the place of logical associations. A large proportion of the material utilized by autistic intellectual activity derives from incompletely considered concepts, false identifications, condensations, flights of ideas, symbols deriving their value from real objects, and analogous abnormal psychisms. It is obvious however, that besides abnormal material, normal material and normal thought processes may also be used." [32; 73]. Noting its similarity to daydreaming, Bleuler found autistic thought to be most clearly manifested in schizophrenia, the most important symptom of which is the active rejection by the patients of the outside world and the predominance of the internal life.

Besides the autism of schizophrenics, Bleuler also describes autistic thought processes during dreams and daydreams, during waking in hysterics and healthy persons, and also in poetry, mythology, and in art in general. His fascinating and clearly written book contains some very interesting and (despite the presence of many false assumptions) clinically correct descriptions of many affectively based errors and distortions of intellectual processes which are involved in the formation of complex psychopathological phenomena, such as delirium. He offers interesting descriptions of the principal cases in which logical thought is weakened and the balance swings in favor of autistic intellectual activity: (1) in the child, who lacks the experience essential for the mastering of logical forms of thinking; (2) in questions outside our realm of knowledge; (3) in persons temporarily overwhelmed by strong emotions; (4) when associations are weakened—both in the dreams of the healthy person and in the state schizophrenia.

It is not our purpose here to give a critical analysis of the whole of Bleuler's clinical and psychopathological concepts, and we shall leave aside, as requiring special examination, the problem of the relationship between the concepts of Bleuler and Freud. The problem of the extent to which Bleuler remained uncritical of the pseudoscientific, speculative construction of Freud's psychoanalytical ideas must also receive special examination. We shall merely note that, despite the praise which Bleuler bestowed upon Freud, Bleuler himself remains incomparably closer than Freud to clinical reality and displays considerable restraint in evaluating the role of sexual inclinations. (He particularly challenged Freud's imputation of the importance of sex in children and in the mentally retarded.)

Let us now turn to some of Bleuler's views on thinking and its disturbances. The historical value of Bleuler's concepts can be seen in the fact that, in contrast to the formal intellectualistic psychology and psychopathology of his time, he stressed the affective basis of thought processes or, more precisely, the fact that the direction of thought is dependent on human needs.

The fact that Bleuler stresses the role of affective desires in thinking, and the fact that he associates the intellect with needs and desires (even though he confines his examination to one need, and to its biological level at that), constitute, in our opinion, an achievement rather than a failing of his book. Our principal objection to his concept of autistic thought is that it unjustifiably divides the "real" from the affectively based thought processes. Although he correctly points out that the former reflect the outside world and are regulated by it, he mistakenly isolates this principal form of thought from emotions, desires, and needs. Real human thinking (that which reflects the outside world) undoubtedly depends on human wants; intellectual activity, like any other human activity, is always directed toward the satisfaction of needs and always dependent on one's desires and feelings. It is, in fact, with the satisfaction of needs that the intellectual activity of man begins. This activity is at first purely practical (perceptual), and only later becomes theoretical.

However, whereas the desire for the satisfaction of his needs leads man to fundamentally correct cognition—to the objective, logically justified, rational reflection of the outside world, the same desires and the same needs may sometimes modify and distort the course of his thought, thereby giving rise to cognitive errors. A valuable feature of Bleuler's writings is his description of the affectively based errors arising in human thinking.* He makes a

---

*Unfortunately, the problem of affectively based errors of thought is hardly mentioned in the principal textbooks and monographs dealing with the psychology of thinking. Yet this problem is of enormous practical significance.

glaring error, however, in his attempt to distinguish that which is affectively based as the principal form of thinking, and to contrast it with an apparently indifferent and higher, extrasensory form of intellect—real or concrete thinking.

Bleuler's concept of autistic thought has a slightly different meaning: in addition to being affectively based, it is also egocentric, uncritical, and subjective, and is not amenable to correction by actual circumstances. It remains apparently in isolation, independent of the signals from the outside world, and is determined exclusively by one's subjective experiences—daydreams, inventions, desires, and fears. This type of thinking does not merely diverge from logical sequence; it does not obey the laws of logic at all—it is alogical.

Other errors arise from Bleuler's fundamentally incorrect concept of an artificial breach and antagonism between real (logical) and autistic (alogical) forms of thought. He thus misinterprets the genesis of these two apparently opposite forms of thought. Although, as has already been made clear, he correctly locates the genesis of man's real intellect in his individually formed experience, since the material of real thinking consists of the reproduction of associations provided by the outside world, Bleuler nevertheless incorrectly asserts that autistic thinking is due to natural mechanisms.

According to Soviet psychology's current understanding of the process of intellectual activity and its genesis, no natural mechanisms or forms of thought can exist. All man's cognitive activity, even the most elementary forms of sensory perception, is based on systems of conditioned connections formed since birth.

Bleuler's attempt to subdivide the single process of rational cognition into two genetically and structurally different forms of intellectual activity and to introduce into the psychopathological terminology the concept of autistic thinking (intelligence independent of the outside world) is absolutely wrong and arbitrary. The basic principle of Bleuler's system (besides a tinge of Freudianism, with its antireflex, intrapsychological interpretation of the causality of mental phenomena) is none other than functional psychology, which subdivides human mental activity into a series of isolated faculties.

In a radical extension of Bleuler's ideas, certain investigators attempted to subdivide disorders in thinking into those which are truly intellectual and those which are extraintellectual. Extraintellectual disorders would thus include all possible cases in which patients' errors in judgment occur as a result of affective disorders.   Hence, an exclusive concentration upon affectively based errors in thinking, although perhaps justified from the point of view of clinical psychiatry, leads to the deduction of imaginary solutions from the matching of isolated faculties and from indifferent and prejudiced reasonings.

Many investigators have thus attempted to resolve disturbances in thinking into disturbances of the functions of affect and will. Admittedly, another point of view has been suggested, according to which the disturbance in thinking was converted into a "basic disturbance" (Grundstörung); all the other psychopathological manifestations of schizophrenia were then derived from it (Akkerman [10] and others).

The theory of the existence of inborn, isolated functions also provides the basis of the explanations of the psychomorphologists, who assume that for each specific mental function there exists a separate brain center, and that a lesion of this area causes a disturbance of that function.   Without entering into the complicated problem of localization, we merely note that, by neglecting the neurodynamic and psychological analysis of disorders in thinking, these investigators arrive at oversimplified psychomorphological correlations.

A considerable influence was exerted by the Wurzburg school of thought, according to which thinking was attributed to a "mental essence," or "an internal mental act," independent of sensory images and divorced from perception and speech.   In consequence of this understanding of thinking, Jaspers, a proponent of German classical psychiatry, contrasted intellect with the act of thinking [422].   Whereas he defined thinking as the manifestation of intrapsychic activity, he regarded the intellect as the sum total of the faculties; memory, attention, and speech were looked upon as the "elements of intellect."   This subdivision is also found in Soviet psychiatry.   For example, in Gurevich and Sereiskii's textbook of psychiatry, we read: "The thinking processes, functionally speaking, are closely related to the nature of the intellect; nevertheless these two concepts are not identical.   When the intellect is undisturbed, as pathology shows, marked disturbances of thinking may nevertheless exist. Thinking represents intellect in action, a manifestation of intrapsychic activity; by using the intellectual powers, the thinking processes embrace the active components of intention, attention, affective tendency, and purposive orientation.   Hence, in contrast to intellect, which is stable within certain limits and capable of

only slow variation (in the direction of development or impoverish-
ment), the thinking processes are dynamic: they change in accordance with various factors even in normal conditions, and show
especially marked, but not irreparable disturbances during pathological states. These changes in either direction (disintegration or
reintegration) may take place suddenly, or in steps." [77; 40]. Many
investigators have noted the simultaneous existence in a patient of an
intact intellect and impaired thought processes.

This distinction between intellect and thinking resulted in
attempts of investigators to seek a separate genesis for the disturbances in thinking in gross forms of organic disease and in schizophrenia. The disturbance of the cognitive processes arising in
severe organic diseases—for example, after trauma—were defined
as disturbances of the intellect, or of the "elements of the intellect";
the disturbances of the higher cognitive processes in schizophrenia,
on the other hand, were interpreted as disturbances of "true"
thinking.

Although the principles of idealistic psychology concerning inborn functions were the dominant explanatory principles used in the
analysis of intellectual disturbances, less noteworthy attempts at
explanation were made from the standpoint of Gestalt psychology.
According to the idealistic principles of Gestalt psychology, which
have been criticized by Pavlov, thinking is in itself incapable of
reflecting the outside world; it is merely a "state" in which a person
finds himself when perceiving an object. The motive of thinking is
attributed to a special property of the object—its "Prägnanz." This
property gives rise to internal connections directed toward transformation of the "bad" Gestalt into a "good" one, and this transformation takes place automatically, and only during perception.
Perception is a universal process which embraces both the material
object of thought and the thinking subject. The process of thinking
is thus reduced by the exponents of Gestalt psychology to an equili-
brium between dynamic forces and fields. Neither past experience,
nor acquired knowledge, nor speech plays a significant role in
thinking. Thinking is detached from the outside world and from
human practical activity. The qualitative features of human thought
processes are eliminated. As Vygotskii so clearly expresses it,
in Gestalt psychology there is no line of demarcation in principle
between human mental activity and the behavior of the earthworm.

Gestalt psychology has had some influence on the work of
psychiatrists and psychologists involved with the problem of the

pathology of thinking (Gadlich, Gelb, Goldstein). In our early investigations [102; 114] we attempted to explain the different forms
of intellectual disturbances from a Gestaltist frame of reference.
Such disturbances were described as "slips" in the "intellectual
field," or as disturbances of communications between systems under
stress. However, the principles of Gestalt psychology have had no
decisive influence on the investigations of Soviet psychiatrists and
psychologists.

* * *

A widely held view of the essence of psychopathological phenomena was that the mental activity of the psychiatric patient
represents regression to a phylogenetically earlier level. In this
connection various authors have tried to draw an analogy between
the thought processes of schizophrenics and those of primitive
peoples (Lévy-Bruhl [166]). Storch [485] and Schilder [471], for
example, considered that in schizophrenia there is a return to more
primitive and archaic methods of thinking; they point out the inadequate differentiation in the schizophrenic's thinking between the
"ego" and the surrounding environment. The patient's subjective
experiences are projected into the outside world, objective phenomena are perceived in private terms, and the outside world is
personified.

Some authors (Kretschmer, Blonskii, and others) have compared
the thought processes of schizophrenic patients with those of the
child at the age of puberty. This point of view, deriving from the
aforementioned theory of phylogenetic regression, tends to elimi-
nate the qualitative difference between the thought processes of the
healthy person and those of the psychiatric patient. We shall later
turn to a critical analysis of this concept.

In concluding this survey, we note that all past explanations of
disorders in thinking have been based on the conceptions of various
idealistic schools and are thus unacceptable to us. Even so, the
facts accumulated in psychiatric practice still provide a rich source
of material for research in both psychopathology and the psychology
of the cognitive processes. However, the collection of this material
has until now been purely empirical in character. The general
principles of the psychology of thinking have been used neither to
explain nor to classify thinking disorders. The undeveloped state of
psychopathological theory is one reason for psychiatrists' disillu-

sionment with the data from traditional psychology. On the other hand, a combination of the data of Marxist-Leninist philosophy and the modern Soviet psychology of thinking, based on this philosophy, would provide a useful contribution to the explanation of disorders of thinking.

3. MODERN DATA CONCERNING THINKING AND ITS DISORDERS

Soviet psychology defines thinking as the generalized and systematic reflection of reality. "Thinking may be defined as a generalized reflection of reality by the human brain, executed by means of speech and based on existing knowledge, intimately connected with sensory perception of the world and with human practical activity." [294; 245].

In describing the dialectical way of perceiving the objective world, Lenin wrote: "The dialectical road to the recognition of truth, to the recognition of objective reality, runs from living contemplation to abstract thought, and from these to practical activity." [4; 161]. Stressing the dialectical unity of the two stages of cognition, the exponents of classical Marxism—Leninism point out that it is in fact the rational stage which makes it possible to probe the essence of objects and events in nature and society. Lenin states that "... all scientific (true, serious, not trite) abstractions reflect nature more profoundly, more truly, more fully," [4; 161]. Consequently, rational cognition is not restricted to the reflection of the unique or the particular, but also reflects the most essential associations of reality. The process of cognition is characterized not only by the transfer from the sensory to the rational, but also by the fact that it must revert once again to practical activity. This process, which reflects the outside world most completely, becomes possible only through the existence of language, which, in Marx's words, is the "very essence of thought." [1; 448].

These general principles of Marxist—Leninist philosophy form the basis of the views of Soviet psychologists on the nature of mental processes, including thinking. Thinking is a special form of human behavior which develops in the course of practical experience, as man is faced with the necessity of solving problems.

To understand the nature of the processes involved in thinking, it is very important to investigate their genesis. Mental properties are formed in the course of ontogenetic development. Vygotskii's investigations aimed to refute the view that mental processes, including thinking, are internal mental properties, or self-contained mental functions. He repeatedly postulated that mental processes arise during group behavior and during social intercourse. In his words, "a function shared by two people becomes the internal psychological function of one person." [51]. Although he adhered to the correct, materialistic principle that mental processes are formed under the influence of the conditions of life of man in society, Vygotskii paid greater attention to the importance of the assimilation of socially developed ideas and concepts than to practical activity itself.

The view that mental activity is formed from external activity was developed most logically by Leont'ev [173] and Gal'perin [61]. In his writings, Gal'perin points out that any process of assimilation begins with a concrete action with objects. To justify this hypothesis he cites the results of an investigation of arithmetical operations in children. These operations (counting matches, for example) are performed initially in the form of an external action—a true manipulation of objects; subsequently, this process, which is accompanied by naming numbers, is modified: the movements of the hands give way to movements of the eyes, for the child no longer counts the matches by handling them but simply by looking at each of them. The child counts with the aid of external speech, but he later counts "to himself," "in his head."

Consequently, the process of assimilation of a mental operation begins with a concrete action with objects. Later the operation loses its character of an external action with objects and is assimilated into external speech, as a result of which it is abstracted from concrete objective conditions and acquires a more generalized character. In Gal'perin's words, a specific "contraction of the process" takes place, so that it becomes automatized and changed into a dynamic stereotype.

Leont'ev calls this factor the factor of formation of the mechanism of the corresponding mental function, and goes on to say that many links of the process become unnecessary, are not reinforced, become inhibited, and disappear. Together with this contraction of the process, a reinforcement of the corresponding reflex connections of the "reduced system" takes place.

Zaporozhets [99] cites this point of view on the basis of the experimental study of the formation of voluntary movements in the child. The regulation of movement takes place at an early age with the aid of uncontracted "finding-out" activity, which consists of a motor-tactile investigation of the situation. On the basis of the behavior, visual orientation develops, which does not require direct contact with the object. In the course of the formation of stable stereotypes of orienting reactions in the child, the conditions for higher forms of movement control are satisfied. "These particular stereotypes are associated with speech and may be activated by means of speech in the absence of directly perceptual conditions of activity." [98].

It should be noted that the understanding of mental processes as processes developing from external activity is also found in the writings of a number of progressive psychologists outside the Soviet Union (Piaget [459], Wallon [41]).

The views developed by Soviet psychologists—namely, that theoretical activity develops from external activity, and that mental properties, both general and special, are the product of ontogenetic development—are based on the doctrines of Sechenov and Pavlov on the reflex nature of mental activity. In his "Elements of Thought," Sechenov states that thought begins with the formation of ideas about an object and then passes directly into the "extrasensory region." He points out that abstract concepts, such as mathematical concepts of homogeneity or invariability, are formed under the influence of real transactions, and are "taken from the facts of real life, the only difference being that in mathematical values all these properties are reduced, as it were, to an ideal, whereas in real objects they are no more than an approximation to the ideal." Sechenov concludes his book with the words: "The transfer of thought from the experiential region to the extrasensory takes place by means of prolonged analysis, prolonged synthesis, and prolonged generalization. In this sense it is a natural continuation of the preceding phase of development, using the same methods and, consequently, the same intellectual processes." [286; 251–252].

The view held by Soviet psychologists that thinking is an activity which develops from practical experience and arises in the course of the life of an individual, rests on Pavlov's teaching. Thinking is based upon conditioned-reflex activity and develops as a result of individual experience.

Hence, by postulating the reflex nature of thinking, Soviet psychologists reject the principles of idealistic, empirical psychology, which regards thinking as an inborn faculty or function, which only increases quantitatively in the course of development.

The psychological investigation of the origin and development of thinking as S. L. Rubinshtein points out, consists of the discovery of its principles as an analytic synthetic activity, in which sensory and rational cognition are merged into one. An important problem confronting Soviet psychologists is "not only to trace the change from one stage to another, but more especially, to unmask at each stage the internal principles of the fundamental intellectual processes and to build, on this basis, a general theory of intellectual activity." [259; 33].

Being a special form of human activity, thinking is manifested as the sum of a series of varied operations; the most important operations are analysis and synthesis and generalization and abstraction.

The principle of the reflex nature of mental activity implies the definition of what is mental as a process. In Sechenov's words, "the idea of a mental act as a process must be held as fundamental." [286; 251–252]. Even the most elementary human mental processes, such as feeling and perception, are processes in the sense that they take place in time and possess somewhat variable dynamics. The discovery of the reflex nature of all these processes, even in the most elementary acts, afforded a particularly clear revelation of their multistage nature. All human intellectual activity is characterized by such processes.

Intellectual activity consists not only of the ability to perceive and be aware of surrounding events, but also of the ability to act in conformity with a set purpose. Thinking is an active, goal-directed process, directed toward the solution of a definite problem.

In S. L. Rubinshtein's book, "Thinking and the Methods of Its Investigation," the role of thinking in human practical activity is revealed as a creative, productive process, possessing its own principles. Starting with the bare conditions of a specific problem, human thought goes on to discover the various unknown and conflicting elements of knowledge involved in the situation; "the normal course of thought not only creates the essential conditions for replying to the questions which a person is asked, but also poses questions...." [262; 15].

Although Soviet psychology has frequently investigated the problem of thinking and its development, the results obtained have not been adequately utilized in the analysis of intellectual disorders.

Modern investigations in the field of the pathology of thinking have proceeded in two opposite directions. The one based on the reflex principle of mental activity forms the main line of investigation followed by Soviet scientists and by certain progressive non-Soviet workers. The other direction, most widespread among American and British psychologists, consists of an eclectic combination of the old line of the psychology of individual faculties, or isolated functions, with Freudianism and Gestalt psychology. This sharp divergence is not accidental, for the problem of intelligence, of its formation and disintegration, is bound up with a whole series of problems of an ideological nature, so that the difference in ideological approaches is very prominent in this field.

The influence of Gestaltism and Freudianism is still seen today in the investigations of American clinical psychologists. The dominant trend in the field of the psychology of intelligence in the USA at the present time remains Gestalt psychology. The work of Wertheimer and Kohler has led to the appearance of a whole series of investigations which attempt to show that the sudden reconstruction—a sudden change in the significance of a problem situation—constitutes the fundamental intellectual activity. This point of view is presented especially clearly in the writings of Dunker [396]. The productivity of thinking is dependent on the forces ("stress systems") of the "internal" and "external field." Goal-directed mental activity takes place under the influence of a definite stress in the system, which tries to discharge itself. The process of the solution of a problem must be understood in these terms as the process of the reconstruction of a situation.

The influence of Gestalt psychology can be discerned in the writings of such American clinical psychologists as Hanfmann, Kasanin, Brown, and Rickers. These workers explain disturbances of intellectual activity in schizophrenia in terms of a splitting of the structure of the intellect and a disturbance of the interrelation and communication of the strained systems.

Psychomorphological conceptions are also found in the writings of some British neurologists and psychologists. Critchley [388]. for example, asserts that the nature of a disturbance of intellectual activity is determined by the localization of a lesion in particular lobes of the brain. Similar views are held by McFie and Piercy [443], who claim that specific types of intellectual functions are impaired selectively by wounds in different situations. Shapiro and Zangwill consider that lesions of the right side lead to a disturbance of abstraction. Freeman came to the conclusion that human fantasy and "capacity for unreality" are contained in the frontal lobes. Psychomorphological principles are also reflected in Pitrich's monograph, "Thinking Disturbances in Brain Injury" [463]. This author describes the results of the experimental psychological investigation of 70 patients with brain injury and manifestations of aphasia in whom disturbances of verbal and logical thinking were found. In this book, with its interesting factual material, Pitrich starts out from Kleist's conception of the two components of intelligence—perceptual and active (sensory and motor). Corresponding to this he divides disturbances of intelligence into paralogical (disturbance of concepts), which are found in lesions of the left side of the posterior, the inferior parietal, and the temporal regions of the brain, and alogical disturbances, corresponding to lesions of the "anterior" brain. The latter disturbances are attributed to inadequacy of motivation. In the course of his comparative studies of speech disturbances, agnosia, apraxia, and hemianopsia, he concludes that the data both of psychological experimentation and of cerebral pathology permit a phylogenetic subdivision of functions into the primitive and the differentiated. If, in a lesion of a particular zone of the brain, a primitive function is disturbed (for example, constructive praxis in a lesion of the parietal region), figurative, spatial intelligence localized in this area will also be disturbed. This subdivision of intellect, in Pitrich's opinion, is of practical significance, for it facilitates the retraining and rehabilitation of patients in accordance with the residual intact elements of their thinking.

In other writings, such as the monograph by André Rey [465], in which the methods of experimental psychological investigation of mental disturbances are described, the disturbance in thinking is regarded as an impairment of an isolated function, which must be expressed as a quantitative ratio, much as the I.Q. is calculated. In Kaplan's monograph [424] the disturbances of the thinking of patients with senile changes and arteriosclerosis of the brain are interpreted as the result of a weakening of the function of attention. During recent years an extraordinarily large number of monographs devoted to problems of clinical psychology have been published abroad. Many different methods of investigation of mental disturbances, including disorders of thought, have been described, systematic classifications of the methods have been given, and the attitudes of different psychologists toward these methods have been reviewed. In these investigations, however, very little has been said about the experimental findings in relation to disturbances in thinking, and no conclusions or generalizations have been deduced from the results of the investigations. Most of these studies constitute no more than combinations of psychiatric essays and lists of technical methods.

It must be noted that during recent years there have been comparatively few investigations devoted specifically to the problem of disturbances in thinking published outside the Soviet Union. There are several reasons for this.

Firstly, many clinical psychologists devote little of their energies to the study of the disturbances of the patient's perceptual activity. Some investigators, such as Mowbray, consider that the clinical psychologist must limit his area of study to the area of individual differences between mental patients. The "area of competence" of the clinical psychologist lies not so much in the analysis of disturbances of mental processes as in the investigation of individual concrete patients. It is not by chance that Mowbray called one of his articles "The Clinical Psychologist as a Human Scientist" [449]. A similar point of view is held by French writers (Lagache, Pichot, Tournai), who consider that the importance of clinical psychological investigations lies in the detailed investigation of individual cases. In their investigations the concepts of normal and pathological are brought closer together.

Secondly, insufficient attention has been paid to the problem of disturbances of intellectual activity because psychopathological symptoms are regarded, not as a distortion of the process of cognition, but as a manifestation of the "play" of fundamental needs. Freud's psychoanalytical concepts still play a dominant role in this realm of psychopathology, although slightly altered in the form of sociopsychological and psychodynamic theory in which the central question involves the possible libidinous nature of the sense of fear as well as of unconscious forces in general. The attempt to link disturbances of thinking with the "play" of subconscious inclinations has become the cornerstone of many psychopathological and psychological investigations. In other studies the problem of consciousness and thinking has been replaced by the problem of the localization of consciousness. In particular, many investigations have been devoted to the relationship between disturbances in thinking and the activity of the reticular system.

In many psychological investigations the principal analysis has been carried out along the lines of existential psychology. This is revealed, in particular, by the survey article of Benedetti, Kind, and Mielke, which describes their investigations in the field of schizophrenia between 1951 and 1955 [366].

Investigations of the intellectual disturbances conducted by Soviet psychologists nowadays rest on a single theoretical foundation: all are based both on the Marxist–Leninist theory of cognition and on the Sechenov–Pavlov reflex theory of mental activity. However, despite the unity of their theoretical foundation, the investigations may be divided into two groups on the basis of their methods and purposes and their relationship to practical problems.

The first group of investigations consists of those carried out by physiologists and a few psychiatrists. Using various modifications of the conditioned-reflex or speech-motor technique of Professor Ivanov-Smolenskii, these workers have sought to study the dynamics of nervous processes and of the inductive relationships between the signal systems in various diseases. (These investigations are the more numerous of the two types, and it will be impossible to discuss them all.)

In 1934 Ivanov-Smolenskii [119] first investigated the pathophysiological basis of the phenomenon of the incoherence of speech in schizophrenia. He attributed the various symptoms to alternating states in the speech region, as indicated by the perseverations and echolalia revealed through association experiments.

Chistovich [334] attempted to determine how far the association experiment reflects the dynamics of a disease and how sensitive it is as an index of the changes taking place in cortical activity. In schizophrenic patients with disintegration of thought he noted the presence of "lower" responses of the type of echolalia, and the concrete and one-word character of the response reactions. In Chistovich's opinion this takes place because a series of visual images spills out in response to the stimulus. Speech loses its symbolic significance, and many of the conditioned connections determining the meaning of the particular word are inhibited.

In recent years many investigations by psychiatrists and pathophysiologists working in psychiatric clinics have dealt with the study of disturbances of the neurodynamics in various mental diseases. For instance, Kaminskii and Savchuk [125] and Kononyachenko [136], who investigated hypertensive patients, found a disturbance of the mobility of the nervous processes and the presence of alternating states in these subjects. The disturbance of the mobility of nervous processes after brain trauma was the subject of the investigations of Melekhov and Kamenskaya. They showed that in patients with remote sequelae due to brain injury, which resulted in permanent intellectual impairment, a disturbance of the mobility of the nervous processes was present [193].

Many studies have been devoted to the pathophysiological analysis of the psychopathological disorders in epilepsy. In most investigations a disturbance of the mobility of the nervous processes and a disturbance of the relationships between the signal systems have been reported (see, for example, [283] and [284]).

Particular attention has been devoted to the pathophysiological investigation of patients with schizophrenia. The work of Ivanov-Smolenskii and his collaborators had demonstrated a disturbance of the relationships between the signal systems in schizophrenia. Popov, discussing the disintegration of intelligence and of speech in schizophrenia, points out that a leading part is played by disturbances of differentiation and of the induction relationships between the signal systems [242].

Rushkevich describes weakness of internal inhibition and inertia of the process of excitation in the second signal system in patients with schizophrenia. The phenomena of "uninhibitability and inertia" in most schizophrenic patients, in Rushkevich's opinion, are "among the clear expressions of that chronic hypnotic state of the cerebral cortex of these patients which, according to Pavlov, constitutes the essence of the cerebral pathophysiology of this disease." Besides the hypnotic phases, forming the nucleus of this syndrome, other phenomena are present, notably: weakness of excitatory and inhibitory processes and a disturbance of their mobility [273; 126].

Disturbances of the second signal system in various forms of schizophrenia are described in studies undertaken by the Department of Psychiatry of the Central Postgraduate Medical Institute (under the direction of Snezhnevskii). For example, the work of Sotsevich [300] showed that in the paranoid form of schizophrenia the activity of the second signal system is too predominant. This conclusion was drawn from the results of an association experiment in which mainly abstract verbal reactions were found in the patients.

The disturbance of the dynamics of the nervous processes in various mental diseases was investigated by a group of workers in the laboratory of the pathophysiology of human higher nervous activity of the I. P. Pavlov Institute of Experimental Medicine, USSR Academy of Medical Sciences. Usov [320] found that in old age the negative induction between the two signal systems is well marked. The same conclusion was reached by Gakkel' [54]. Investigations by the same author established the presence of a disturbance of the induction relationships between the signal systems in oligophrenics. The degree of this disturbance was found to depend on the severity of their condition.

A particularly noteworthy investigation of the comparative pathophysiological characteristics of patients with schizophrenic and epileptic defects was conducted by Kaufman [128]. He found that patients with schizophrenia could grasp a problem which was presented in verbal form and which called for the stereotyped reproduction of old verbal experience. Problems requiring orientation in a visual situation without verbal evaluation and problems requiring the verbal evaluation of a visual situation (for example, the description of thematic pictures) were less easily grasped. Schizophrenic patients with intellectual impairment had no trouble in reproducing verbal instructions, but they had difficulty in forming, by means of verbal instructions, new, stable reflexes in response to direct stimuli. These facts indicate, in Kaufman's opinion, a profound disturbance of the mechanism of elective irradiation, which is ordinarily responsible for maintaining the proper interaction between the two signal systems in the process of acquiring new experience. The new experience acquired through the second signal system was transformed into verbal reactions, but was not passed on to the first signal system, so that it could not be utilized in practice; while, conversely, the associations of the first signal system were not passed on to the second (the patients could not discuss a picture demonstrated to them). It was easier to form conditioned reflexes to verbal stimuli; these were quickly automatized, but they remained so widely generalized that it was impossible to define the limits of this generalization.

Kaufman concludes that in patients with a schizophrenic defect a tendency is observed in the first signal system for positive conditioned associations to be inhibited in the absence of their generalization. In the second signal system a tendency is revealed for the disinhibition of inhibitory associations in the presence of irradiation of the process of excitation. The less habitual, less stable associations are disinhibited. Under these circumstances the systems of speech associations, belonging mainly to the higher and more complex forms of speech experience, are disinhibited.

In the same investigation it was shown that completely different results are obtained during the investigation of epileptics: against a background of general depression of the cortex, there is a greater possibility of integration in the first signal system than in the second.

* * *

These investigations attempt to describe the neurodynamic basis of disorders in thinking. However, the principles found in these writings are still of a far too general character; they deal mainly, as we have seen, in terms of disturbances both of the relationships between the signal systems and of the mobility of the nervous processes. These investigations were unable to study the different types of disturbances of thinking as such (i.e., of the process of generalized and systematic reflection of the outside world), although the methods they used were of an experimental character. However, generalizations from the results of these pathophysiological investigations can be of importance to psychiatric theory and practice; these investigations, together with additional, psychological studies, supplement the data obtained in the clinic.

Investigations of a different character were conducted by those pathophysiologists who attempted to replace psychology by the pathophysiology of higher nervous activity. In this category are Rushkevich's investigations, which were devoted to the study of the disorders of abstract thinking in mental patients [273].

Recognizing that the types of intellectual disorders studied by psychiatrists have not been systematically classified, Rushkevich (in a paper written jointly with Protopopov) appeals to psychiatrists to study disturbances of thinking in the context of the principles of normal thought processes established by logic: "These forms of human abstract thinking have long been studied in logic, and in this way general principles have been established which govern the intellectual activity of the normal adult person. Psychiatry, in studying disturbances of thinking in mental patients, classifies the forms and functions of thought in terms applicable to logic (i.e., instead of excited, inhibited, disintegrated, incoherent intellectual activity it speaks of assimilation, reasoning, consideration, combinatory abilities, etc.). Classification is not based on any definite principle, but depends rather on the necessity for registering the complete, wide range of disturbances of intellectual activity observed clinically in mental patients." [246; 5].

Rushkevich makes no distinction between the subject matter of psychology and logic, and he incorrectly defines the objects of logic. In this connection he disregards the psychological study of the principles of the intellectual activity of the normal adult person, although when he wishes to gain insight into the distinctive features of the intellectual activity of the patient, Rushkevich is compelled to make use of the methods of psychology (for example, such tests as the description of thematic pictures and the classification of objects). However, his disregard of psychological theory prevents him from reaching any productive conclusions from his experimental findings and from arriving at satisfactory descriptions and classifications of the typical forms of intellectual disturbances of mental patients. This unsound theoretical basis also led Rushkevich to arrive at clinically unsound conclusions. Thus, for example, he characterizes the intellectual activity of patients with schizophrenia as being basically similar to that of oligophrenics. It must be noted that, despite the admonition in the journal "Voprosy Psikhologii" [347], in subsequent publications Rushkevich continued to develop the same views.

Hence, despite the value of the pathophysiological analysis of the relationship between the signal systems in various forms of disease, investigations which attempt to disregard the data of modern psychology are unproductive and cannot reveal the true nature of disturbances of thinking as a cognitive activity.

The second group of investigations consists of a much smaller— indeed, a disproportionately smaller—number of studies devoted to the analysis of the pathology of thinking as a mental process. These investigations, which regard thinking as a generalized and systematic reflection of the outside world, seek to determine the nature of the changes which different diseases effect upon the various types of intellectual activity (such as analysis and synthesis, generalization, etc.).

The reorganization of psychiatry on the basis of Pavlov's teaching increased the importance of objective methods of investigation of mental disturbances. Several clinical psychologists have devoted themselves to the development and description of methods of investigation of disturbances of mental and, in particular, of intellectual activity.

This series of investigations includes those conducted by Myasishchev and his co-workers. Following the tradition of Bekhterev, Myasishchev attempts to introduce objective methods of investigation into clinical psychiatry. Most of his studies, which are concerned with the analysis of disturbances in the working capacity and the attitudes of patients to their environment, have made a significant contribution to the development of the theory and technique of investigation of perceptual activity [209].

Among work of a technical nature we may mention some sections of the technical writings of Zeigarnik and S. Ya. Rubinshtein [116], in which are described the experimental psychological methods of investigation of mental patients; and the technical sections of the writings of Dukel'skaya and Korobkova [85], which are concerned with the assessment of the working capacity of schizophrenic patients.

In addition to the above-mentioned studies, which are of practical significance, in recent years various investigations of greater theoretical significance have been undertaken. Such studies include the investigations of the intellectual activity of oligophrenic children. For example, the collection entitled, "Perceptual Activity of Pupils at a Special School" [298], describes a series of investigations of the intellectual activity of mentally retarded children in which a detailed analysis was made of the distinctive features of their modes of thought. In his article, "Intellectual Activity of Mentally Retarded Schoolchildren during the Solution of Arithmetical Problems," Solov'ev states that, instead of generalization, mentally retarded children resort to the comparison of old knowledge with the elements of the new problem; such children are unable to find the common link between the various elements of an entity. The mentally retarded child tries to apply a scheme or pattern from an old problem to the solution of the new one." [299].

The work of Zankov [95, 96] is devoted to the study of disturbances of cognitive processes of the mentally retarded child. He points out that the principal difficulty for these children is in shifting to intellectual problems requiring for their solution a change in previously used patterns of behavior.

Lipkina [177], in a paper entitled, "Analysis and Synthesis in the Perception of Objects by Pupils at a Special School," declared that mentally retarded children can recognize only the individual parts of an object; these parts acquire an independent meaning for them. In a paper published jointly with Zvereva [101],

Lipkina states that as the complexity of the objects increases, so does both the number of parts into which they can be subdivided and the difficulty of comparing these parts.

Investigations of the distinguishing features of the intellectual activity of mentally retarded children were published in the collection, "The Mental Development of Pupils at a Special School" [342].

Disturbances of perceptual and cognitive activity were studied in investigations by Luria [182, 183, 185] and by his collaborators (Meshcheryakov [200], Tikhomirov [314], Khomskaya [328], and others). This group of studies deals with the analysis of the formation of perceptual processes in oligophrenic children and the role of speech in the establishment of new conditioned connections. It was found that new conditioned connections are more easily formed at the level of the first signal system than at the level of the second; the neurodynamics of verbal connections is disturbed to a greater degree than the neurodynamics of motor reactions.

The investigation conducted by Nepomnyashchaya [211] under Luria's direction on the subject of the compensation for defects in mentally retarded children is of considerable theoretical interest. From an analysis of the process of learning arithmetic, Nepomnyashchaya shows that the solution of problems is achieved by oligophrenics at the level of objective action; the children had difficulty in changing to a more abbreviated level of action. In pointing out ways of compensating for this defect, Nepomnyashchaya stresses that the training of mentally retarded children must start from the most elementary level, that of concrete operations with objects.

Perel'man's book [226] is a psychiatric treatise dealing with the systematic analysis of intellectual disorders. Although this book must be regarded as one of the most recent in the field of the psychopathology of thinking, all our previous remarks concerning the psychological literature on thinking apply to this book as well. A good feature of the book is its truly comprehensive character; despite its small size, it provides the reader with examples of nearly every type of phenomenon in the intellectual disorders observed to date in clinical psychiatry. However, inadequate classification and interpretation mars the wealth of data and the vividness and variety of description. Thus, Chapter 1 describes the phenomena of "diffuse" intelligence (a frequently observed symptom of schizophrenic patients); Chapter 3 describes the intellectual activity of schizophrenics; and Chapters 4 and 5 analyze obsessive ideas and delirium, quite without regard to their nosology. The second part of the book, which contains these chapters, is entitled, "Pathological Disturbances of Thinking," and the third part, "The Intellect and Its Disorders." In this book, therefore, the tendency is once again revealed to draw a distinction between thinking and the intellect.

Perel'man confines himself to the enumeration and brief explanation of the symptoms of disorders of thinking. For example, when describing such phenomena as agglutination, symbolism, ambivalence, "sliding," Sperrung, stereotype, mentisme, banality, and overreasoning, he makes no attempt at a theoretical explanation and generalization.

A virtue of Perel'man's work lies in his attempt to classify the various disorders of intelligence according to their pathophysiological bases. In regard to all the above-mentioned extremely varied symptoms of disturbances of thinking, however, he mentions only a more or less intensive inhibition of the second signal system and a disturbance of its interaction with the first signal system. Such a general description can hardly be productive.

In experimental psychological investigations the disorders of thinking have been examined in connection with the requirements of clinical practice. One of the problems with which the clinician is concerned is the assessment of the degree of impairment of mental activity. The psychologists of the Central Institute of Assessment of Working Capacity raise the question of the relationship between disturbances of thinking and the nature of the activity to be performed. Korobkova [140] showed that the intellectual powers of patients following head injury varied in accordance with the nature of the activity: the more closely it resembled the patient's previous experience, the higher the residual level of his intellectual powers. The investigations of Kogan [130] show that the disturbances of the intellectual activity of patients with cerebrovascular diseases come to light during the performance of tasks which require the observance of several conditions. The disturbances of working capacity observed in schizophrenic patients are described in a paper by Dukel'skaya and Korobkova [85]. On the basis of the comparison of the results of experimental psychological and clinical investigations and observations on patients at work, these authors concluded that the solution of problems connected with working capacity is dependent, not so much on the degree of preservation of perceptual processes, as on a combination of this preservation with the personality trend of the patient.

Evaluation of the degree of intellectual impairment of patients with organic brain lesions was studied by S. Ya. Rubinshtein. Her investigations, conducted in the experimental psychological laboratory of the Institute of Forensic Psychiatry, were directed toward the study of the structure of intellectual activity during deliberate feigning by patients with various degrees of intellectual impairment. Differences were found between true exacerbation and the hysterical retreat to illness found in pseudodementia: with exacerbation the arbitrariness of thinking is preserved or even increased, while in pseudodementia it disappears. At the same time, differences in the degree of arbitrariness of the thought processes may be used to estimate the degree of intellectual disturbance [270].

The problem of disturbances of thinking has been examined by clinical psychologists in relation to the clinician's overriding practical problem—differential diagnosis. A paper which I published jointly with Birenbaum [31] describes experimental psychological results relating to the thinking disorders of schizophrenics and epileptics: diffuseness and lack of differentiation of judgment characterized the former, while in the latter sluggishness of intellectual activity predominated. Shubert [348] investigated the pattern of disturbance of intellectual activity in patients whose illnesses had been caused by a traumatic situation (such as reactive depression and pseudodementia); with a comparatively high level of generalization and abstraction, these patients showed an absence of logic in their judgments and inadequate control over their associations. Comparison between these findings and clinical and pathophysiological results suggests that the pathophysiological basis of these disturbances rests in the intermittent appearance of manifestations of protective inhibition.

Polyakov [240] studied the disturbances of thinking in schizophrenia. He investigated the intellectual activity of patients whose illness was not marked by well-defined psychotic features, and concluded that these patients tended to grasp the nonessential properties and aspects of objects, those facts not particularly related to the requirements of the concrete intellectual problem.

In her study of the comparative characteristics of the classification of words and of objects in schizophrenic and cardiovascular patients, Tepenitsina demonstrated the existence of a difference in the relationships between the processes of generalization and abstraction and the experimental material.

Several recent studies have been concerned with the development and trial of experimental methods of investigation of the intellectual disorders (for example, the diploma theses of Aseev, Zadruzhinskii, and Urozhaeva).

As already noted, none of these contains either the unified conceptual system nor the comparative material so essential to the analysis of clinical problems in differential diagnosis. It was impossible to consider the problem of the disintegration of thought as a whole when studying an isolated type of disturbance of limited extent. Psychopathology was faced with the urgent task of making the primary generalization from the data of the pathology of thinking. The need had arisen for the generalization, analysis, and classification of the principal types of disturbance of thinking, using the system of concepts of modern materialistic psychology.

The solution of this problem required the use of experimental methods. Disorders of thinking could be classified on the basis of the experimental analysis of the intellectual activity of mental patients. Not until the types of disturbance of thinking had been defined could their relationship to individual diseases be established.

Chapter 2

Methods of Investigation of Disturbances

of Thinking

1. PRINCIPLES OF DESIGN OF EXPERIMENTS
IN PSYCHOPATHOLOGY

In psychology the choice of concrete methods of experimental investigation is a problem not only of method but also of methodology and fundamental principles. The rejection of the view of mental processes as inborn faculties or functions and the approach to the analysis of mental phenomena from the standpoint of the reflex theory of Sechenov and Pavlov have altered the methodology of the design construction of the experiment and the interpretation of its results.

The view that mental processes are inborn functions which change only quantitatively during development led to the idea that a "metric" psychology could be created. The experimental investigation of mental processes was reduced to the determination of the quantitative characteristics of an individual mental act. An example of such a method used to measure an individual mental function is the test known as the "choice reaction." First, the time of the subject's motor reaction to the appearance of a stimulus is measured (the subject has to press a key when a stimulus of any color appears); the subject then has to give a reaction only to a definite stimulus of this particular type (for example, to a red light). The duration of the simple reaction is subtracted from the duration of performance of this sensorimotor act by the subject, and the difference in time is a measure of the act of choice. The magnitude of this difference is a quantitative characteristic of the "higher volitional process," which is thereby detached from the sensorimotor act.

A similar principle of quantitative measurement of inborn faculties lay at the basis of the psychological methods of investigation used in psychiatric and neurological clinics. Investigation of the disintegration of any function consisted of the determination of the degree to which it deviated quantitatively from the "normal standard."

In 1910 Rossolimo, a leading neurologist, developed a system of psychological experiments which, in his opinion, would enable the level of the individual mental functions to be expressed quantitatively when impaired by a disease of the brain [253]. This method is known in the literature as "Rossolimo's profile." The quantitative measurement of individual functions was brought to its furthest extremes in the test investigations of foreign psychologists.

These test methods were used for "pedological" psychometric examination of schoolchildren. These investigations were rightly judged as pseudoscientific by a decree of the Central Committee of the CPSU dated July 4, 1936. The object of these investigations was to select children with inadequate mental development for admission to special schools. By means of these pedological test procedures, children apparently born "smart" were separated from others, whose retarded mental development also appeared to be the result of inborn factors.

These unscientific methods of investigation penetrated into the Soviet Union from the pedagogics of the capitalist countries; they are essentially an attempt to justify the class character of their educational system. At best, such a purely quantitative method of investigation provides an estimate of the quantity of acquired knowledge, and not of the possibility of its further development. Children of the higher strata of capitalist society, having been brought up in favorable conditions and having received a better education, reveal a wider range of knowledge in these tests and are thereby enrolled in schools with a higher educational standard than children of the less wealthy strata of society.

It should be noted that the voices of progressive teachers outside the Soviet Union have been raised against selection by means of such tests. The British psychologist Simon [275] is one such critic of the system.

This test method still dominates the field in the writings of clinical psychologists outside the Soviet Union. Many monographs and articles published during recent years on clinical experimental psychological investigation describe such test methods; even the determination of the patients' I.Q. is included. Among such works we may mention: "Thinking Disturbances in Brain Injury," by Pitrich [463]; "Methods of Investigation of Dementia," by Plugfelder; "Clinical Psychology Monographs," by Rey [465]; and the monograph, "Progress in Clinical Psychology," by Brower and Abt [380].

During the evaluation of patients by means of tests, no regard can be paid either to the qualitative aspect of the disturbance or to the relationship between the disturbances and the conditions of life. The question of ways and means of compensation for the defective function is similarly ignored. When the clinician requests the psychological examination in order to obtain help with the problem of the compensation of a disturbed activity (for example, under the influence of treatment), no answer can be given if the test method is used, for this method will investigate an inborn function, which has already been proved an erroneous concept.

Side by side with this purely quantitative method of psychological test, the tendency has recently appeared abroad in clinical psychology to use "projective" methods of investigation. The problem presented to the subject does not admit of any definite method of solution. In contrast to the test which requires a problem to be solved in accordance with specific conditions, the projective test uses any type of problem, merely as a pretext for the subject to exhibit his experiences and the traits of his personality and character.

As a concrete method the patient may be asked to describe thematic pictures ("thematic apperception test"—T.A.T.) or pictures not representing any particular theme. In the latter case "ink-blots" are used, as suggested by Rorschach; these consist of symmetrically placed configurations of the most curious shapes, which may be obtained by folding a sheet of paper on which a few ink drops have been placed. The thematic pictures presented for description illustrate actions of varied complexity. The subject must first describe the picture and then relate everything that comes into his mind—what the pictures remind him of, what he was thinking about, or what he felt. The experimenter notes the subject's remarks.

The projective method thus represents essentially the antithesis of the test method. In the opinion of its authors it allows a qualitative assessment of the subject's behavior to be made. The test method gives an estimate only of the results of work; the process of the work itself, the attitude of the subject to the problem, the motives leading the subject to choose one or other method of action, personality orientations, desires—in a word, the whole diversity of qualitative attributes of the subject's activity—cannot and must not be taken into consideration when this method is used. With the projective method, on the other hand, no question of a correct or incorrect solution of the problem generally arises. The investigator using the projective method is not interested in the result of the subject's actions or in the possibility of assessing his mistakes or incorrect solutions quantitatively, but rather in the possibility of determining the subject's personal reactions, the character of the associations springing up in these conditions, and the subject's attitude toward these associations. In brief, in the opinion of its sponsors, the projective method helps to reveal the subject's personality. In the words of the French psychologist Ombredane [453], "personality is reflected by means of this method, like an object on a screen" (hence the name "projective"). This method is often called "the clinical approach to the mind of the healthy person." Clinically, this method is used by those psychologists who consider that the psychologist is competent, not to investigate a disturbance of cognitive processes, but only to determine the individual peculiarities of each patient (Lagache [434], Pichot [460], Ombredane [453]).

When, however, we consider what personal experiences and orientations are being discussed, we see that the investigator is trying to reveal by means of this method the "unconscious, latent" motives and desires of the patient—his libidinal complexes. · The peculiarities of the subject's behavior during perception (for example, whether he sees objects in movement or at rest; whether he directs his attention to the large portions of the Rorschach patterns or to the small details, etc.) are interpreted as indications of character traits or suppressed experiences.

Though this method, unlike the quantitative measurement of individual functions, is supposed to give us a qualitative analysis of the whole personality, it is likewise used for a misconceived purpose. The grain of reason embodied in the projective test cannot be utilized, for the results of the investigation are interpreted and the personal experiences are analyzed from Freudian or neo-Freudian standpoints.

It should also be noted that the adherents of the projective method have not entirely abandoned the formal quantitative interpretation to which they objected in their criticism of the test method. For example, the assessment of the results of the Rorschach test is made partly on the basis of the fact that the presence of a particular complex is judged by the number of details of a particular shape or size that are perceived. Hence, the falsity of the initial theoretical principles determines the formal character of the experimental methods and their interpretation: whereas the purely quantitative character of the intelligence tests derives from the theory of individual inborn mental faculties, the banal interpretations drawn from the projective methods can be ascribed to dependence on the Freudian theory of the unconscious.

The principles of experimental psychological investigation in Soviet psychology are totally different. The doctrines of materialistic psychology assume that thinking is not an inborn faculty but rather an activity developed during life; this means that in psychological experiments thinking disturbances must be investigated as disturbances of activity. Individual experimental methods must show how particular intellectual operations are impaired in a patient; how operations are formed in the course of his practical experience; how the processes of generalization and abstraction and of synthesis and analysis are disturbed; how the process of acquisition of new associations is modified; and what distortions have taken place in the ability to use the system of old associations formed in the course of past experience. Because thinking is a goal-directed process possessing its own dynamics, it is to be expected that experimental investigation will also be able to reveal a disturbance of the purposeful character of thought. Hence the results of the experiment must give not only the quantitative, but also the qualitative characteristics of the thinking disturbances. One of the more important aims in the design of psychological experiments is to achieve qualitative analysis of the distinctive features of the course of the patient's mental processes, rather than a merely quantitative measurement. It is important to know not only how difficult or how extensive the problem was that the patient had to understand or solve, but also how he came to understand it, and why he made mistakes or had difficulty. (It should be emphasized that the analysis of the patient's mistakes in the course of the performance of experimental tests is most interesting and provides demonstrative material for evaluating particular attributes of his intellectual activity.)

In other words, the clinical psychological investigation must be equivalent to the functional test, a method widely used in medical practice, which involves the testing of the performance of a given organ. For example, when the physician wishes to test the activity of the heart, he first has the patient perform some action which will place a demand on his organ (for example, running); subsequent auscultation tests the organ and its specific activity. In the psychological experiment the role of the functional test may also be played by experimental methods which have been designed to reflect the mental operations employed by man during work and study.

We must dwell further on the features which distinguish clinical experiments from the experiments designed to investigate the mental activity of the healthy person—those directed toward the solution of problems of a general psychological nature. The principal difference is that, in the former, we cannot always take into account the patient's specific attitude toward the experiment; this varies in accordance with his individual pathology. The presence of delirium, excitation, or inhibition will compel instances of variation in the experimental design, and even occasional modifications in it while the experiment is in progress.

With all their individual differences, healthy subjects nevertheless usually attempt to carry out the instruction, while in psychiatric practice it may be necessary to conduct an experiment with patients who not only do not try to carry out the task but misinterpret or actively resist the instructions. For example, the directions for the association experiment on a healthy subject include a warning that words will be spoken and that he must listen to them; the subject will almost invariably direct his attention actively toward the words spoken by the experimenter. In conducting the same experiment with a negativistic patient, a more subtle technique must be used, for if the patient is instructed to listen he will most likely wilfully fail to do so. In such conditions the experimenter must proceed in a roundabout way: he pronounces the word quite incidentally and notes the patient's reaction.

In other cases experiments must be conducted on patients who form a delusional interpretation of the experimental situation. They consider, for example, that the experimenter is an enemy acting on them by hypnosis or by rays, that there is a thought-reading apparatus in the room, and so on. This attitude of the patient to the experiment naturally influences his reactions; he frequently deliberately carries out the experimenter's instructions incorrectly, delays his replies, and so on. In such cases the design of the experiment must also be modified.

The design of the experimental psychological investigation as used in clinical practice differs from that of the usual psychological experiment in one further detail: the great variety and larger number of techniques used. This may be explained as follows. During the performance of any task, including an experimental problem, the subject (healthy person or patient) reacts and acts as an integral personality; by generalizing and synthesizing the material he thereby assesses his action and assumes a definite attitude toward his work and the situation. During the solution of any problem every aspect of the intellectual activity of a person (healthy or sick) may be revealed.

Furthermore, the process of disintegration of thinking does not take place at one level only. It does not happen in practice that in one patient only the processes of synthesis and analysis are impaired, and in another the defect is present in the purposiveness of the intellectual act exclusively. Hence, when a patient performs any test, evidence of various forms of disturbance of thinking may be obtained. However, despite this fact, each method will reveal the form or degree of disturbance with variable ease, accuracy, and reliability.

Of necessity, the experimental conditions with patients as subjects may change during the course of the experiment, and these variations must be accounted for in analyzing the experimental results. Very often a change in the instruction or some slight difference in the method of conducting the experiment will alter the significance of the results. For example, if in introducing an experiment on the memorization and reproduction of words the experimenter stresses the evaluation aspect of the task, the results of this experiment will most likely be of more value in illustrating the subject's attitude toward his work than in evaluating his memorization processes. Also, during an experiment with a sick person, changes in the patient's condition may necessitate alterations in the course of the experiment. Another factor which may demand a comparison of the experimental variations is as follows: In striving to correctly perform the experimental task, the patient often becomes acutely aware of his defect; he will strive to find a means of compensating for it, to find external aids to help him correct his mistakes. Different problems may present greater or lesser opportunities for this to occur. It frequently happens that the patient can solve more difficult problems correctly but cannot solve the simpler ones. Analysis of the nature of this phenomenon is possible only if the results of different tests are compared.

A final factor necessitating this comparative method is the frequent fluctuations in the degree of the patient's intellectual disturbance. With an improvement in the patient's condition, some features of his disturbances in thinking disappear while others resist amelioration. The character of the disturbances observed may also change under the influence of the experimental method itself. Only by a comparison of the results of the different variants of any method, applied many times, can a reliable estimate be made of the character, quality, and dynamics of a patient's disturbances in thinking.

There therefore exists a rational explanation for the fact that during the investigation of intellectual disturbances it is often necessary to use not one method, but a group of methods.

2. DESCRIPTION OF EXPERIMENTAL TECHNIQUES

We have already mentioned that the performance of any test may reveal disturbances of widely different aspects of thinking; nevertheless individual experimental methods are still the most suitable means of revealing a disturbance of particular intellectual operations or of particular components of thinking. During our subsequent descriptions of concrete forms of disturbances of thinking we shall describe these individual methods in detail. At this stage we shall merely describe some of the most commonly used techniques.*

Classification of Objects

The subject in this test is shown a series of objects (actual objects or cards) which he is asked to arrange in different groups on the basis of some general sign. This method was first used for the investigation of aphasia by Goldstein [406], who had the patient arrange a group of real objects in accordance with the character of

---

*Full technical details are described in the Technical Letter of the State Research Institute of Psychiatry, compiled by Zeigarnik and Rubinshtein [116], and also in the textbook on the experimental psychological investigation of mental patients prepared for publication by the same institute.

the material. The psychological difficulty of performing the test was that the "general" principle of classification—the property of the material of the object—was often contrary to the customary concrete associations between the objects (for example, in accordance with the principle of the material a pen should be placed in the same group as a spoon; the habitual association arising between a pen and a book interfered with this grouping). Consequently, to classify on the basis of a common principle it is necessary to inhibit the concrete associations between objects and to subordinate the process of classification to an abstract principle. This method was subsequently modified (in the investigations of Vygotskii [50], and Birenbaum and Zeigarnik [31]): instead of real objects, pictures of objects on cards were shown to the patients. Besides the purely technical advantages of this method, the conditions of grouping may be varied more widely: the objects may be given an unusual color or an unusual shape, etc.

A variant of this method is as follows: The subject is shown an assortment of 70 cards on which are pictures of a wide variety of objects, such as domestic animals, wild animals, instruments, people in various occupations, furniture, fruits, vegetables, and trees. He is instructed to sort the cards into several groups in accordance with a given principle. The cards may be classified on the basis of function or of type of material. Without discussing the characteristics of all the possible types of classification, suffice it to say that however different in nature the group of objects, the task of classification requires both the detection of only an elementary similarity or difference between the objects and the ability to distinguish an essential sign common to the various objects.

This test thus provides a means of determining the level of the process of generalization; we may learn whether the subject forms groups only on the basis of special, concrete associations or whether he does so also at the level of wider generalizations (and whether he is guided by this level throughout the experiment).

In the experiment we may also learn how the patient copes with the problem: Does he group the objects together initially on the basis of a narrow, exclusive principle, with his choice only gradually subordinated to higher levels of generalization (for example, does he at first put only birds into one group, then group birds with animals, and only as a last resort include people, to form the group of "living creatures"); or does he form groups in accordance with the more general signs at once ("living creatures," "plants," "inanimate nature")? Does he solve the problem by himself, or does he call on the experimenter for help?

This experiment is free and dynamic in structure; the experimenter not only observes what associations the subject uses when classifying groups, but also actively intervenes, helping or "hindering" the subject by prompting the right answers or provoking mistakes. If properly conducted, the experiment reveals not only the subject's level of generalization, but also his attitude toward his mistakes; since the experimenter verbally indicates the subject's mistakes during the experiment, it is important to note whether the subject corrects them or persists with an incorrect method of classification.

The method of classification of objects permits of many variations. Instead of pictures of objects, the subject may be given words to sort which represent the names of objects. Polyakov's variant, as another example, involves the classification of pictures according to shape and color.

The Method of Exceptions

Among the methods used to investigate forms and ways of generalization, mention must be made of the experimental test known as the method of exceptions.

The subject is given cards on each of which are drawn four objects, chosen so that three of them are related to each other while the fourth does not match the rest. The subject is asked to say which of the four is superfluous. For example, he may be shown a card with pictures of a protractor, scales, a clock, and spectacles, in which case the spectacles must be the exception because the first three articles are measuring devices.

The psychological essence of this method is that the subject must first understand the conditions governing the entire operation. Only when the subject has found the principle of generalization joining the three objects can he exclude the fourth. This method also demonstrates whether or not the subject can find the correct word formula to justify his chosen principle of selection. It also allows one to note if and when the subject changes from one method of solution to another.

The Method of Pictograms

One of the techniques used to investigate the ability to generalize and abstract is the method of forming conventional meanings, or the method of pictograms.

The subject is required to remember 14 words. As an aid to memorization he is instructed to think of something which will help him to reproduce the required words in the future, and to draw it on paper. He is forbidden to take notes or to jot down letters as mnemonic devices. The subject is told that the quality of the drawing is immaterial. There is no time limit for the test.

This method was first suggested by Luria for investigating the use of drawings as aids in memorization. It was later used with slight variations to study intellectual processes. The experiment is conducted in such a way that while the subject assumes that it is only his memory that is being investigated, the experiment is in fact mainly concerned with studying the general nature of his intellectual processes.

The task of creating a conditioned connection during the memorization of words itself gives rise to considerable difficulty, since it is not always possible to reflect the whole range of meaning of a particular word by means of a drawing. The choice of what to draw thus requires a considerable degree of intellectual freedom.

Birenbaum [30], who used this method to investigate the disturbance of ideas in mental patients, delineates this fundamental difficulty, the range of meanings of the group of words is wider than can be represented by a single drawing, while the meaning of the drawing is wider than the meaning of each individual word; the meanings of the picture and of each word can thus only partially coincide. It is this ability to detect what is common to the drawing and to each word which is the fundamental mechanism of the active formation of the conditioned meaning. Although this intellectual operation takes place relatively easily in a person of normal intelligence, even in in an adolescent, in the presence of pathological changes of thinking the formation of these conditioned associations becomes difficult.

The pictogram test may be conducted in two ways. In the first of these the picture is a conventional representation of the concept included in the word. For example, to memorize the word "development" any small and large figures (squares, circles) may be drawn; to memorize the word "doubt" a question mark may be used. This method is satisfactory with a subject who has achieved an adequate level of education. In the second method the drawing consists of a less general concept than the given word; the first must serve as the conditioned stimulus for the second. For example, the same word "development" may evoke such associations as "development of industry," "mental development," and "physical development." The drawing of any object associated with such a less general concept (a factory, a book, some article connected with sport) may then act as a stimulus for the concept of "development."

Hence, this test requires the ability to coordinate the concept denoted by a word with a more concrete concept; this is possible only when the subject is able to abstract from the whole range of concrete concepts contained in the given word, and when he can inhibit all the special associations connected with this word. The performance of this test is possible only when the subject has attained a definite level of generalization and abstraction.

This pictogram method provides the means of judging the degree of generalization and relevance of the associations formed by the subject. As a rule, healthy subjects, even if they have not completed their high-school education (ninth or tenth grades), can easily perform this test. If the subject encounters difficulty in understanding the task, as soon as he is shown how the test should be performed, he will thereafter solve the problem correctly.

Indirect or Aided Memorizing

An experimental method similar to that just described is that suggested by Leont'ev [171] and known in the literature as the method of the indirect memorization of words. We shall now describe one of the variants of this method.

The subject is asked to commit 15 words to memory. To facilitate memorizing he has to choose a suitable picture to correspond to each word from among 30 pictures which have been placed in front of him. After choosing the pictures, the subject must explain what association he made between each word and the object in its corresponding picture. The subject is then shown the pictures and asked to recall the corresponding words.

The chief advantage of this method over that of the pictograms is that here the experiment can be carried out with subjects with both little education and little or no drawing ability. The method also gives an idea of how fully and differentially the subject reproduces the material, and to what extent he is capable of mastering a particular technique for aiding the process of memorizing.

The Understanding of Metaphorical Meaning

Variant A. Explanation of Proverbs and Metaphors

The subject is given proverbs and metaphors and is asked to explain them. The proverbs chosen are common and not too complicated. In addition, the subject is asked either to think of some example from everyday life to which the particular saying applies or to point the similarity or difference between two other proverbs. If the subject's interpretation of a proverb is not clear to the experimenter, he is asked to write a short story to illustrate its meaning.

The experiment proceeds in the form of a conversation, in which the experimenter plays a very active role. By asking appropriate questions he can verify the accuracy and the depth of the patient's comprehension of the metaphorical meaning and elucidate the difficulties which may arise. For this reason the questions must be put carefully to the subject.

The severest disturbance of intellectual activity which this test may reveal is the complete inability to understand the metaphorical meaning, in which case the subject renders a literal interpretation of the proverb or metaphor. However, the ability to correctly interpret proverbs does not necessarily indicate the subject's level of generalization. Some proverbs may be so familiar to the subject that a correct interpretation of them means no more than that the subject already knows their meaning; in these cases no generalization of new material has taken place. A far more demonstrative method is that which requires the matching of phrases and proverbs.

Variant B. Matching Phrases and Proverbs

The subject is given a series of proverbs written in tabular form and cards on which certain phrases are written; some of these phrases may have nothing to do with the meanings of the proverbs, but may contain words reminiscent of the proverbs. The subject is asked to arrange the phrases and proverbs by meaning, so that each proverb is matched by only one phrase. Several series of proverbs and phrases are presented, graded in difficulty. By way of illustration we show the first and easiest of the series.

Proverbs: 1. Murder will out. (Literally: You cannot hide an awl in a sack.)
2. Strike the iron while it is hot.
3. All that glitters is not gold.
4. Take care of the pennies and the pounds will take care of themselves.
5. As the ale is drawn, so it must be drunk.

Phrases: 1. Gold is heavier than iron.
2. The cobbler mended the boots with an awl.
3. Everything that looks good isn't good.
4. If the snake went anywhere it came back late. (This sentence in Russian is phonetically similar to proverb No. 5.)
5. The blacksmith worked all day today.
6. By combined effort all difficulties can be overcome.
7. The truth cannot be concealed.
8. Don't put things off until tomorrow.

This variant of the method differs in certain respects from Variant A. The understanding of the metaphorical meaning of a proverb is here facilitated by the fact that although the subject may have only a confused understanding of the meaning, the phrase acts as a prompting device. The phrases provoke a difficulty of another sort, however. The chances of slipping into an approximately similar meaning are increased, for some words duplicated in the phrases and proverbs may easily provoke uncritical matching in cases when the metaphorical meaning is not completely clear. The critical factor in Variant B is thus not the ability to understand the abstraction, but rather the ability to inhibit what does not correspond to the meaning of the proverbs. The implementation of both variants will thus reveal not only the subject's general level of abstraction, but also the extent of its stability.

Whereas the methods described above are mainly aimed at investigating abstraction and generalization, other methods used in clinical practice are intended for the study of the logicality of argument. As an example of these we will describe the method known as "the establishment of the succession of events."

Establishment of the Succession of Events

The subject if given a series of 5 pictures depicting successive stages of an incident (for example, the breaking and repairing of a cartwheel).

Picture No. 1.   A road with a cart loaded with sacks. A wheel has come off the axle. The carter stands looking at it perplexed.

Picture No. 2.   The same background.   The carter is walking towards a village.

Picture No. 3.   The carter is walking along accompanied by a wheelwright carrying his tools.   The cart and the broken wheel can be seen in the distance.

Picture No. 4.   The background as in the first picture.   The carter and the wheelwright are mending the cart and have raised the shaft.

Picture No. 5.   The carter is driving off. The wheelwright is standing in the foreground. His tools are lying on the road.

The subject is instructed to arrange the pictures in order of succession of the events which they depict.   After this has been done, the subject must describe the incident in his own words, according to his arrangement of the pictures.

This simple method reveals whether the subject has understood the theme of the individual pictures, whether he can compare several elements, and whether he can reason logically when changing from one element to another.   In addition, during the performance of this test the character of the subject's attitude toward and arrangement of his work is revealed; it may be observed whether the subject notices his mistakes and corrects them quickly or is quite unconcerned by them.

The theme and presentation of the pictures used in this experiment may be modified in accordance with the degree of disturbance of the patients' mental activity.

Variants of the Association Experiment

The association experiment has long been used in psychology and psychiatry.   It originated with Sechenov [286].   In the course of an argument with Kavelin, Sechenov claimed that associations were determined in character, and to prove this statement he conducted what was essentially an association experiment. The association experiment has been used extensively by Soviet psychiatrists to investigate the intellectual activity of patients (Bekhterev [29], Tokarskii [315], Pavlovskaya [220, 221], Il'in [121, 122], Osipov [216], Dovbnya [82], and others).

However, as with other methods, the association experiment has been used for other purposes, depending upon the different theoretical viewpoints of the investigators. Exponents of idealistic psychology have interpreted associations as connections of ideas, so that they have reduced the investigation of associations to the analysis of the link between ideas, or the formation of "chains of ideas." The association experiment has also often been used by followers of the psychoanalytical school. By presenting words connected with a psychologically traumatic situation, and obtaining certain responses to these words, Jung drew conclusions regarding latent "complexes" allegedly responsible for the patient's illness.

Pavlov introduced a new, materialistic understanding of the association, which he defined as a temporary connection. It is the process of verbal association that most adequately reflects the dual physiological role of the cerebral cortex, as stated by Pavlov, in his article, "Healthy and Pathological States of the Cerebral Hemispheres," as follows: "The physiological role of the cerebral cortex is one of integration (as regards its mechanism), on the one hand, and one of the interpretation of signals, on the other..." [217; Vol. III, part 2, p. 53].

During the investigation of disorders in thinking, in addition to the methods we have already described, several variants of the association experiment may also be used. Let us examine certain variants of the association experiment.

Variant 1

The experimenter recites to the subject a standard series of words and asks him to respond to each word with another word, the first that springs to his mind. The response words are written down, and the subject's reaction time is measured in seconds with a stopwatch. This experiment can be used to analyze the content of the subject's associations, the degree of their generalization, and their rate of formation.

In healthy subjects the association experiment usually reveals a short latency period (0.5–2.0 sec) and a relevancy of the response reactions to the meaning of the word stimulus. Although they reflect the subject's experience, the response reactions are always evoked by a word stimulus. Each new word stimulus causes a change in the response reaction. This experiment can also be conducted in an informal manner upon patients who may not be able to understand or who may not be listening to the instructions. For example, it was found that excited patients, even though they were not listening to what was said to them, responded to individual words or injected into their own flow of words replicas of those addressed to them.

Variant 2

The process of association in the healthy subject is characterized not only by its degree of generalization, but also by its dynamic nature. Human associations are distinguished by their mobility and are subject to inhibition. The variant suggested by Kogan [131] may be used to investigate the extent of this mobility.

After the subject has been presented the entire series of word stimuli, the experiment is repeated once more without instructions. If, during the second presentation, the subject gives the same responses as before, the series of stimuli is presented a third time, but this time with the new instruction: "When you answer don't use the same word as before." Healthy persons experience no difficulty with this variant of the test; only an increase in the latency period is observed.

Variant 3

Sechenov [286], in his article, "Remarks on Kavelin's Book 'Problems in Psychology,'" pointed out the determinate character of associations and stressed the factors of selectivity and control. The first two variants of the association experiment do not, however, afford a measure of the extent of selectivity and control of the associations. In those variants the indeterminate nature of the instructions facilitates the appearance of associations of a different order. If, for example, the word "table" ("stol") evokes an association of the species—genus type ("table"—"furniture") or an association of the same category ("table"—"chair"), all such responses correspond to the instruction, "Answer with any word." These variants therefore cannot be used to judge the selectivity of the subject's associations. It is nevertheless extremely important to measure precisely this attribute of the patient's associations, for properly constructed judgments and conclusions imply the selective and deliberate character of the associations.

In order to determine whether the subject is capable of maintaining definite control of his associations throughout a period of time, the experiment is conducted as follows. The subject is asked to respond to each word with another which bears a specific relationship to it. He may be told, for example, to respond with a word opposite of meaning, to name a species in response to a generic word, or to name the parts of an object in response to the name of the object as a whole. A healthy subject encounters no difficulty in carrying out these instructions, which require selective response reactions. In some cases the subject does not find the required word immediately or may even not find it at all; he nevertheless has grasped the instruction and thus does not respond with any word at all.

Variant 4

This method is designed to investigate the free flow of associations, in contrast to the first three variants, in which the associations investigated arose only in response to a presented stimulus. The subject is asked to name as fast as possible a definite number (usually from 30 to 40) of words at will. The experimenter writes down these words and records the latent periods by means of a seconds counter. Analysis of the spoken words and of the associations between them will reveal the specific nature of the association connections and the speed with which they are formed. In the healthy subject the associations arising in this way are grouped in accordance with a particular conceptual principle or stimulus.

* * *

In addition to the tests included in the methods described above, another method consists of having the subject relate the theme of a story or fable. This test can be used to determine the extent to which a subject understands the theme of the story, the extent to which he generalizes and successively relates the theme, and the extent to which he maintains a consistent plot sequence throughout the experiment. His account should be tape-recorded or taken down in shorthand wherever possible.

The patient may also be asked to describe a picture. This apparently simple task may be of great value in revealing whether the subject perceives the material in generalized form or whether he dwells only on unessential details—whether he immediately describes the general meaning or becomes fixated upon the parts. This simple test may be used to detect the subject's attitudes toward work and toward his incorrect interpretations. The experimenter is able to judge whether the subject is capable of fixing his attention for long periods or whether he is soon bored and abandons the problem.

Such are the principal methods used to investigate the intellectual activity of patients. In the course of the investigations additional methods may sometimes be used in order to obtain more detailed and convincing evidence in support of the conclusions already reached. These methods will be described later, in the course of our descriptions of the relevant material.

Chapter 3

Characteristics of the Patients Investigated

In Part II we shall examine typical examples of the various types of disturbances of thinking; the characteristics of these disorders are presented on the basis of the results of our experimental psychological investigations conducted on a large sample of mental patients. The distribution of these patients according to their diagnoses is given in Table I.

Detailed clinical descriptions of these patients will be given in the following chapters in the course of the descriptions of the individual types of intellectual disturbance. Here we shall briefly summarize the main types of disease.*

*This summary is given for the nonspecialist. Students of abnormal psychology may refer themselves to textbooks of psychiatry.

TABLE I

Distribution of Patients According
to Diagnosis

Diagnosis	Number of patients
Schizophrenia	175
Epilepsy	50
Cerebrovascular diseases	155
Brain trauma	185
Oligophrenia	40
Encephalitis	30
Progressive paresis	30
Manic-depressive psychosis	15
Psychopathy	30
	Total 710

Schizophrenia is the severest and most widespread of the mental diseases. It is characterized by progressive deterioration, often proceeds in the form of long attacks, and frequently culminates in marked changes in the patient's intellectual activity and personality. The symptoms of schizophrenia are varied. It may manifest itself in the form of delusions, hallucinations, psychomotor disturbances, or obsessional states. Depending on the course of the disease and the various combinations of syndromes, different forms of schizophrenia are distinguished.

There are various theories as to schizophrenia's etiology and pathogenesis, which are at present the subject of intensive scientific discussion. Pavlov considered schizophrenia to be the result of a weakening of the cerebral cortex, leading to a transitional state between sleep and wakefulness. He considered schizophrenic symptoms to be an expression of a chronic hypnotic state.

At the time of investigation, our schizophrenic patients differed as regards their mental states and the stage of the disease. Some of them were in a stage of remission or of residual defect, while others were investigated during a relapse (or attack). In many patients a "productive" symptomatology predominated, with delusions and hallucinations. Other patients were more sluggish and exhibited such neurotic features as asthenia, anxiety, and apathy.

Epilepsy is a progressive disease of the brain characterized by two different syndromes: (a) transient, periodic paroxysms, including epileptic fits of the grand mal and petit mal type, and associated symptoms, such as disorders of consciousness; (b) permanent, progressive changes in character and the intellectual sphere; these include signs of developing dementia and a narrowing of the range of interests.

Pavlov considered that epilepsy develops against the background of a strong but unbalanced type of nervous system. He regarded the epileptic attack as a manifestation of the pathological inertia of the process of excitation in the motor analyzer. The same pathological inertia of the nervous processes is also manifested in the permanent mental changes in epilepsy.

Cerebrovascular diseases include hypertension, cerebral atherosclerosis (starting from early mental disturbances and ending with postapoplectic dementia), hypotension, various forms of vasopathy, dystonia, etc. In cerebrovascular diseases mental disorders are occasionally observed, and the basic pattern of the mental disorder is formed by the slowly progressive disturbances of the capacity for mental work.

Brain trauma. Depending on the character of the trauma, patients may be divided into two groups: (a) patients with open wounds, i.e., those in whom the shell splinter or bullet, etc., injured the dura and, usually, the brain substance, and (b) patients with closed brain injuries, such as concussions or contusions, unaccompanied by disturbance of the cranial bones. In accordance with the duration of the "traumatic disease" (a term introduced by the Soviet pathologist Smirnov), subacute and acute posttraumatic states (such as war casualties, the chronic cases in military hospitals) and patients with late sequelae of trauma may be distinguished.

Oligophrenia is the condition of incomplete mental development as a result of injury to the child's nervous system in the period of intrauterine development or in the first years of life. These conditions may result from congenital lesions of the brain, such as is found in cases of microcephaly, Down's disease, congenital neurosyphilis, etc. Para-infectious encephalitis and brain trauma affecting children under the age of $1\frac{1}{2}$–2 years may also lead to the development of oligophrenia.

The investigations of Krasnogorskii, Ivanov-Smolenskii, and other physiologists have shown that the weakness of the association function of the cortex characteristic of oligophrenia is based on a weakness of the nervous processes—in some cases mainly of excitation, and in others mainly of active inhibition.

Children with oligophrenia of varying etiologies are very frequently referred to the pediatric psychiatric clinic. Adult oligophrenics are rarely referred to the psychiatric clinic. When they are, it is mainly either in connection with the medical board's assessment of disability or on account of concomitant diseases.

Manic-depressive psychosis is another disease whose course is defined by various periods. The excited, extremely gay, active manic state of the patients gives way to an inhibited, depressed, melancholy state. The disease often consists only of a series of either depressive or manic phases. Each attack ends in recovery and the disease does not lead to permanent personality disorders, but the attacks may be repeated after short intermissions.

Great importance in the pathogenesis of manic-depressive psychosis is attached to the increased excitability of the thalamohypothalamic region. The causes of manic-depressive psychosis are not clear. Sometimes manic or depressive states are observed in clinical practice in patients with other diseases. It is very difficult or impossible to carry out experimental psychological investigations on manic patients; such patients can be investigated as a rule only in the hypomanic phase.

Progressive paresis is a severe mental disease caused by an involvement of the nervous system in the syphilitic attack upon the body. The main symptoms of progressive paresis are increasing dementia, disturbances of speech and movement, exaggerated self-importance, occasional delusions of grandeur, and and inadequate and uncritical behavior. At the present time, as a result of the successful treatment of neurosyphilis, progressive paresis is rare in the Soviet Union.

Encephalitis (inflammation of the brain substance) often leads to various forms of mental disorder (hallucinations, delusional syndromes, disturbances of intellectual activity of varied degree, uninhibited or uncritical behavior, etc.). Many different forms of encephalitis may occur. In this book the experimental data were obtained during the investigation of patients suffering from various forms of encephalitis, mainly the epidemic encephalitis described by von Economo and Geimanovich.

Psychopathy describes the dysharmonic development of the personality as a result of either constitutional or acquired abnormalities of the nervous system. Psychopathies are not mental diseases, although the intellectual and emotional-volitional spheres in these patients exhibit many symptoms. These mental idiosyncrasies of psychopaths may become so acute in connection with the difficulties of life or episodic diseases that they come to resemble pathological mental disorders. Diagnostic difficulties consequently often arise in clinical psychiatry when distinguishing between psychopathy and schizophrenia or organic brain diseases.

PART II

EXPERIMENTAL RESULTS

The intellectual disturbances observed during experimental psychological investigations may be grouped into the following three types: (1) disturbances in the process of generalization; (2) disturbances in the logical course of thinking; and (3) disturbances in the purposiveness of intellectual activity.

The intellectual attributes of each individual patient rarely fall into definite categories representing one type (or subtype) of intellectual disturbance. Complex combinations of different types of disturbance are often observed in the structure of the individual patient's particular defect of thinking. For example, in some cases a disturbance of generalization is combined with a disturbance of critical thinking, while in others faulty generalization may be found together with various subtypes of disturbances of logical thinking.

This grouping should not be regarded as a strict classification of the disorders of thinking; it is rather a list of the parameters around which are grouped the various types of disturbances of thinking encountered in psychiatric practice. Hence, during the investigation of the intellectual activity of mental patients it is unnecessary to divide the patients in accordance with the types of disturbance we have distinguished. With such a division it would be difficult in each individual patient.

It is more logical to proceed from the grouping of the patients in accordance with the nosological principles generally adopted in clinical psychiatry, and to compare the types of intellectual disturbance revealed by the experimental results with this grouping. The presence of a certain disturbance may be considered to be established in a given patient if, during the performance of the principal experimental tests (classification of objects, interpretation of proverbs, etc.), methods of solution are used which are characteristic of a particular type of thought disturbance. For example, we felt justified in concluding that the level of generalization was lowered in a patient because he solved experimental problems of this type with the aid of associations based on concrete situations.

We will turn now to an examination of the various types of disturbance in thinking. We shall begin with an analysis of the disturbance of the processes of abstraction and generalization.

Chapter 4

Disturbances in Abstraction
and Generalization

Thinking, as a generalized and indirect reflection of the out-side world, is manifested in practical life as the assimilation and utilization of knowledge, as the acquisition and application of new methods of intellectual activity. This assimilation is accomplished not as the simple accumulation of facts, but rather as a process of synthesis, generalization, and abstraction. When applying various methods of solution to a mental problem, man picks out the most general and essential principles and stimuli; that is, he generalizes the phenomena presented to him.

The psychological investigation of thinking and of its appearance and development consists of the determination of its principles as an analytic–synthetic activity which combines sensory and rational cognition into a single activity.

This view of thinking is based on the Marxist–Leninist theory of cognition, which postulates that the process of reflection of the outside world includes two stages of cognition—sensory contemplation and rational thinking. Stressing the dialectical unity of these two stages of cognition, the founders of Marxism–Leninism point out that it is the rational stage which makes it possible to probe into the essence of things and events in nature and society. "Imagination cannot grasp movement as a whole; for example, it cannot grasp movement with a velocity of 300,000 km per second. But thought can and must grasp it" (Lenin [4; 220]).

It is only generalized thinking, or thinking which employs concepts, which can provide the fullest reflection of reality. We can also understand reality by means of sensory images and visual ideas, but this method of cognition does not enable us to determine the internal connections of phenomena. Only by intellectual activity in terms of concepts can the true principles of phenomena be revealed.

This thesis of dialectical materialism is in harmony with Pavlov's dictum that speech, the "signal of signals," enables the direct impressions obtained from the outside world to be analyzed and synthesized afresh. Because of the connections of the second signal system, our reflection of the outside world is raised to a new level, surpassing the limits of direct impressions and images given by the organs of the senses.

Considerable attention was given by Vygotskii [50] to the problem of generalization. He approached the process of development of the mind historically, considering that human mental processes develop from external activity, and repeatedly emphasized the secondary character of mental processes. Human behavior and mental development find their origin in human interrelationships, which develop during material enterprise. In discussing the role of the use of tools in mental development, Vygotskii attached particular importance to language. He saw speech as a phenomenon of objective activity which arises in the process of social practice. It is used initially as a form of communication, and subsequently develops into a means of organization of human actions. Speech almost by definition implies the possibility of executive power, that of initiating and controlling action. Speech is a system of relationships and associations of social experience; it is always nothing more than the generalization of social experience.

We shall not examine in detail here the contradiction in Vygotskii's conceptual system which was so well delineated by Leont'ev and Luria [175]. As these authors rightly point out, Vygotskii's general theoretical views, in which the conscious is understood to be the product of interaction with the outside world, conflict with his experimental conclusion that consciousness is a product of human psychological intercourse. The unit of individual consciousness for him, therefore, was the meaning of speech—the product of the cultural and historical life of society. However, despite this contradiction, Vygotskii's theoretical principle that the possibility of generalization and abstraction is a most important stage in human mental development remains a significant contribution to scientific knowledge.

In his criticism of the work of Ach, Vygotskii showed that the main, and indeed decisive, factor in the process of generalization is the change from direct intellectual operations to indirect operations.   He considered generalized thinking, or thinking in the form of concepts, to be not a stepped-up version of a lower form of behavior, but a completely different type of activity.

On the basis of his own investigations and of the work of his collaborators (Zankova, Solov'eva, Shif), Vygotskii analyzes the different degrees of generalization corresponding to the different genetic stages of development—from intellectual operations by syncretisms to intellectual operations with concepts, the latter being a higher form of reflection. In Vygotskii's words, intellectual operations with concepts assumes the enrichment of reality, and the strength of scientific concepts "is shown in that sphere which is entirely determined by the higher properties of concepts—reality and arbitrariness" [50; 289]. Consequently, intellectual operations with concepts must imply a different attitude toward an object, one in which the opportunity is allowed of establishing different relationships both between objects and between the concepts themselves. Meanwhile, the systems of connections established and generalized in previous experience are not now annulled, for the formation of a generalization proceeds not only by means of the newly created generalization of single objects, but also by means of the generalization of previous generalizations. Vygotskii often returned to his conceptual nexus in Lenin's principle, which we have already mentioned: that intellectual operations with concepts enable man to take a long view of the impressions and ideas directly received by the sense organs so that, when he reverts to practical activity, he obtains an even fuller and more detailed reflection of objective reality.

The determination of the unique level of generalization in each individual is subject to innumerable variables. The nature of the problem to be solved is itself a principle factor—in healthy persons—in determining the level of generalization. Previous knowledge must be abstracted and applied to the special conditions of the problem; these operations are indirect in character.

The problem of generalization and abstraction has been the subject of many investigations by Soviet psychologists (Gal'perin, Menchinskaya, S. L. Rubinshtein; see especially Vygotskii's description of the disturbances of concepts in schizophrenic patients). Many other psychologists have devoted their work to defining the disturbances of thinking in patients suffering from various diseases of the brain (Anikina, Birenbaum, Hanfmann, Zalmanzon, Zeigarnik, Kasanin, Kogan, Kononova, Korobkova,

Kostomarova, Lebedinskii, Pitrich, S. Ya. Rubinshtein, Shubert, and many others).

Investigations of the intellectual operations of patients with different brain diseases have shown that disturbances in the process of generalization may assume various forms. Notwithstanding their great variety, they may be grouped into two types: (a) a lowering of the level of generalization; and (b) a distortion of the process of generalization. We shall describe the most general characteristics of this disturbance, illustrating it with typical examples, and we shall then go on to make a systematic analysis of the material.

1. LOWERING OF THE LEVEL OF GENERALIZATION

The lowering of the level of generalization implies that the patients' judgments are dominated by direct ideas of objects and phenomena; operations with general signs are replaced by the establishment of concrete connections between objects. During the performance of an experimental task such patients are unable to select from the full assortment of signs (stimuli, or principles) those which disclose the concept most fully. For example, in an experiment using the classification method, one such patient refused to place a cat and dog in the same group "because they fight." Another patient would not group together a fox and a beetle because "the fox lives in the forest while the beetle flies." The special signs "lives in the forest" and "flies" determined the patient's arguments to a greater degree than did the general sign "animals."

With a well-marked lowering of the level of generalization, the patients were generally incapable of performing the classification test. It seemed to them that the objects differed so much in accordance with their concrete properties that they could not be grouped together. Even the table and chair could not be grouped together because "you sit on a chair but you work and eat on a table." One patient refused to group together a key and a pair of scissors, because they are different: "This is a key and these are scissors, what can they possibly have in common?" In some cases the patients formed a large number of small groups on the basis of an extremely concrete link between them, for example: key and lock, pen nib and penholder, thread and needle, exercise book and pencil. Sometimes the subjects grouped together objects as elements of a theme (telling some story about the objects), but produced no classification. One such grouping, for example, consisted of an egg, a spoon, and a knife; another, an exercise book, a pen, and a pencil; a third, a key, a lock, and a cupboard; a fourth, a tie, a glove, a thread, and a needle, etc. The subject explained his choices as follows: "He came home from work, ate an egg with the spoon, cut a slice of bread, and then did some work, took an exercise book, pen and pencil...." Erroneous solutions of this type are called concrete-situation combinations.

The ability to operate with generalized signs characterizes thinking as an analytic–synthetic activity. For this reason disturbances of the type of concrete-situation combinations were most frequently found during the performance of our principal tests (classification of objects, explanation of proverbs, etc.), in which these mental operations are conspicuously present.

Among all the patients we investigated there was one group who performed these tests on the concrete-situation plane, as described above. Table II classifies these patients according to their specific diagnostic categories.

Such solutions were found principally in oligophrenics (95% of these patients) and in epileptic patients who have had the condition

TABLE II

Performance in the Object-Classification Test Using Concrete-Situation Combinations

Diagnosis	Total number of patients	Number of patients performing test using concrete-situation combinations
Schizophrenia	155	14 (9.0)*
Epilepsy	50	43 (86.0)
Cerebrovascular diseases	125	5 (4.0)
Brain trauma	170	7 (4.1)
Oligophrenia	40	38 (95.0)
Encephalitis	30	21 (70.0)
Progressive paresis	30	11 (36.7)
Manic-depressive psychosis	15	3 (13.3)
Psychopathy	30	—

*The number of patients is given in percent in parentheses.

since childhood (86%). Solutions of this type were also observed in a high proportion (70%) of patients with severe forms of encephalitis. As a rule, the mental states of these patients showed no psychotic symptoms (delusions, hallucination, disturbances of consciousness, etc.); a general intellectual deterioration merely predominated.

These patients could perform a simple task correctly if its conditions were firmly delineated in advance. Subsequent changes in the conditions evoked confusion and erroneous behavior. Although they readily followed the hospital routine, performed relief duties, and generally aided the staff, they often came into conflict with their surroundings, did not understand jokes, and engaged in arguments with other patients.

In some cases, in more advanced stages of disease, the patients had difficulty in sorting even with the use of a concrete sign. For example, one patient with epilepsy formed the following group: Cock, goat, dog, horse, cat. It appeared that he had formed this group on the basis of the general sign "animals," but he at once explained: "This old peasant had a dog, a cock and a goat—these were all in the farm; perhaps he didn't need a cat, although if there was a dog, perhaps there was a cat as well." The group which he had formed was not a group of "animals" in general, nor even a group of "domestic animals," but concrete animals belonging to a concrete master, who might not have a cat. Sometimes we found a solution to a problem in which the patient proposed dividing objects in accordance with the sign of a particular type of industry: paper making, agriculture, tinplating, etc.

Sometimes the objects were sorted in such a way that only the two nearest objects were grouped together. For example, table was grouped with sofa ("you have to sit at the table"); sofa was grouped with book ("it is nice to read on a sofa"), exercise book ("perhaps to write something"), pencil ("you write with a pencil or a pen and there isn't a pen here"). The patients made no attempts at classification.

All these examples indicate that the operation of classification, which is based both on the detection of the dominant property of an object and on abstraction from a large number of other concrete properties and attributes of objects, gives rise to difficulty, forcing many types of mental patients to resort to grouping on the basis of concrete-situations.

* * *

Similar results were obtained in this group of patients when they performed the test utilizing the method of exceptions (for a description of the method, see p. 50). In Table III we show the distribution of the solutions using concrete-situation combinations in this experiment.

Since any one patient did not always perform all 10 tests given to him in a particular manner, the total number of tests given and the total number of concrete-situation solutions for each group of patients are given in the table. The highest percentage of these solutions was found among the oligophrenics (87.5%) and in the patients with epilepsy (78.9%), i.e., in the same patients who, in the object-classification test, had used concrete-situation combinations (95% and 86% of solutions respectively). For example, when presented with a card on which were drawn three watches and a coin, one of the patients of this group would not agree to exclude the coin: "No, the money is not superfluous. In the first place, you can't live without money, and secondly, only with money can you buy a watch." When, in the course of the investigation, the experimenter explained that the coin was superfluous in this case, the

TABLE III

Performance in the Exclusion-of-the-Superfluous-Object Test Using Concrete-Situation Combinations

Diagnosis	Number of patients	Total number of tests undertaken	Number of concrete-situation solutions*
Schizophrenia	155	1550	230 (14.8)†
Epilepsy	45	450	355 (78.9)
Cerebrovascular diseases	125	1250	350 (28.0)
Brain trauma	160	1600	316 (19.8)
Oligophrenia	40	400	350 (87.5)
Encephalitis	20	200	84 (42.0)
Progressive paresis	30	300	220 (73.3)
Manic-depressive psychosis	10	100	30 (30.0)
Psychopathy	30	300	50 (16.7)

*This number includes refusal to do the test.

†The number of concrete-situation solutions is shown in percent in parentheses.

patient objected seriously and attempted to prove that the watches
and money fell into the same category by saying that "both watches
and coins are kept in the pocket." Another patient from this group,
when shown as objects "a thermometer, a watch, scales, and a
pair of spectacles," exclaimed that the thermometer ought to be
excluded, because "only a sick person needed it." A patient from
the same group suggested grouping together the watch, the thermometer, and the spectacles, because "if a man is shortsighted, he
will look at the thermometer and the watch through his spectacles."

When presented with four objects, three of which bore some
relation to sources of artificial light (a kerosene lamp, a candle,
an electric flashlight) and one to natural light (the sun), the patients
often chose the kerosene lamp as superfluous, explaining that nowadays it is no longer necessary, for "even in the most remote
places electricity is available." Other patients excluded the candle
for the same reason.

Typical examples of responses of this type are given in
Table IV. We may see that the patients employed properties of
the objects and formed associations between them which were
valueless for performance of the test.

In cases in which the patients' degree of intellectual defect was
more marked, they could not understand the purpose or conditions
of the test. When ordered to exclude the fourth, superfluous object,
they could not grasp that they had to combine three objects in
accordance with a definite principle. The mental operations of
comparing and contrasting appeared to be beyond their capacity.

Sometimes, immediately upon attaining an understanding of the
instructions, the patients would protest: "There is nothing superfluous here, all the objects are necessary." For example, patient D.,
the examination of whom will later be described in detail, when
shown pictures of a boot, a slipper, a shoe, and a foot, exclaimed:
"Excuse me, nothing is superfluous here. This is a man's foot, and
you can put a slipper, a boot, a shoe, or a sock on it.... Of course
there is no sock here.... If it had been a woman's foot, the slipper
would have fitted.... And perhaps if her foot had been lame, the
boot.... I think the shoe would fit a man's foot." When the experimenter suggested eliminating the foot, since it is a part of the
body while the other three objects are articles of footwear, the
patient burst out laughing: "You must be joking. How on earth can
you take away the foot? If a man had no feet, why would he need
footwear?"

TABLE IV

Typical Replies of Patients with Lowered Levels of Generalization in the Exclusion-of-the-Superfluous Objects Test

Pictures presented	Patient	Patient's responses
Kerosene lamp, candle, electric flashlight, sun	K. (oligophrenia)	You must take away the candle. You don't need it if you have a flashlight.
	D. (epilepsy)	You don't need the candle, it soon burns down so that it is useless, you may fall asleep, and then it may flare up again.
	S. (epilepsy)	You don't need the kerosene lamp, for electricity is available everywhere now. You can take away the candle, too. No, you had better keep the candle in case the electricity supply breaks down. This often happens where I live, and so we keep a stock of candles.
	K-n (epilepsy)	If it is daytime you must take away the sun, for it is light without it, but if it is night, then... (the patient is lost in thought). In any case there is no sun at night... No, that is wrong, in the daytime you must take away the candle and leave the sun, but at night you don't need the sun.
Scales, watch, thermometer, spectacles	K-n (epilepsy)	The thermometer is unnecessary. There isn't a doctor here, or a hospital. The scales are superfluous. They are needed in a shop when things have to be weighed.
	S-v (oligophrenia)	Take away the thermometer; it is only needed in the hospital.
	R-v (epilepsy)	I don't know, everything is necessary — the watch for the time, the thermometer for measuring the temperature. Perhaps the spectacles, if the man can see well, but if he is shortsighted, he will need them. Scales are not always necessary, but they are useful in business.

Another patient (an oligophrenic) also could not agree with the experimenter's suggestion to exclude the foot: "There is only one slipper, one boot, and one shoe, not a pair. How can they be worn? Better to throw them away and keep the foot. If you have only one foot you can walk with a crutch, although not so well." The patients approached the pictures of the objects from the point of view of their practical utility, and they could not perform the theoretical operation which the test required.

* * *

The impossibility of performing the test on the level of generalization and the inability to abstract from the individual concrete properties of objects were due to the fact that the patients could not grasp the conventions of the test. This inability to understand the conventions was particularly prominent during the tests requiring the interpretation of proverbs and metaphors.

Proverbs constitute a type of folklore in which a generalization or conclusion is transmitted through the image of an individual fact or event, a concrete-situation. The true meaning of the proverb becomes clear only if a person can abstract from the concrete facts mentioned in the proverb, and when the concrete, isolated events acquire the character of a generalization. It is only by the satisfaction of this condition that the gist of the proverb can be transferred to similar situations. This transfer is similar in its mechanism to the transfer of the method of solving one problem to another, as is seen especially clearly when phrases are matched with proverbs. In discussing the problem of transfer, S. L. Rubinshtein remarks that "at the basis of transfer lies generalization, and generalization results from an analysis which reveals the essential relationships." [262; 67].

Both Soviet and non-Soviet authors have investigated the understanding of metaphors. The work of Piaget [234] and Vygotskii [50], for example, has demonstrated the connection between the understanding of metaphors and the level of concept formation. Schneider [477], Gadlich, and Goldstein and Gelb [406] found that patients with diseases of the central nervous system often cannot grasp the figurative meaning of proverbs and metaphors. These authors obtained interesting experimental findings, although they attributed an independent significance to this disturbance of understanding, erroneously associating it directly with the altered meaning of the words. Moreover, we now know that this failure of understanding is not always due to the same cause. Also, the complete inability to understand metaphorical meaning is rarely observed.

Difficulty in understanding the metaphorical meaning of expressions depends not only on the altered meaning of the words but also on such other possible factors as a negativistic attitude of the patient and possible changes in the dynamics of his intellectual activity. All these factors will be discussed in the following chapters, at this stage we shall merely mention that patients who could not distinguish a generic sign in an experiment on the classification of objects frequently could not understand the metaphorical meaning of proverbs. "Strike the iron while it is hot" means, according to one patient, that "iron must not be forged when it is cold." Another patient said: "There is no such thing as an iron hand. If you mean an artificial limb, that is made of wood and not of iron." Another patient, given the proverb, "Sit on your own sledge" ("Know where you belong"), said: "Why should I sit on somebody else's sledge? Why should I? It isn't pleasant to sit on a strange sledge." The experimenter tried to explain that this proverb can apply to other situations than those concerning sledges. The patient disagreed: "How did it come about that somebody sat on a strange sledge? Was he perhaps deep in thought, thus absent-mindedly setting off with the wrong sledge?" Experimenter: "Now, if a man was doing something that wasn't his own affair, could you use this proverb?" Patient: "No, you couldn't, in one case it is 'affair' and in the other it is 'sledge.'" Only with great difficulty could the metaphorical meaning in some cases be explained to the patient; however, when the next proverb was presented to the same patient he again refused to consider anything other than its literal meaning. Since these patients interpreted words only in concrete terms, they had no conception of the metaphorical interpretation of proverbs.

In some cases, when the patient was able to understand a metaphorical meaning, the proverb nevertheless appeared to him to be insufficiently precise since it did not reflect every practical possibility. One patient, for example, disagreed with the proverb, "Truth will out" ("An awl cannot be hidden in a sack"), saying: "This isn't always true. Sometimes things hidden by thieves are not found. I know of such a case." Another patient, of the proverb, "If you are afraid of wolves, don't go into the forest," responded: "This proverb isn't true. Sometimes there is no danger. The proverb preaches cowardice." Thus, in these cases the patients' judgments are also excessively attached to the concrete facts, and their inability to abstract from them leads to failure to arrive at the conventional interpretations of proverbs and metaphors.

* * *

The inability to grasp the nature of the task in experiments involving systematic memorizing (using pictograms) is readily observable in those subjects who fail to do so. As mentioned in Chapter 2, this task is difficult because the picture cannot (and must not) reflect the whole range of associations activated by the perception of a word. The subject must select only certain of the associations which can replace the word, and he can do this only after attaining a sufficiently high level of generalization.

Birenbaum [30], using the pictogram method, found that associations to concrete-situations were predominant in patients with gross organic brain lesions. She observes that difficulty in establishing correct conventional associations was related to a disturbance in the ability to form ideas.

Our own investigations confirmed these findings. In the group of patients presently to be described, the experimental task caused considerable difficulty. For instance, when required to find a picture for memorizing the word "development," patient K. said: "What sort of development? There are different sorts—muscular development, mental development. Which do you want?" The same patient could not think of a picture for memorizing the words "heavy work": "What do you call heavy work? I found it hard to solve problems in school, and you may be weak and would find it hard to do physical work. I don't understand what I should draw." Another patient had difficulty in finding a picture for memorizing the phrase "the sick woman." He tried to draw a bed, but immediately declared that this drawing was unsuitable, because a sick woman would not necessarily be confined to bed: "She might have influenza, in which case she could be up and about." The patient then decided to draw the medicine trolley, but even this did not satisfy him: "A sick woman need not be taking medicine. She might be having physiotherapy. She might only have a toothache, or perhaps be having a baby.... Although, of course, having a baby is not an illness," and so on.

Some patients try to reflect a situation almost photographically. When asked, for example, to memorize the expression "happy holiday," the patient says: "What am I to draw? There must be an accordion, a dance, and also, perhaps, a table with a cloth, a bottle, and food. How am I to draw all this? I'm not an artist, and you would need an artist to draw it properly."

In her investigations of patients with severe brain lesions, Birenbaum observed that the difficulties in performing the pictogram task are so great that sometimes patients are unable to choose a drawing, for none seems to convey with sufficient precision and comprehensiveness the concrete significance of the words. We obtained similar results with our patients. One of them for instance, in order to memorize the words "a starving man," wanted to draw a loaf of bread; he immediately rejected this drawing as incorrect, however: "Of course, a starving man would never have any bread." He then decided to draw a thin person's face, but this did not satisfy him, for "a person can be thin through illness and not through starvation."

Being unable to grasp the nature of the task, many subjects frequently attempt to interpret the literal meaning of the word. For instance, this same patient retorted indignantly to the experimenter: "You never told me what sort of a man was starving, or why he was starving—whether it was because of a famine, or because he was out of work in a capitalist country, or because he simply was unable to eat." Instead of the general concept of "a starving man," the patient forms different ideas of a starving man in various concrete situations. We give below a few typical examples of pictograms of patients with epilepsy.

Patient A. A happy holiday. — "How can I draw this? You can be happy in different ways. One person likes to go to a movie on his holiday; that is happiness for him. Another likes to go out drinking.... This is bad, of course.... But some people I know do it all the same.... Others are happy when they go for a walk with their family, or when they take the children to the circus. How am I to draw all this? Of course, you can look at it from a different point of view, from that of society. We have national holidays, for everybody. May Day, for example. I could draw a demonstration, with a lot of flags. (The patient draws a flag, but still is not satisfied.) One flag isn't enough, there ought to be lots of flags and a crowd, but I don't know how to draw them...."

Patient M-va. A dark night. — "How can you draw a picture to make it clear, first that it is night, and second that it is dark? I could draw a moon, but then it would be light.... Of course, when there is only a half-moon, halfway through the month, then it would not be light. But still it doesn't show me that the night is dark. I shall draw a cloud (draws shading on the paper). But you can have clouds by day as well as by night, for black clouds gather before a storm and it grows dark. Turgenev gave a good account of a threatening storm, I think, in "Notes of a Hunter," but this does not refer to night. I should do better to draw a lamp, which burns at night. Admittedly, it often burns during the evening, in the twilight.... Many people light their lamps in the twilight, although it is bad for the eyes. I don't do this; I like to watch the twilight fall. What am I to draw to help me remember "a dark night"?... I shall draw a moon and a lamp to remind me that it is dark. But it isn't so, and I don't like what I am drawing. It isn't what it should convey."

Patient M-va. Heavy work. — "It is absolutely impossible to draw anything the least like heavy work. For some, mathematics is hard. I never liked it and never had to do any. Others don't take to literature. And, of course, for a weak person physical work is heavy.... Anything can be heavy. I shall draw a stone; it is hard work piling stones. Now, of course, they have cranes to lift heavy loads.... No, I cannot draw stones, but I shall draw a hammer, like the one a blacksmith uses. But there, again, there are no more hammerers nowadays, it is all done by machines. I don't know, doctor, what.... Oh, well, it can be a stone and a hammer.

Patient K-v. Doubt. — "How can I do this, what is it that is in doubt? You can have doubts about people, about what you don't know, about what decisions to make. Weak-willed people often have doubts. You can also have doubts about material things. You buy something, for example, perhaps some material for a suit or a dress. How do you know whether it is pure wool or not? You see that you can have doubts about so many things, and yet you want me to draw about it at once. I should need to have plenty of talent for this, to be able to draw all these things. I don't agree that they can all be represented by any one drawing...."

Hence an analysis of the data obtained by different methods (classification of objects, method of exclusion, explanation of proverbs, and method of pictograms) revealed disturbances of the process of generalization in epileptic, encephalitic, and oligophrenic patients; their arguments were of the concrete-situation type and they did not understand metaphors and conventions. We included these patients in a single group in which the intellectual disturbances focused upon the lowering of the level of generalization.

A lowering of the level of generalization was found not only in their performance on the above-mentioned experimental tests which required some degree of complex analytic–synthetic activity, but also in the activation of latent associations.

An association experiment carried out with the patients of this group, which consisted of 30 epileptics and 20 oligophrenics, revealed the lack of generalization of their associations. In 33.3% of the cases (altogether 1050 words were presented) no response reaction was present; the actual request, "Answer as a single word," was too conventional a task for the patients: "A table is a table, what else can I say?" In 34.3% of the responses the patients named the function or a particular attribute of the object ("pencil"— "write"; "berry"—"red"); 11.4% of the responses consisted of synonyms of the presented word; only 21% of the replies were adequate.

As a further illustration of the lowering of the level of generalization in these patients, we now present extracts from case records together with the results of the experimental psychological examination of several individuals.

Patient D., male (case notes of Dr. Ya. I. Chekhovich), born 1921. At the age of 11 months he had an attack of meningoencephalitis. Development was retarded. He attended a special school and did not qualify for any trade. At 16 years of age he began to work as an assistant laborer. Although he liked physical work and was diligent and efficient, he was irritable and prone to quarrel. Attacks of psychomotor excitation with impulsive fits were observed (tearing off the bedclothes, throwing things through the window); it was mainly because of these that he was several times admitted to the hospital.

In the hospital the patient was properly oriented in space and time, fussy, talkative (repeating the same phrases in a stereotyped manner), quarrelsome with the other patients, and disinclined to obey the rules of the ward; nevertheless, he did his share of work.

In the object-classification test, the patient did not at once understand the instruction ("They are all different"), and attempted to count the pictures. After further explanation by the experimenter, he placed into one group the pictures of a cart and a horse, and those of a doctor and a thermometer into another, with the words: "Let him measure the temperature." Into a third group he placed a cupboard, a saucepan, and a beetroot: "You can cook this in the pan and put it in the cupboard." He included a flower with a beetle and a bird, with the explanation: "The beetle must settle on the flower. Birds eat beetles, but this one is too big. ... I have seen how mother birds feed their young." He combined a dress with a charwoman: "She will wear it." A fox, a bear, and a tree were placed in the same group: "These live in the forest." The experimenter tried to help the patient to form more general associations between the objects, but without success. For instance, the patient replied to the suggestion to place the cat and dog into one group by saying: "They don't live peacefully together." In the same way the patient did not agree to classify together a fish, a fox, a wolf, and a goat: "No, this won't do. A fish swims, foxes and wolves live in the forest, and goats run about the farmyard. They cannot be placed together." The patient was unable to place pictures together in accordance with some common generalizing sign, but was guided in the performance of his task by purely concrete, special signs.

When the task was to arrange pictures in serial order, the patient described the details of each picture individually without integrating them into a single whole: "Here the cart has broken, and here (picture No. 4) it is being mended; here the man is going for a walk (pointing to picture No. 2, which illustrates the driver going to the village to seek help). Here the cart is moving (picture No. 5)."

Experimenter. Where does the story begin?
Patient. Here (pointing to picture No. 1). The wheel was broken.
E. What comes next?
P. This one; it is being mended (No. 4).
E. And next?
P. Here he comes with an ax. Probably to chop some timber (No. 3).
E. Where is the driver going?

P. To chop wood.
E. Or, perhaps, to the village to seek help?
P. Yes, of course, so that this will be the second picture. Correct.

The patient placed the second picture after the first, then the fourth, and then turned to picture No. 3, where the driver was shown returning with a helper. Not until the experimenter had given leading questions was the patient able to arrange the pictures in the correct order.

For a long time the patient was unable to understand the instructions in an association experiment: "A table is a table, what else is there to say about it?" After further explanations and examples, the patient began to solve the problem. His response reactions (see Table V) consisted either of adjectives qualifying the word stimulus ("air"—"fresh") or of words indicating its immediate function ("lamp"—"burning"; "bread"—"eating"). Of 21 response reactions 3 were qualifications, 7 denoted function, and 10 were mere repetitions of the word stimulus ("fall"—"to fall"; "brother"— "a brother is a brother"). The patient's associations were thus not generalized in character and their range was narrow. His limited range of associations was particularly obvious after the test was repeated, using the same word stimuli but with the instruction to respond with a different word from the one he gave during the first test. As shown in Table V, our patient either responded with the same words as before, or merely repeated the word stimulus. Only in five cases did he react with another word (one of which was a synonym of the word stimulus—the two names for the bell).

It was also difficult for the patient to understand metaphors and proverbs. When asked to explain the metaphor "golden head," the patient replied: "There is no golden head, only the head on a statue may be gilded." He explained the proverb, "Strike while the iron is hot," as follows: "If iron is cold it isn't soft and cannot be forged; it cannot be made into horseshoes." In reply to the experimenter's question as to whether this proverb can be applied to doctors, the patient said: "No, it cannot. Doctors heal the sick, they don't forge. They aren't blacksmiths." The results of this experimental test thus showed that the patient could not draw abstract conclusions from concrete, habitual associations and relationships between objects.

Patient S., female (case records of Dr. A.S. Remezova), born 1905. Diagnosis of epilepsy. At the age of 3 she suffered a head concussion. She was slow to learn at school and achieved little. At 15 years of age she began to have epileptic fits, with loss of consciousness, which gradually became more frequent, and her memory and intellect began to deteriorate sharply. After 1941, on account of the worsening of her condition, she was periodically admitted to a psychiatric hospital, where she was treated with Luminal; she was last admitted in 1952. On the ward the patient was lethargic and taciturn. Her movements and responses were slow. Her store of words was poor and her circle of interests narrow. With the staff she was officious and sometimes fractious and malicious. Frequent epileptic fits were observed (approximately once a week), with convulsions and loss of consciousness, which terminated in sleep.

Pathophysiological investigation (by S. M. Pavlenko) revealed an instability of differential reaction, signs of successive inhibition, weakness of stimulation, and a weakening of internal inhibition.

TABLE V

Results of an Association Experiment (Patient D.)

Stimulus word	First presentation		Second presentation*	
	latency period (in sec)	response reaction	latency period (in sec)	response reaction
bread	1.5	eat	1.5	loaf
lamp	2.5	burning	2	to burn
singing	2	better	2.5	better
wheel	2.5	turns	2.5	turns, it is round
beauty	3.5	beautiful	2.5	good
war	2.5	war	2	war, war
red	1.5	color	2	dark red
air	2.5	fresh	2.5	air, don't know
blue	2.5	color	2.5	color
bell (electric)	3.5	rings	4.5	hand bell
mountain	1.5	high	2.5	high, not a chimney
moon	2.5	month	2.5	month, half-month
brother	2	a brother is a brother	3.5	brother, one's own brother
treatment	1.5	cure	2.5	treat, treatment is better
ax	2.5	ax	3.5	ax-handle
falling	2.5	to fall	5	don't know
head	1.5	aches	3.5	head
to run	2.5	fast	3.5	to run, to go on foot
berry	2.5	raspberry	3.5	cranberry
to make a noise	2	loudly	2.5	to cry
depth	2.5	deep	3.5	don't know

*Instruction: "Don't reply with same words you used before."

In the object-classification test the patient for a long time could not understand the instruction and kept looking at the pictures. Picking up the picture of a goose, she said: "There is nothing more like this here, this a gander, there are no more ganders" (she put the picture to one side. Taking a picture of a carrot, she said: "This is a carrot.... Just look, what a fine red carrot, there are no more like it." The experimenter asked her to place the carrot into the same group as the beetroot, but she protested: "That is a carrot and this a beetroot; they are different." On reflection, she continued: "You can make soup from them, and put cabbage in as well." She looked for a picture of a cabbage: "There isn't one." The experimenter repeated the instruction once more and asked her to place suitable objects into one group. The patient placed the cow with the goat, saying: "They graze together." The experimenter asked the patient to place the bear in the same group, but she replied with fear: "What do you mean? The bear would eat them." When the experimenter suggested placing the blacksmith and the charwoman together in the same group, the patient replied: "Let them, they are man and wife, but where are the children?" She looked among the pictures and found a skier: "This is their son."

The task of establishing the sequence of events was performed as follows. The patient picked up picture No. 3 and said: "They are walking, and here (pointing to picture No. 5) he is riding into the forest.... You know, they wanted to go for wood, they went, but this one is staying behind, this one wants to go home." She picked up picture No. 4: "Here the wheel has broken." She glanced at picture No. 1: "They had piled a lot of sacks." The experimenter repeated the instruction. The patient turned to picture No. 4 and said: "The driver went somewhere." She arranged the pictures in the order, 5, 3, 4, 2, 1, with the following explanation: "The driver was going somewhere, and on the road he saw something.... The wheel fell off.... Then he ran.... He needed a hammer, you know.... And this one (picture No. 1) is keeping watch to see that it is not stolen. The one in blue ran off and the one in the red shirt stayed behind. Where is he running?... Somehow the wheel fell off. The cart was so heavily laden with flour that it broke.... They did not look at it, it was not properly managed."

The results of an association experiment (see Table VI) revealed the restricted, elementary character of this patient's associations. Basically, her response reactions consisted either of a very elementary qualification of the stimulus word ("singing"—"better";

TABLE VI

Results of an Association Experiment (Patient S.)

Stimulus word	First presentation		Second presentation*	
	latency period (in sec)	response reaction	latency period (in sec)	response reaction
bread	2	ear of corn	2	paper
lamp	2.5	light	2.5	to shine
singing	2.5	better	3.5	to sing
wheel	1.5	round wheel	3	wheel...don't know
beauty	3.5	don't know	3	don't know
war	3.5	they fight	5	he is silent
red	3	color	2	a blue color
air	5.5	in the room	5	air is what...
light blue	1.5	dark blue	2.5	light blue
bell	8	rings	3	happy
mountain	3.5	high mountain	4	high
moon	3.5	round	3.5	moon, sun
laughter	8	they roar with laughter	3.5	they roar with laughter
brother	2	kin	2.5	sister
treatment	3.5	they treat patients	5	don't know
ax	5	they chop wood	4	a sharp ax
head	3	head aches	4.5	head
to run	3.5	to run	3	he stands
berry	2	sweet or sour	3.5	sour
to make a noise	2	noise	3.5	to make a noise
depth	5.5	don't know	3	deep in a well

*Instruction: "Do not reply with the same words you used before."

"wheel"—"round") or of echolalia ("to run"—"to run"; "to make a noise"—"noise"). When the stimulus-word was presented a second time, the patient either declined to answer or merely repeated the stimulus-word or emitted the previous response.

Patient K., male (case records of Dr. Ya. I. Chekhovich), born 1917. Diagnosis: para-infectious encephalitis. Hallucinatory-paranoid syndrome.

The patient was born prematurely. In early childhood he had frequent illnesses (pneumonia, diphtheria twice). He was late starting to walk and talk. Mental retardation was noticed from early infancy. He studied at a special school. Since childhood other children had made a laughing stock of him, and he could not stick up for himself. He had always been slow in his movements and thoughts. In later life all attempts to train the patient for work had been unsuccessful because of his extremely slow tempo of work, although everything he did, he did thoroughly. Since 1944 he had worked in the bookbinding workshop of the day hospital of a psychoneurological outpatient treatment center. At the end of April 1950, after an attack of influenza, he began to have delusions of persecution accompanied by hallucinations, heard voices "threatening to kill him or summoning him to go somewhere." He appeared to be very alarmed and excited, especially at night.

Neurological State. Gordon's sign positive on the left. Exophthalmos. Reaction to light sluggish. During convergence the left eye deviates outward. Asymmetry of the nasolabial folds. Marinesco's sign positive on the right. Loss of tone in the limbs. Knee and ankle jerks brisker on the right. Unsteadiness during Romberg's test. Hypermimia. Tremor of the eyelids, tongue, and fingers. Salivation.

Mental state. Sluggish and importunate. Makes stereotyped requests. Speaks eagerly about his experiences. Convinced that he is being persecuted by a certain group of persons living in his house. In the hospital he does not hear voices, but thinks that some of the patients are "associated with his enemies or friends." The store of knowledge which he acquired at the special school is preserved. His interests are extremely narrow.

In an experiment on the classification of objects, the patient asked: Do I have to count?" Experimenter: "No, there is no need to count, but you have to arrange similar things in groups." The patient looked at the cards without understanding. The experimenter then took two cards containing pictures of an elephant and of a shovel, and said: "Look here, for example, an elephant and a shovel do not belong to the same group." · The patient smiled, happiness spread over his face: "I understand, animal goes with animal." He began to arrange them, and formed the following groups: (1) pig and horse ("They are animals"); (2) blacksmith and charwoman ("people"); (5) violet and bush ("flowers"); (6) cat and dog (he was silent); (7) cupboard and bookcase ("They are in a room"). He did not arrange the remaining cards (cart, airplane, beetle, shovel, goose, etc.) into groups. The experiment subsequently proceeded as follows.

Experimenter. (Pointing to the second group.) What do you call this group?
Patient. They are animals.
E. What can you put there?
P. I don't know.
E. Shall we put the goose there?
P. No, we can't. It swims.
E. Shall we put the beetle there?
P. No, we can't. It is an insect.
E. Then shall we put the goose and the sparrow together?
P. No, we can't. The goose swims and the bird flies.
E. But surely a goose is a bird?
P. Yes.
E. Well then, we will put them together.
P. No, the goose swims and the bird flies, and it lives in the forest.
E. Can we put a bear and a fox together with a cat and dog?
P. No, we can't. The cat and dog live in a house, but the bear and fox live in the forest or at the zoo, for I have seen them there.
E. But surely the fox and bear are animals, too?
P. Yes.
E. This will be the group of all the animals. Let us put them together.
P. No, they are different. But have it your own way (reluctantly, still thinking it over). It won't be right.

E. Now, can we put the cupboard and bookcase together?
P. Yes, we can.
E. Can we put the cart and the automobile together?
P. No, we can't. They are different.
E. Surely you can ride in a cart and you can ride in an automobile?
P. If the cart is tied with a rope to an automobile it can be pulled. I have seen this done.

Let us now turn to the results of the performance of tests involving the "establishment of the sequence of events." The patient begins to explain the third picture (the driver and the foreman are going for the tool): "Here they are walking with the ax. They will probably chop some wood." He picks up the second picture: "And here he is going for a walk. You see that he has gone." He pays no attention to the remaining pictures. The experimenter again explains that the pictures must be arranged in the proper order. The patient picks up the fourth picture, exclaiming: "Here the wheel has broken. He picks it up and mends it. ... And here (looking at picture No. 3) they are going to look for wood." The experimenter helps the patient by saying that the broken wheel is also shown in the second picture. The patient thanks him ("Yes, it is broken"), but draws no conclusion and continues to examine the picture. He moves on to picture No. 4: "Here he is riding somewhere, and here stands a man." Then, after considering the matter, he returns to picture No. 3 and exclaims: "Here they are mending the wheel." He looks at picture No. 1: "They have mended it, but it has fallen off again." As a result, the following sequence of the pictures is obtained:

No. 5. "The sawed plank of wood. The man on the cart is carrying a basket."
No. 1. "The cart has broken down; the wheel has fallen off."
No. 4. "Here it is being mended."
No. 2. "It has fallen off again."
No. 3. "The workmen are going with axes, most certainly to chop wood."

These experimental results show that these patients are unable to distinguish the essential properties of objects or to discover the principal relationships between them. When patient D. sees the cards showing a dress and a charwoman, the association, "A woman wears a dress," springs to his mind. On the other hand, the more logical associations do not occur to him: "A woman is a living being," or, "A dress is an article of clothing."

As a result of their inability to form abstract generalizations from the concrete properties and details of objects, these patients cannot solve even the simplest problem if its solution requires the comparison of these properties, the rejection of some, and the selection of others. When performing the task of establishing the sequence of events (such as in the breaking and mending of a wheel), the patients fixate upon individual details of the picture and find it impossible to join them. For instance, patient D. at first begins to argue in support of the wheel having fallen off, but when he sees the next picture of the woodcutter with the ax, he makes a suggestion about where he is bound for with the ax: "Probably to the forest to chop wood." In precisely the same way patient S., when shown a series of pictures depicting how wolves attack a boy who is walking through the forest, and how the boy climbs a tree, exclaims: "He is picking apples, that is why he climbed the tree." After the experimenter had turned the patient's attention to the snow and pointed out that apples do not grow in winter, the patient replied: "Yes, that is true, how can I have said that ? ... Why did he climb the tree?", but did not correct his mistake. Any stimulus arouses standard, stereotyped associations: the boy climbed the tree, consequently he was picking apples, the man had an ax in his hands, consequently he was going to the forest to chop wood. The individual details are neither joined nor integrated, thus precluding any understanding of the situation as a whole. This extremely narrow range of association, in combination with a usually limited range of knowledge and ability, affords these patients very limited possibilities for effective action in real-life situations; they behave satisfactorily only in certain rigidly predetermined conditions. Patient T., for example, an oligophrenic, worked as a messenger and performed adequately all the duties expected of him. When, one day, he was instructed to obtain the signatures of all of his colleagues to a document, he burst in on a closed meeting explaining that the person speaking at that moment must sign the paper. Suggestions that this could all be done at a later time were to no avail, and the meeting was interrupted. T. would not leave, but burst into tears and exclaimed: "I have been ordered to see that everybody signed it." The special conditions of the situation caused no change in patient T.'s behavior.

Tokarskii describes an instance of this type of behavior in his paper, "On Folly" [316]. He cites the fool from the folk tale who was beaten after making merry during an accidental fire, with the reprimand that a fire must be put out with water. When, the next day, the fool saw people roasting a pig over a fire, he seized a bucket of water, poured it on the fire, and was beaten again. The fool had thus grasped only part of the command—that fires must be put out with water; he had not understood the fundamental difference between the two fires. Tokarskii correctly remarks in this context that although the fool had grasped the instruction and remembered it, he had not taken into account the changed conditions. The fundamental characteristic of foolishness, according to Tokarskii, is the "failure of action to correspond to the demands of the actual situation." This failure to correspond occurs because the fool is unable to stretch his field of perception to include everything taking place around him. "The fool," remarks Tokarskii, "sees and hears only a small part of everything that exists in the world of reality." His deficiency in the ability to abstract and generalize places him in the same category of behavioral disability as are the patients we have just described.

It is interesting to note that Seguin [279] claimed that the intellect of a mentally retarded child (in Seguin's terminology, an idiot) "is excited only by one particular aspect of a phenomenon which possesses many such aspects." Moreover, when preparing to react to such concrete phenomena, the mentally retarded individual, in Seguin's opinion, "not only limits their number to the minimum possible, but even within this limited sphere his ideas are neither complete nor constant."

Authors discussing the psychology of the mentally retarded child cite experimental findings that show that such children cannot discover the common element from among a variety of single phenomena. During the 1930's, Vygotskii and Shif found that the mentally retarded child who has learned to work with visual systems of associations is unable to systematize his experience through generalization and abstraction. The structure of associations based on words is abnormal in the mentally retarded child. Solov'ev [299] points out that instead of generalizing, mentally retarded children tend to compare their previously acquired knowledge with the elements of the new task. Zankov [95, 96] states that for such children the difficulty arises when they turn to intellectual tasks whose solution requires the utilization of new patterns of behavior. Investigations conducted on mentally retarded children at the Institute of Defectology of the RSFSR Academy of Pediatric Sciences by Luria and his co-workers (Khomskaya, Tikhomirov, Lubovskii, Meshcheryakov) revealed a disturbance of the cortical neurodynamics [182].

By the use of a motor–speech technique, Meshcheryakov [200] found that the mentally retarded child formed associations which were fragile and unstable because of their inadequate basis in speech. Tikhomirov [314] found that in mentally retarded children the associations of the speech system exert an inadequate control over their behavior. If the verbal associations come into conflict with direct, concrete associations, the latter prove dominant, and the former, although preserved in the speech system, cease to regulate the child's behavior. Martsinovskaya [187] found that verbal analysis and generalization of direct or concrete systems of associations were absent in schizophrenics. Her results agree with those obtained by Krasnogorskii [153], who discovered weakness of excitation and disturbance of differentiation in oligophrenic children.

It can be said that the intellectual activity of such patients represents an imperfect reflection of objects, phenomena, and their interrelationships. A perfect process of reflection of the objective properties and principles which underlie material objects always assumes the ability to abstract from concrete details. In discussing the sensory–abstract–practical nature of thinking, Lenin stressed that the act of generalization is a deviation from concreteness. "The approach of the (human) mind to an individual object, and the acquisition of an impression (an idea) from it is not a simple, direct, rigid act, but a complex, bifurcating, zigzag-shaped act allowing for the flight of fantasy from life." [4; 370].

In our patients this "flight" from single associations was extremely difficult. Words did not serve for them as a vehicle of generalization, but remained, in Sechenov's definition [286], "nick-names." In discussing the process of the formation of ideas in the child, Sechenov points out in his book 'Elements of Thought' that not every meaning or use of a word implies realization of its true significance; although a small child may use correctly words such as "plant" or "animal," these words are no more than "nicknames" for the corresponding objects.

It is only the use of general concepts that can convey a correct understanding, lead to adequate action, and provide man with his (to use Pavlov's expression) "extraordinary advantages." "Nick-names," on the other hand, are imperfect instruments of intellectual activity.

* * *

From superficial observation it might be said that the intellectual activity of patients with an impairment in the ability to generalize resembles to some extent the thought processes of the healthy small child; this, however, is not so. The associations formed during the child's life experience are still insufficiently generalized; ideas have not yet assumed a dominant, controlling role in the child's activity (in some cases they have not yet even been formed). By itself, however, the process of formation of new ideas is within the child's range of abilities. (We are not concerned, here, with the fact that this process of the formation of ideas is limited, of course, by the child's age.) In the course of his development the child learns to master the operations of metaphorical interpretation and abstraction. The formation of ideas goes on continuously in the normal child, despite the small range of his knowledge and skill.

It is a different matter with the intellectual disintegration of the adult patients with impaired generalization. During investigation they revealed (especially in the cases of well-educated professional persons) an integrity even of general ideas and were still able to perform certain intellectual operations, but they were unable to form new ideas or to acquire new mental skills. This inability to form new generalizations, even in the presence of an adequate stock of previously formed ideas and knowledge, is the characteristic feature of organic dementia.

We should not conclude, however, that generalization in the demented patient regresses to the level of the child. It is not that the process of the lowering of the level of generalization, on the one hand, and the development of the generalizing skill, on the other, merely originate at opposite ends of the same continuum. The low level of generalization in the demented patient does in fact differ qualitatively from the inadequate level of generalization of the small child. We must therefore examine the structure of the intellectual activity of the mentally retarded child.

The diagnostic differentiation between dementia and mental retardation must often be made in clinical practice. It is often suggested that in dementia there is a quantitative reduction of acquired associations, whereas in the mentally retarded patient they do not accumulate. Not by chance do we often find in the psychiatric literature vivid comparisons between the patient with an organic dementia, who has "dissipated his wealth," and the oligophrenic, who is poor and has never acquired any.

This view of the nature of dementia and mental backwardness is incorrect. Dementia and mental backwardness are different in principle. In the mentally retarded child the process of acquisition of new ideas—especially general concepts—is extremely slow and difficult, and the limitations of age are much more marked than in the healthy child. The oligophrenic child's knowledge of objects and events and his general abilities and skills are poor and imperfect, yet such a child can still acquire some new ideas and skills; he can therefore be educated. Patients with dementia, on the other hand, although they retain the traces of previous generalizations, are unable to acquire new material or to make use of their previous experience.

Consequently, the intellectual activity of the demented patient is not similar in structure to that of the retarded child. Demented patients cannot be educated.

2. DISTORTION OF THE PROCESS OF GENERALIZATION

The disturbance of the thought process which we call distortion of the process of generalization is apparently the antithesis of that just described.

Whereas the judgments of the patients described above do not go beyond the bounds of single, individual associations, in the patients whom we shall now discuss the "flight" from concrete associations assumes a grossly exaggerated form. In their judgments these patients reflect only some random aspect of phenomena, and they pay little attention to the essential relationships between objects, and disregard the objective value of things and events. For example, when asked to classify objects, these patients are guided by excessively general signs and respond inadequately to the real relationships between objects. Patient M., for example, grouped together a fork, a table, and a shovel in accordance with the principle of "solidity"; and a mushroom, a horse, and a pencil in accordance with the "principle of joining the organic to the inorganic."

We describe this manner of performing experimental tests as formal, illogical, or capricious. Table VII shows that it is found most frequently in patients with schizophrenia (in 67% of the patients whom we examined), mainly with the hallucinatory, paranoid form of the disease, and in psychopaths (33%).

TABLE VII

Performance in the Object-Classification Test Using Formal, Illogical Combinations

Diagnosis	Number of patients investigated	Number of patients making mistakes during performance of tests
Schizophrenia	155	107 (67.1)*
Epilepsy	50	2 (4.0)
Cerebrovascular diseases	125	–
Trauma	170	4 (2.4)
Oligophrenia	40	–
Encephalitis	30	6 (20.0)
General paresis	30	–
Manic-depressive psychosis	15	–
Psychopathy	30	10 (33.3)

*The number of incorrect solutions is shown in percent in parentheses.

TABLE VIII

Performance in the Object-Classification Test Using Formal and Illogical Associations

Objects classified in the same group	Patients	Explanation
cupboard, saucepan	M. (schizophrenia, paranoid type)	"Both have an opening."
automobile, spoon, cart	G-n (schizophrenia, paranoid type)	"A spoon also moves, toward the mouth."
beetle, spade	G-n (schizophrenia, paranoid type)	"You dig the earth with a spade, a beetle also digs the earth."
flower, spoon, shovel	D-n (schizophrenia)	"All these objects are long."
goose, pig	K-v (psychopathy)	"The goose and pig aren't friendly."
shovel, horse	E-n (schizophrenia, paranoid type)	"They both begin [in Russian] with the letter 'L.'"
clock, bicycle	M. (schizophrenia)	"A clock measures time, and if you are riding a bicycle, it also measures space."

Such patients live in a world of their own hallucinations and have little interest in the real situation. They attempt to approach unimportant, commonplace events "from theoretical standpoints." In conversation they can discuss matters of a general character, but often they cannot give a simple answer to a concrete question. Their language is flowery. For example, when talking about a cupboard, one such patient called it "a circumscribed part of space," and when discussing a friend, whom he described as a good man, he said: "What is good and evil? This definition is relative—positive and negative, like the problem of electrons and the universe. If something is bad, this is a qualitative aspect, and it means that something else must be good. But bad may be taken for good, and the two are not opposite."

Some of the more demonstrative examples of how such patients perform tests on the classification of objects are shown in Table VIII. They either make use of signs which are so general (hardness, movement) that they go far beyond the essential signifi-

TABLE IX

Examples of Performance of Pictogram Tests Using Formal, Illogical Associations

Words given for memorizing	Patients	Drawings and explanations
development	M-v (schizophrenia)	Two arrows
development	Od-ov (schizophrenia)	A rope. "It can develop."
razluka (separation)	M-v (schizophrenia)	Onion (luk)
somnenie (doubt)	E-n (schizophrenia)	Catfish (som)
somnenie (doubt)	Sim-v (schizophrenia)	A clay ball (in Russian "kom gliny"). "Glinka wrote a novel 'Somnenie,' let it be 'gling' (clay)."
devochke kholodno (the girl is cold)	L-aya (schizophrenia)	$\frac{\pi D^2}{4}$ "They both have a letter D."
devochke kholodno (the girl is cold)	R-v (schizophrenia)	Two squares. "You said two words."
devochke kholodno (the girl is cold)	K-v (schizophrenia)	Some dots and a triangle. "The dots are snow, let the triangle be the girl."
pechal' (grief)	K-v (schizophrenia)	To print (pechat'). "It begins with pech."
pechal' (grief)	L-na (schizophrenia)	Stove (pechka). "It begins with "P."

TABLE X

Diagnostic Breakdown of the Performance of Test Involving
"Composition of Pictograms" Using Formal, Illogical Associations

Diagnosis	Number of patients	Total number of drawings	Number of illogical drawings
Schizophrenia	150	1500	960 (64.0)*
Epilepsy	35	350	30 (8.6)
Cerebrovascular diseases	105	1050	95 (9.0)
Brain trauma	140	1400	80 (5.7)
Oligophrenia	10	100	—
General paresis	15	150	—
Manic-depressive psychosis	10	100	—
Psychopathies	30	300	99 (33.0)
Total	495	4950	1264 (25.4)

*The numbers of illogical drawings are given in percent in parentheses.

cance of the phenomena, or they work on purely external, immaterial signs (an opening).

The illogical, aimless character of the judgments of the patients
of this category is particularly obvious when they attempt to com-
pose pictograms. One such patient, for example, in order to memorize the words "teplyi veter" (a warm wind), drew two triangles
(treugol'niki), and to memorize the expression "veselyi uzhin" (a
jolly supper), two circles (kruzhki). Another patient of this group,
to memorize the word "somnenie" (doubt), drew a catfish (som),
and to memorize the word "razluka" he drew an onion (luk).

Patients with a lowered level of generalizing ability have difficulty in composing pictograms because they cannot form abstractions when presented with individual concrete word meanings.
Another group of patients could perform it very easily, since they
produced any associations at random which bore no particular
logical relation to the problem. The drawings were interpreted so
widely and unobjectively that the result bore no logical relationship
to the word or words.

In Table IX we show the most typical examples of performance
on this task in which illogical and formal associations are used.
Table X shows that such associations were formed mainly by
patients with schizophrenia (64%).

The illogical character of the mental activity of these patients was also demonstrated by an association experiment. Such an experiment, conducted on 50 patients with schizophrenia, showed that adequate responses were given in only 30.4% of cases (altogether 1050 words were presented). Nearly half the answers (45.8%) were echolalic in type ("koleso"—"kolesnitsa"), consonant ("lechenie"—"techenie"; "topor"—"bor"), or were stereotyped phrases ("aim"—"the aim justifies the means"). Irrelevant responses also appeared: "luna" (moon)—"yad" (poison). Response reactions denoting the concrete function of the object or its concrete properties occurred in only 11.4% of the cases. So far as refusal to reply is concerned (12.4%), this was due not to any difficulty, as in the patients of the first subgroup (with a lowered level of generalizing ability), but more to a negativistic attitude toward the task.

TABLE XI

Examples of Definition of Ideas by Patients with Distortion of the Process of Generalization

Words to be defined	Patients	Definitions
Clock	O-v schizophrenia	A mechanical object, a form of objectiveness, or an object of logic.
Clock	A-v schizophrenia	The impulse or pulse of the vitality of all mankind.
Clock	Z-na schizophrenia	A measure of a definite property of matter, what do they call it in philosophy? An attribute, isn't it?
Cupboard	M-v schizophrenia	This is an object belonging to inanimate nature; it has practical application for the preservation of other material particles.
Cupboard	A-v schizophrenia	An element of the conditions of life.
Cupboard	D-na schizophrenia	An object of daily use, a collection of atoms.
Horse	A-v schizophrenia	A being in close relationship to people.
Horse	K-i schizophrenia	An animate object, no longer essential, for technical progress has made it obsolete.
Horse	K-n schizophrenia	This is an animate object; no, better to say a phenomenon, helping man with his work.

TABLE XII

Examples of Comparison of Concepts by Patients with Distortion of the Process of Generalization

Words for comparison	Patients	Patients' statements
Rain and snow	A-v schizophrenia	"Objects of humidity, distinguished by the displacement of certain substances in relation to the circumference of the earth."
Deception and error	A-v schizophrenia	"The life relationships of humanity as a whole, the rejection of particles of nonliving substances, but an error is an inappropriate act in human relations."
Deception and error	K-n schizophrenia	"Deception is an immoral behavior, a defect in the relationship to production; an error is also a defect, but a permissible one. It ought to be corrected. Then it is not an immoral attitude to life."
Sledge and cart	A-v schizophrenia	"A modification of appearance."
Sledge and cart	P-v schizophrenia	"From the grammatical point of view both these words are nouns, but "sani," the word for sledge, does not exist in the singular, while cart may be either singular or plural."

The predominance of formal, random associations, coupled with a departure from the sense of the problem, forms the basis of the fruitless hairsplitting which characterizes such patients and which is known clinically as "ratiocination."

Ratiocination is frequently exhibited by these patients during the simplest forms of mental operation, such as the description of pictures illustrating a theme. Unable to grasp the concrete meaning of the theme, these patients seem compelled to perceive the pictures from the viewpoint of grossly overgeneralized principles. For example, one such patient described the picture of a woman chopping wood as follows: "The theory of the establishment of living conditions." Another patient said in regard to the same picture:

"Here we see everything for man; this is called his way of life"; a third patient explained it as "...woman and her fate."

This symptom of sterile reasoning is especially prominent during the performance of tasks requiring verbal formulation, for example the definition and comparison of concepts (see Tables XI and XII). It stands out even more clearly in experiments with tasks involving the explanation of parables. Patient E. (this patient will later be considered in greater detail) interpreted the proverb, "All that glitters is not gold," as follows: "Whatever happens, you must say that not everything that glitters is gold. It would be truer to say that this proverb stands by itself; it soon exhausts itself. Here there is a depreciation of gold as a metal, from the philosophical point of view. The essence does not lie in gold. Possibly another metal, not so contemptible as gold, shines and is more useful to man. A ray of light, falling on glass, shines and may also be useful.... Now, any form of radiation.... But then, generally speaking, one must not look on man and his affairs from a purely external standpoint."

Although this patient grasped the idea of a metaphor, his statements were only partly concerned with defining its meaning. Fundamentally, the patient indulged in futile reasoning in relation to the subject under discussion, in this particular case the "value" of gold, and the social and ethical problems related to gold ("gold, the contemptible metal," etc.). These futile statements are evidently due to various causes. On the one hand the word strikes the patient from different aspects; selection of the meaning appropriate to the particular concrete-situation does not take place. On the other hand, the task itself presented to the patient (in this case, the relationship between phrases and metaphors) does not guide his thoughts, and he sets out from more general principles.

In describing these disturbances of intellectual activity in patients with schizophrenia, Bassin [24] uses the vivid term, "a tumor of the intellect." Pavlov declared more than once that the gift of speech is an advantage to mankind, but that, at the same time, it contains within itself the possibility of a divorce from reality, a departure into the realm of sterile fantasy, unless speech is kept strictly to the course laid down by reality. The logic of the thinking process must be under the control of practical experience, or, in Pavlov's striking phrase, of "mistress reality." Because of the absence of verification by practice, the intellectual activity of the patients becomes inadequate and their judgments are converted, in Pavlov's expression, into "mental cud."

This absence of verification may, perhaps, also explain the paradoxical fact that in these patients speech does not facilitate performance of the test, but rather adds to the difficulty: the words pronounced by the patients evoke new, often random associations, which they do not inhibit. Having completed a task correctly in real life, the patients may then proceed to conduct an absurd discussion about their performance and its implications. In experiments on the relationship between phrases and proverbs or metaphors, the patients often choose the appropriate phrases but then give a completely nonsensical explanation of their choices, thus nullifying their correct performance.

To further illustrate this type of random associative behavior, we give a few extracts from the case histories and results of investigation of patients of the group under consideration.

Patient P., male (case history of Dr. Gogolev), born 1927. Diagnosis: schizophrenia. Until 1951 he was apparently healthy, and his growth and development were normal. He was a good pupil at school and graduated in 1950 from GITIS. After starting work in his specialty he became excitable and fussy, and wrote poetry at night. Soon he began to say at home that he was being persecuted at work, that agents in disguise were following him, that he was being acted on at a distance by electric currents, and that his thoughts were being detected by a radio network. He became aggressive. In this state he was referred to the clinic of the First Moscow Medical Institute, from which he was transferred to the Kashchenko Hospital, where he was given insulin therapy. He was discharged only very slightly improved. At home he behaved badly and was aggressive toward his family and friends. He heard many different noises in his head. He declared that he was tuned to a radio network. He was then admitted to the Gannushkin Hospital.

Mental State. On admission he was oriented but apathetic. At times he spoke to himself, made absurd gesticulations, and laughed to himself. Sometimes he was stupid and affected in his behavior, and inclined to make grimaces. At times he was excitable and aggressive, and demanded to be disconnected from the radio network; he said that his head had been turned into a grandiose receiving and transmitting station, and that people around him knew his thoughts. He had vague dreams while awake. He was reluctant to speak about his experiences. He was rude, malicious, and tense. He was uncritical of his own condition.

After a course of insulin therapy the patient's condition improved. His obsessional ideas gradually disappeared, and during his stay in the hospital he began to regard them as a pathological manifestation. His behavior became more regulated, and he was more sociable and approachable. He developed a wish to go home.

In a test involving the classification of objects the patient grouped the pictures together as follows:

(1) A skier and a pig: "This denotes the contrast between winter and summer; winter is a boy on skis, while the pig is on the grass."

(2) A pencil and a goat: "Both pictures were drawn with a pencil."

(3) An airplane and a tree: "This is the sky and the earth."

(4) A cat, a table, and a plum: "The cat is on the table and so is the plum."

(5) An exercise book, a sofa, and a reading book: "You can work on a sofa."

(6) A watch and a bicycle: "A watch measures time; when you ride a bicycle, it also measures space."

(7) A fork, a spade, and a table: "These are all solid objects: they are not easily broken."

(8) A saucepan and a cupboard: "Here there is an opening."

The experimenter asked: "Can you arrange them another way?" The patient replied in the affirmative, broke up the previous groups, and placed together a bush (kust), a saucepan (kastryulya), and a goat (kozel), with the explanation: "They all begin with the letter "k."

The patient's manner of performing a test involving the rejection of a superfluous object also showed certain distinctive features. For instance, when examining a card on which were drawn three types of clock and a coin, the patient declared: "There is nothing here which does not go with the others, as I shall explain. If you take the first card, they are all measures of divisibility; there is absolutely no incompatibility between them. Each object can be used to perform definite functions. If you take the coin, it is a measure of divisibility, it is accepted in human consciousness as a unit of something. A coin determines the value of human labor; clocks determine longitude." When asked to pick out the odd object from the group, "clock, scales, spectacles, thermometer," the patient exclaimed: "Surely they are all compatible from the philosophical point of view. The clock indicates the flight of time, the fact that everything follows a certain course, that everything is in motion; I must pick that out from the rest."

When asked to define certain concepts, the patient defined the word "table" as follows: "Table is a word of direct social significance. In relation to each other, the objects will be regarded as dead. By comparison with nature, it may be said that it is made of wood, and wood grows and exists in nature. Here it has been destroyed and it is an inanimate, indefinite standing object, the form of which possesses both quality and quantity." This was the extent of the patient's definition, and apart from saying that the table is a dead object, and discussing the ruined tree, he made no attempt at a definition in concrete, functional terms.

An association experiment revealed a high frequency of stereotyped responses ("fire"—"the Moscow fire crackled"*; "illusion"—"optical").

Patient E., male (case history of Dr. G. Ya. Avrutskii), born 1928. His development as a child was normal. He was reserved, did not play with the other children, and was always capricious. He started school at the age of 8 and was an excellent pupil. After the age of 13 he became still more reserved, and he shunned the society of other people. He was evacuated during the war and had to endure hardships. On his return to Moscow in 1945, his relatives noted his very marked reserve, silence, timidity, and irritability. He attended a railroad technical school but could not learn despite great efforts. He did his homework carefully, but could not answer questions in class. He always had difficulty in thinking, and his "thoughts were scattered." He changed schools several times. Recently he abandoned his studies and made no attempt to do any form of activity.

He was fearful in front of people, and felt more at ease when alone. At times he had a distressing feeling that it was difficult to think, that his thoughts were torn apart and were being broken to pieces. Sometimes he had a "flood" of thoughts. It was particularly difficult for him to think when he was with other people. It appeared that some form of misfortune must have beset him. He avoided walking along the street, because he could feel on his back the gaze of a person walking behind him, which gave him a sort of cold sensation, and he spoke of certain dangers which were threatening him.

He felt that he was talented and that his future lay in art. He was particularly attracted to motion pictures, and he wrote a script which "will surprise the world." He decided to devote his life to this goal, and he was prepared to endure all manner of privations and sufferings for it.

Neurological examination revealed no abnormality.

Mental State. The patient was properly oriented in regard to place, time, and environment. He was somewhat uninhibited and self-confident. His movements were sudden, angular, and jerky. During conversation he would not look the other person in the face. He easily established contact and answered all questions freely and without restraint. He spoke quickly and correctly, with an adequate range of shades of meaning and with smooth transitions, and his modulation was good. His facial expressions were adequate. The fact of his hospitalization did not worry him and he did not mention his family, to whom, he said, he felt no obligations. He did not occupy himself on the ward.

In the object-classification test the patient began to sort correctly on the basis of the relevant sign (people, animals, plants), but soon gave it up and said: "There is no future in this, this is an uncultured and blind way of dividing them; surely they are all different objects with specific features. You have to look at them from the point of view of the actor, using the principle of the motion picture, to make them look at each other.... The bear can see the small insect, and the elephant can see the horse, but not the fish, although the fish, when it swims away, can see the elephant. Of course, the eyes of fish are constructed differently.... What do they call this in zoology?" The patient discussed the objects from the point of view of "motion pictures."

The experimenter asked him to find some other principle of division. The patient replied: "You can do so from the philo-

*Perhaps this is something of the style of "London Bridge is falling down."—Tr.

sophical point of view, from the point of view of the conversion of inanimate into animate matter. Things are the product of human labor. People, animals, plants—these are the product of nature.... Or it would be even more correct to place everything in the same group; it is all nature."

In a test of his systematic memorization, involving the composition of pictograms, the patient formed the following associations: to memorize the expression "a happy holiday," he drew a flag; for the word "development," he drew two dots, a large and a small; for the expression "hard work," he drew a circle ("This is a flight into the stratosphere; that is hard work"). He considered "a bold deed" for a long time: "What is boldness? It isn't the same as courage; courageous people reflect upon their deeds, but bold...." The patient thought for some time, and then abandoned the problem. When given the expression "a jolly supper," the patient said: "Supper means the ingestion of inorganic matter by an organic being although food is also organic matter." He drew circles and an arrow: "The circles are matter and the arrow represents the change from one form of matter to another." The patient interrupted his argument: "Well, if you look at it from the actor's point of view, you must express a tasty supper purely symbolically."

To memorize the words "a warm wind" the patient drew two squares and a triangle, with the explanation: "These are two concepts, an adjective and a noun. Of course, from the point of view of the producer, you should also give a picture of the other, but I cannot do that."

In the proverb interpretation test, the patient performed easily and correctly but made mistakes in the modification of the test which involved choosing from among given phrases those equivalent to the proverbs. For example, he matched the proverb, "All that glitters is not gold" (the meaning of which he had previously explained correctly), with the phrase, "Gold is heavier than iron," giving the explanation: "According to the principle of negation, in the proverb the value of the other shining metal is negated, and in the second phrase the comparison of the heaviness of gold and iron is negated."

An association experiment revealed a combination of adequate response reactions with responses of the type of habitual verbal stereotypes ("falling"—"from a pedestal"; "moon"—"the man in the moon").

These tests show that the intellectual processes of the patients of this subgroup are dominated by verbal and logical associations which are not controlled directly by the particular concrete relationships of the situation and which are inadequately based on sensory ideas.   The patients could grasp problems demanding generalizations, they could distinguish a common sign, and they could convert the concrete meanings of words into abstractions, but the temporary "flight" from concrete meanings inherent in any form of generalization acquired an exaggerated and, at times, grotesque character. So that his thinking was incapable of comprehending not only many individual details but also many of the more important relationships.

Disturbances of intellectual activity in schizophrenic patients were described by Vygotskii [51]. He postulated from his experimental findings that in such patients the function of concept formation had disintegrated; concepts had degenerated to the level of complexes, or concrete meaning-patterns. This phenomenon was based on changes in the meaning of words.

While we may agree with Vygotskii that patients with schizophrenia often show changes in word meaning, we cannot agree that in these cases concepts are degraded to the level of complexes. A complex as Vygotskii understands the term, involves a generalization of phenomena on the basis of concrete associations or concrete ideas. As our experiments showed, "concrete" association takes place in only a very small proportion of schizophrenics. In most cases the process of generalization is disturbed not because the patients operate with concrete association but rather because their intellectual activity is dominated by associations which are inappropriate to the concrete relationships of the situation. In our earlier researches, and in the work of Birenbaum [31], it was shown that the disturbance of concepts takes a unique form in schizophrenics. Even when their judgments are concrete, they reflect not only the concrete relationships between phenomena or objects, but also, and perhaps to a greater degree, their random, incidental characteristics. (We named this pathological behavior, at that time, "lability, or the lack of differentiation of word structure.") Such patients have lost their ability to be guided by the objective meaning of the problem, so that they often perform the experimental task (as well as problems in everyday life) by applying specific conditions completely irrelevant to the demands of the particular situation. Their sterile reasoning is caused less by a disturbance of concepts than by a tendency to classify any and every insignificant phenomenon as a particular "concept."

We shall return to this point in Chapter 4; at this stage we merely emphasize that we are inclined to interpret this disturbance not as the disintegration of concepts but rather as a distortion of the process of generalization.

We thus may conclude that the single process of reflection may manifest two types of distortion. Whereas the associations of the patients of the first subgroup (with a lowered standard of generalization) never rise above the level of special, single associations, and whereas the direct impressions which they obtain are not integrated and their verbal and logical associations do not attain dominant significance, in the patients of the second subgroup (with distortion of the process of generalization) the converse is true: their verbal and logical associations derive little support from the concrete properties and signs of objects and phenomena. Whereas the intellectual operations of the first group of patients are characterized by a narrow range of associations, those of the second group are characterized by the appearance of a very large number of associations, but these associations are uncontrolled, random and, what is more important, they reflect only excessively general relationships.

In both variants of the disturbance of the processes of generalization, speech is no longer an instrument of generalization. Whereas in the first case the patients' speech reflects only unessential details, in the second case it is reduced to the level of a meaningless abstraction.

Chapter 5

Disturbances of the Logical Course
of Thinking

Any definition of thinking should regard it as a process, and this applies not only to the general theoretical characteristics of thinking but also to every particular human thought. Even the elementary mental acts of a person, such as feeling and perception, are processes in the sense that they occur in time, possess a certain variable dynamic pattern, and take place as an active human function. The discovery of the reflex basis of even these most elementary acts revealed very distinctly that they are processes carried on in many different stages. This "process" type of structure is manifested to its maximal degree in every act of human thinking.

One of the special features of thinking as a higher form of cognition is its systematic nature. Of course, this systematization comes about only as a result of the correct structuring of ideas. The cognition of facts hidden from direct perception is possible only when man is capable of generalizing and analyzing from the facts he perceives. This systematization, involves the transition from one group of judgments to another and the formation of a long chain of conclusions. The chain of conclusions, transformed into reasoning, is a true manifestation of thinking as a process. It is not by accident that in many languages we find the expression, "to lose the thread of an argument." It is only through the correct sequence of judgments that the systematic generalization of facts is rendered possible. When the order of the conclusions is very sequential and orderly, we speak of the logic of human reasoning. Conversely, illogical human reasoning can exist side by side with an adequate grasp of the material and with an adequacy of individual judgments when the necessary order in the exposition of the material is not present. It is not without reason that students are specifically taught how to attain a logically correct course of thought.

It is a familiar fact that in their everyday speech small children associate by means of their "impressions," or associations of a sensory character. As they grow older they begin to grasp relationships of cause and effect, and to draw simple forms of deductive and inductive conclusions.

The physiological basis of this logically correct thinking lies in the domination of associations by the second signal system—in contrast to the rudimentary forms of the preschool child's "seeing-and-doing" thinking, which is mainly conducted by associations based on the first signal system.

In the formation and disturbances of investigating thinking, it is not enough simply to analyze the formation and disturbance of ideas, or simply to describe the characteristics of intellectual operations.   Our investigations show that the disturbance of the process of generalization, although the most common, is not the only type of thinking disturbance. Moreover, the simple disintegration of ideas does not represent the most common disturbance of thinking. It is the various pathological states of the brain which most frequently lead to dynamic disturbances of thinking.

Little research has been done into the disturbance of the dynamics of thinking.   Although in many psychiatric investigations mention is made of the dynamic character of certain disturbances of thinking, underlying this concept is the suggestion that they are reversible.   In a joint study which we made with Birenbaum [31], devoted to the comparative analysis of disturbances of thinking in schizophrenics and epileptics, we mentioned several differences in the respective dynamics of their intellectual activity. Whereas the latter were characterized by inertia or "stagnation" of thinking, the former most often exhibited extreme lability in the course of their intellectual processes.   Having noted that the manifestations of disintegration in the patients of both groups are opposite in character, and that the distinguishing features of these disturbances cannot be divorced from the distinguishing features of the patients' affective structures, we nevertheless classified all disturbances of thinking under the disintegration of ideas.   Having examined disturbances of thinking as integrally connected with changes in affective dynamics, we described the various manifestations of the disintegration of thinking under two headings—pseudoabstract and excessively concrete judgments.

In studies of the disturbance of intellectual activity following closed brain injuries [108, 109], we distinguished a type of disturbance of thinking in which the patients' mental activity was characterized by its superficiality and flatness, and by the rapid extinction of the thinking process. This type of disturbance of thinking was not classed as a disturbance of ideas; it was defined instead as a dynamic disturbance, a manifestation both of the rapid exhaustion of the patient's mental activity and of the lowering of the "tone of consciousness."

Ease of exhaustion of the intellectual processes of patients with brain trauma was described by Kogan [130], Korobkova [138], and Kostomarova [148], in the course of their investigations of the working capacity in such patients.

Subsequent investigations of our own confirmed the view that rapid exhaustion plays an important role in the genesis of disturbances of the intellectual activity of patients with organic brain lesions. It was also revealed not only that dynamic disturbances of thinking are a manifestation of fatigability, but also that their nature is much more complex, and their various symptoms are much less conspicuous than previously imagined. We described them as disturbances of the logical course of thinking.

These dynamic disturbances arise from many different causes, and may manifest themselves clinically in widely different forms: "flights of ideas" in manic patients; the "stagnation" of the thinking processes of the epileptic; the illogicality of judgments of cerebrovascular patients; and the "sliding" characteristic of schizophrenics. In the present chapter we shall analyze these different types of disturbance of the logical course of thinking.

1. FLIGHTS OF IDEAS

The term "flight of ideas," widely used in psychiatry, denotes a peculiarity of thinking observed in patients in the manic phase of a manic-depressive psychosis. This phase is characterized by euphoria and psychomotor excitation. The patients speak loudly and without stopping, they laugh, joke, and accompany their speech with lively, expressive gesticulations and facial movements; they are extremely distractible. Every new impression, be it a spoken word or a perceived object, directs their thoughts and ideas, which replace one another so rapidly that the patients cannot register them in their speech. They cannot finish one thought before going on to the next; sometimes they shout only a single word. Characteristically, despite their extreme distractibility and scattering of attention, manic patients actively observe what is going on around them, and they frequently elicit surprise by their quick wit and pointed remarks.

As a rule, experiments cannot be performed on manic patients because of their extreme distractibility, which prevents them from fixing their attention on the experimental situation. Such patients can be investigated experimentally only when at various levels of a hypomanic state, in which certain pathological changes in their intellectual activity may be observed.

These patients have retained the capacity for analysis and synthesis in the appraisal of a situation, although during the performance of any experimental problem their superficiality of judgment is readily apparent. The patients pay little attention to thinking over the problem presented to them and they fail to grasp the meaning of the task. For example, when comparing ideas, they often remark on their similarity and difference in accordance with external signs. When asked to explain the similarity and difference between the concepts of "table" and "chair," one patient (with only a high-school education) replied: "They have in common the fact that both the chair and the stool have four legs; the difference is that the chair has a back while the table has none." The same patient gave the correct, generalized reply when he was guided and prompted in solving the problem. When required to arrange pictures in consecutive order, although these patients immediately understand their theme, they proceed to arrange the pictures in any random order. In the proverb-and-phrase test, hypomanic patients often choose phrases according to similarities between words rather than from their individual meanings, although they are capable of the latter. If the patient's attention is drawn to the incorrectness of his answers, he easily corrects his mistakes.

The intellectual activity of patients in a hypomanic state is characterized not only by a superficiality of judgment, but also by a lack of inhibition of many random and chaotic associations. Individual words evoke new thoughts, which the patients immediately put into words; their speech reflects a multitude of ideas and emotional experiences. In cases of extreme hypomania, the patients can concentrate on an experimental problem only for a very short time. Although they may understand the meaning of a proverb perfectly, they fail to explain it. Often one particular word in the proverb will evoke a whole chain of associations. Instead of explaining the proverb, a patient may cite a relevant example from his own life; this will in turn remind him of something else, and his thoughts then begin to run in haphazard directions. For example, a hypomanic patient explained the proverb, "All that glitters is not gold," as follows: "Gold—that is the beautiful gold watch my brother gave me, he and I get on well together. When we were at school we use to quarrel, but since then we have lived in peace. My brother is very fond of the theater, and I went with him to see a play...," and so on. The chaotic character of his associations prevented him from giving the correct explanation of the proverb, and the word "gold" immediately led to a complete chain of reminiscences. However, other variants are possible, in which patients may omit a link in the course of their explanation. Another patient, for example, immediately understood the meaning of this proverb, and as an example, in the course of his subsequent explanation, he wanted to describe the case of an apple which, although good on the outside, was bad inside. This, however, was not what the patient said, for he at once began: "Apples, of course, are sometimes wormy. There are some sorts of apple, for example, which you would never suspect.... Our neighbors had some Michurin apples. Naturally the development of Michurin's theory is very important...." He then went on to give various reminiscences of friends of his who were trained in Michurin's ideas.

Often the disturbance of logical reasoning in patients in a hypomanic state is somewhat different in character. The patients solve intellectual problems very quickly and correctly, but immediately after doing so they began to pour out a stream of words which have nothing to do with the task in hand. Sometimes the patient could be stopped and given the next problem, which he solved correctly, after which something else distracted him or he started talking about something. After this "jerky," impulsive performance of a problem, a stream of words poured out, reflecting the patient's general state of hyperactivity. This alternation of correct solutions and absurd statements sometimes lasted throughout the whole investigation. The correct and rapid solution of the problem was embellished by a system of thoughts and expressions running in different directions.

Particularly marked abnormalities were found in experiments involving the explanation of proverbs. A female hypomanic patient compared two proverbs: "Two minds are better than one," and

"Make up your own mind." She soon grasped the opposition in meaning between these proverbs: "These proverbs are different. In the first, one mind is complementary to the other, but the second means that you must stand by your own opinion." However, immediately after this correct explanation she poured out a stream of words: "A group, of course, is better than an individual.... In our collective farm the harvest was good last year, my father who drives a tractor harvested much more rye than the plan anticipated.... I love working in the field."

The disturbance of the logical course of thinking in patients of this group is also manifested during their performance on the object-classification test. They immediately understand the instruction and begin to sort the pictures correctly into groups, often in accordance with a general sign, but any chance association which may arise turns the course of their thinking into another direction. One such patient, for example, having formed a group of live objects, including several human beings (i.e., having performed the task on the correct level of generalizations), suddenly exclaimed when he saw the picture of the blacksmith: "We are blacksmiths and our friend is the hammer.... I love... the old revolutionary songs.... A song...is our friend. And is art in general to be found among these cards reminding me of a song? The pictures aren't drawn particularly well: who drew them, a "khudozhnik" (an artist)? From the word "khudo" (bad)." The patient laughed, held a picture in his hand, and did not carry out the test. When the experimenter asked him to turn to the problem, the patient continued to sort the pictures without returning to the previous principle of solution, but began with new associations which had arisen: "Where can I put the smith, surely there is no smith here?" When he saw a horse, the patient said: "Let us shoe it." Experimenter: "You have begun to arrange them differently." The patient replied: "Yes, I wanted to separate people from animals," and continued to arrange them in accordance with the generic sign.

The patient had grasped the meaning of the problem and, what is more, he could solve it at the generalized level, but any stimulus (a word spoken by himself or by the experimenter, something which he saw, etc.) evoked random associations and often led him away from the immediate problem. If the experimenter gave him guidance, he would eventually correctly sort the cards and define the ideas, but the independent path of his reasoning, proved inadequate or incorrect.

The disturbance of the dynamics of thinking becomes prominent in association experiments, where the following features of the patients' association may be observed:

1. The response reactions of the patients consist of large numbers of words. At times they could not conform to the instruction to reply in a single word. In some patients most of the answers were multiverbal (see Table XIII). For example, patients S-v, V-n, Ch-n, and M-v gave multiverbal answers in 13 or 14 of 20 tests, and patient Kr-i did so in 16 of 18 tests.

2. In the variant of association experiment in which the instruction required an antonym as a response, many incorrect answers were observed (an average of 32% in each case; see Table XIII).

TABLE XIII

Results of an Association Experiment on Hypomanic Patients

Patients	Variant I			Variant II*		
	latent period (in sec)	number of response reactions	number of multiverbal reactions	latent period (in sec)	number of response reactions	number of undirected reactions
1 S-v	1.5–2	20	13	2–2.5	20	6
2 K-k	1–2	20	5	1.5–2	20	8
3 V-n	1–2.5	18	13	1–1.5	20	10
4 Ch-n	1–1.5	20	14	1.5–2	18	8
5 Kr-i	1–2.5	18	16	1–1.5	18	11
6 L-va	1.5–2	18	7	1–1.5	20	3
7 S-i	1.5–3	20	8	1–2	20	0
8 Ch-o	1.5–2.5	20	10	1.5–2	20	0
9 Yar-1	1–2.5	20	11	1–1.5	20	7
10 M-v	1–2.5	20	13	1–1.5	18	9
11 S-n				1–1.5	20	8
12 P-ni				1–2	20	7
13 R-na				1–1.5	20	6
14 K-na				1.5–2	20	6
	Total 194		110 (57%)		274	89 (32%)

*Instruction: "Answer with a word opposite to the one I say."

Associations appeared which had been established in the patient's past experience but which were irrelevant to the present situation. For example, instead of responding to the word "cold" with the word "warm," the patient answered with "winter." From Table XIII, we see that of the 14 patients, only 2 always responded as directed; in 3 patients (V-n, Kr-i, and M-v) half of the responses were not made in accordance with the directions.

The presence of a large number of undirected associations represents a deviation from the normal. As we have already mentioned, Sechenov originally stressed the fact that the associations of a healthy person are distinguished by their directedness. The responses of the healthy person are selective; they arise in relation to the concrete nature or the conditions of the task while any inadequate associations are ordinarily inhibited. In our patients, on the other hand, this normal process of inhibition of inadequate reactions was impaired.

3. The latent period is close to normal, and sometimes slightly above normal (1.5–2.5 sec). (This somewhat paradoxical fact was discussed some time ago by Aschaffenburg [360].) In this connection it must be noted, in particular, that some patients at times emitted multiverbal reactions and at others, reactions of a perseveratory type. This presumably indicates that prolonged excitation in the speech areas leads to inhibition in these areas.

From a comparison of these experimental findings it may be concluded that flights of ideas are based on the increased lability of the cortical processes. The process of the concentration of the excitatory process which arises during the hypomanic's performance of the test gives rise, not to negative induction, but rather to pathological irradiation.

2. "SLUGGISHNESS" OF THINKING

This clinical manifestation represents the antithesis of the type of disturbance we have just described. Patients characterized by "sluggishness" of thinking cannot change their mode of work or their opinions, or switch from one type of activity to another. Such disturbances are often found in epileptics and in patients with late sequelae of severe brain injuries.

Sometimes these patients are able to work, but then only with frequent interruptions, loss of their former skills, and difficulty in acquiring and applying new skills. They usually arrive at the mental hospital after having failed to compensate for their defects, often having become addicted to alcohol. Their case histories show that these patients can work, read newspapers, and often show an interest in ward affairs; at the same time, their mental production is of a low calibre and they can work only very slowly.

Experimental psychological investigation further reveals the slowness and sluggishness of their intellectual processes. Although they may both comprehend the instructions and exhibit ample capacity for generalization in the classification experiment, they are unable to adjust to modifications in the experimental procedure. A change in the conditions impairs their standard of performance.

This sluggishness of intellectual processes so impairs the patients that they cannot cope even with the most elementary problems if a change in conditions is required. One patient, for example, in the pictogram test, was quite able to invent conventional signs for the classification of words if he was allowed to draw "a man," but he could not do so if he was forbidden to draw "a man."

Such patients are also characterized by a lack of flexibility. In experiments requiring systematic memorization, having chosen a particular picture to aid in memorizing a particular word, the patients are then unable to choose another picture for this word when asked to do so. Thus, the patients can solve the problem only if it can be done by one particular method. Even in experimental tasks requiring the classification of colored pictures—which requires no complex analysis and synthesis—they cannot switch to another sign from one that they have already distinguished. Having grouped the pictures by their color, they cannot then categorize them in accordance with their form.

This type of disturbance can be described as "inertia of the associations of previous experience." Sluggishness of thinking, a disturbance of the dynamics of intellectual activity, results in a lowering of the level of generalization. The intellectual activity of the patients also disintegrates at the level of concrete generalizations. For example, these patients not only would not group together wild and domestic animals, but they regarded each domestic animal as a single specimen. Consequently, the task of classification could not be carried out even at the concrete level; the patients "marked time." Because of this hesitation the patients have trouble finishing this task, even when they comprehend the principles of classification, for the sorting process itself requires the inhibition of some elements and the comparison of others (i.e., it requires some degree of flexibility of operation, of switching from one to another).

One patient, for example, distinguished many small groups by a concrete, yet generic sign: domestic animals, wild animals, furniture, transport. He formed the pictures of people into two groups: people engaged in physical work and those doing mental work (he included a skier among the latter).

The experimenter suggested certain groupings, such as domestic and wild animals, people in various occupations, etc. The patient agreed and started to sort the pictures afresh, but having already accomplished the task by the previous method, he gave up: "Let it be like that." Although he had understood the principle of classification suggested by the experimenter, and although he had even begun to act accordingly, he could not switch over to a different method of work.

This same difficulty was also revealed in an experiment involving the exclusion method. One patient, for example, when shown a card on which a table, a chair, a sofa, and a table lamp were drawn, exclaimed: "Of course, this is all furniture, exactly, but the lamp is not furniture. But surely there must be a lamp on the table if it is night, or even twilight.... In winter it grows dark early, and then it is better to remove the sofa.... If there is a chair, you can do without the sofa." When the experimenter said: "But you yourself said that the lamp is not furniture," the patient replied: "Of course, that is right, you must pick out the furniture, but the lamp is a table lamp, it stands on the table. I suggest we take out the sofa." Despite the fact that the experimenter tried several times to guide the patient into the proper direction; despite the fact that the patient himself not only understood but also mentioned the principle of generalization (furniture); in the actual test—sorting the objects—he returned again and again to the property he had picked out: "The lamp is a table lamp; it must stand on the table." The patient could not switch from the decision he had made.

The concrete associations with previous experience inertly dominate the intellectual activity of the patients and determine the entire subsequent course of their reasoning. They frequently cannot discard a single detail during the test, or let a single property of the objects escape, so that they cannot achieve even elementary generalization. For instance, in an experiment involving the use of the exclusion method, one such patient, when shown a card with pictures of a table, a chair, a sofa, and a table lamp, argued for a long time: "It would not be hard to leave the chair out, for if there are many people they can sit on the sofa. That is the first possibility. The second possibility is if fewer people are there...one person, then the sofa can be left out. Admittedly it is soft and comfortable, while the chair is hard. As a third possibility, the table can be left out; it is possible to sit on the sofa, put something on the chair, and write on it. Of course there are drawbacks to this, but they can be overcome. The lamp can be left out, because it doesn't belong to the same family, but this is impossible if this happens in the evening...." So that this patient recognized to some extent the basic sign of classification: although he understood that the lamp "did not belong to the same family," he could not adhere to this principle and straightaway began to consider the fact that in the evening the lamp was essential. This attempt to be precise and to exhaust all the various factual relationships when solving any problem, results in the ratiocination characteristic of the epileptic. Such attention to superfluous detail is known generally in clinical practice as "tenacity" of thinking.

This inertia of the associations of previous experience stands out especially clearly during tests demanding a fuller explanation—the definition of concepts. To illustrate this statement two typical examples of patients' attempts at the definition of simple concepts are given below.

Patient B-n (epilepsy). Cupboard. — "This is an object in which things are kept.... However, dishes are also kept in a sideboard—food, too, and clothes can be kept in a cupboard. although food is often kept in a cupboard. If the room is small and a sideboard will not fit inside, or if there simply isn't a sideboard, the dishes will be kept in a cupboard. We have a cupboard; on the right side there is a large empty space, and on the left four shelves; that is where the dishes and food are kept. This is bad management, of course, because the bread often smells of naphthalene from the mothballs. Again, there are cupboards for books, but they aren't deep. They have shelves, lots of shelves. Cupboards now are sunk into the walls, but still they are cupboards."

Patient A. (epilepsy). Table. — "A table is made of wood. This is not quite true, and it is not acceptable as a definition of table, for there are tables made of other things than wood — metal or tiles. A table is an object with four legs, on which rests a flat board, parallel with the floor or ground; a table may even have size. This is the general concept of 'table,' and it is essential to state that tables have different purposes, The most typical feature is that they stand, for the legs may differ. Tables may also be divided into kitchen and writing tables, or Swedish tables with small drawers. I should say that not one of the existing definitions is adequate. An object consisting of legs and a top, the top being flat in form and resting on props. Their different heights must also be mentioned. It is difficult to define restaurant tables, for they are very high. A board, resting on props, and for man's use...but this might be a plank and not a table. A table is characterized by the fact that it is at a certain height from the ground and satisfies man's needs."

These illustrations show that the patients began correctly to define the concept of "cupboard" or "table" but then at once made all sorts of deviations from their definitions, going into detail over all the possible alternatives. As a result of these clarifications and descriptions the patients were unable to arrive at a single, clear definition. The patients themselves, however, were unsatisfied with their explanations, because they felt they were insufficiently complete.

Inertia of the concrete associations of previous experience also was exhibited in a variant of the association experiment: "Answer with the first word that comes into your head." Twenty epileptic patients were given 420 words. The results show that the latency period was fairly long, its average duration being 6.5 sec, and at times in individual patients it reached 20—30 sec. The responses were adequate in 48.4% of cases and consisted of synonyms in 8.3% of them; in 11.9% of the total number of reactions the patients refused to answer.

A noteworthy feature was the large number of delayed reactions (31.4%); the patients replied, not to the word presented, but to the one before. For example, when replying to the stimulus "song" with the word "silence," in response to the next stimulus "wheel" he gave the reply "stillness"; having responded to the word "deceit" with "trust," he responded to the next stimulus "head" with the word "lie." In some patients delayed reactions were observed in 7 or 8 of 20 response reactions.

The delayed reactions in our patients are an important deviation from the normal course of the process of association. They demonstrate that the subsequent stimulus is of greater signal value than the original stimulus. To clarify the mechanism of these phenomena it is necessary to turn once again to the analysis of the structure of the association experiment.

The word with which the subject reacts to the stimulus is not the only association which arises. However, the fact that he reacts with only one word is explained by the experimenter's instruction to give only one word, and that which first springs to the subject's mind. The other associations arising under these circumstances are inhibited. The presentation of another word stimulus evokes new associations. In other words, the patient's response reaction was prompted each time by the actual stimulus. The current action of the stimulus is dependent on the problem set—the instruction given.

Soviet psychologists have studied the relationship between the formation of associations and the conditions and meaning of an activity. Leont'ev and Rozanova [176] showed that following a change in the meaning of a task (instruction), the same stimuli evoke different associations. The consolidation and reproduction of associations must take place in relation to the instructions given.

As applied to our experimental situation, this must mean that only the words spoken at a given moment could evoke associations, and that only then could they be the signals for the response reaction. The associations evoked by stimulus words spoken previously, on the other hand, could not be made to apply at the current time; the previous stimuli must remain neutral and must lose their signal value.

In our patients, however, the presented stimulus did not acquire the necessary value. Because of the inertia of their nervous processes, our patients responded to the echo of a previous word stimulus.

Similar results were obtained in the second variant of the association experiment, in which the patients (after the main experiment) were again presented with a word stimulus and instructed to respond with a different word from that previously used. This experiment revealed the presence of perseverations (in 44% of cases the patients responded, contrary to the instructions, with the same word as before) or a refusal to answer (10.7%). Adequate replies accounted for 45.3% of the total number of response reactions. The latency period was long, with an average duration of 8.5 sec.

This variant of the association experiment evoked such great difficulties in some patients that at times they could not respond with an adequate word: perseverations represented their predominant reactions (as, for example, in the case of patient T., the results of whose tests will presently be given).

By way of illustration of the intellectual disturbances in patients with "sluggishness" of thinking, we give below a few short extracts from a case report, together with the results of an experimental psychological investigation.

Patient T. (case report of Dr. L. N. Balashova), born 1909, high-school education. Diagnosis: traumatic encephalopathy. In 1941 sustained concussion with no apparent aftereffects. In 1952 sustained another head injury with temporary loss of consciousness. Persistent headaches, sleeplessness, and irritability developed; he worried over trifles, cried, and his work was impaired.

Mental State: oriented; conformed to ward discipline. Passed unnoticed on the ward and had little to do with the patients. Usually in a depressed mood. He complained of persistent headaches, sleeplessness, a tendency to cry, and absent-mindedness. He could tolerate neither acute stimuli nor noise, including the other patients' conversation; he was lethargic and apathetic. His memory was poor and his range of interests limited: he did not read newspapers and he was not interested in the radio programs. He was considered incapable of work.

In all the experiments the patient grasped the instruction slowly and had difficulty in understanding the conditions of the test. In an experiment requiring the arrangement of a consecutive series of pictures, the patient thought for a long time: "The uncle rode on a cart. Where does he start to ride? Everywhere here the axle is broken. Here is the beginning (No. 3). The carrier arrived at the blacksmith's and said: 'The wheel has broken.' Here they are mending it (No. 4). He had mended it and gone (No. 5). And here.... No, that's wrong." He took card No. 1 in his hand: "Here he is worried.... Yes, that is earlier." He began to sort them again: "Here is the beginning (No. 3), here they are repairing it (No. 4), and here it has been mended (No. 5). This is wrong again. How on earth can I do it?"

Five times the patient sorted the series of cards and every time he began with picture No. 3, until the experimenter suggested that he start with picture No. 1. Only then did the patient perform the task correctly and convey the theme. Hence, during the performance of this task, the nature of the patient's difficulty was that, having once identified picture No. 3 as the first stage in the theme, he could not at the next attempt start with another, even though he realized that his solution was wrong.

In performing the object-classification test, the patient examined the pictures for a long time, shifted them from place to place, and then formed the following groups: "objects in a room" (including furniture, scales), "dishes," "domestic animals," "wild animals," "birds," "transport" (here he included a sailor: "he is on a steam-ship"), "working people" (a doctor, a blacksmith, and a charwoman), "flowers," and "trees." He did not know in what group to place a beetle, a fish, a skier, a bush, and a thermometer. The experimenter explained to him that some groups could be put together. The patient thought for a long time. The experimenter suggested forming a group of people and including in it the skier, and also combining all the species of plants. The patient agreed and added: "Right. I made all those groups to no purpose; I can combine many of them. Why didn't I guess as much?" He started to do the test again and formed the groups as follows: "objects in a room," "dishes," "animals" (he combined the domestic animals, the wild animals, and the birds), "plants" (he combined the trees and flowers, but did not include the bush), "people" (doctor, blacksmith, char-woman, skier); he again included the sailor with the steamship: "He is on a steamship." The beetle, fish, bush, and thermometer remained unclassified in the groups; the scales again were included with the "objects in a room." The experimenter asked him to check whether he had done the test properly. The patient examined all the cards and made no corrections. When the experimenter suggested to him that the fish should be included with the animals, the patient did not object; in the same way he agreed that the sailor should join the group of people. When, however, the patient was asked a third time to check the classification, he again tried to group the sailor with the steamship, to separate the trees from the flowers, and to place the scales with the furniture. After more leading questions, the test was eventually done correctly: the patient arranged the cards into three groups, although while doing so he was all the time trying to revert to his previous method of solution.

This experiment also shows that the patient could not switch from his adopted method of solution to another. Although the patient was guided by concrete signs in the performance of his task, the dominance of specific, concrete differences between objects complicated the correct course of his reasoning. It was not by chance that he did not say that the wild and domestic animals could not be grouped together, as we often found with patients in whom we observed a lowering of the level of generalization. Moreover, having combined the wild and domestic animals, the patient himself added the birds to them. Consequently, although he was able to find the general principle of solution, he consistently could not place the beetle in this group, which previously had been left out of all the groups. In the same way, having combined the trees and flowers, he could not add the bush, which had not previously belonged to this group. Having formed a group of people, the patient did not include the sailor with them, but left him, as at the first attempt, in the same group as the steamship. In other words, in his performance the patient repeated the same mistakes he had made previously, simply because he was unable to switch over to a different method of solving the problem.

In an experiment involving systematic memorization using pictograms the patient formed excessively uniform associations; everywhere he drew a picture of a man. To memorize the expression "a happy holiday," the patient drew a man holding a flag; for the word "development," he drew a large and a small man; for the expression "heavy work," a man with a wheelbarrow. For the words "a dark night," the patient was unable to invent a picture: "How can I draw a man in the dark?"

The patient's performance in this test shows that he understood the conventions of drawing (for example, the patient easily systematized the memorizing of an abstract word such as "development," and drew adequate pictures of a large and a small man), but he was unable, as we stated above, to invent any association not involving a man.

The results of the association experiment with patient T. show the following:

(1) a long latent period (average 6.3 sec, in some cases up to 15-21 sec);

(2) the limited range of associations; the patient's response reactions often consisted of nothing more than naming the functions of an object or defining it: "wheel"—"it turns"; "ax"—"to chop";

(3) the instruction to reply with a different word from that given during the previous presentation of the stimulus leads to a considerable increase in the latency period (average 10.5 sec) and to a refusal to answer ("I don't know");

(4) the presence of delayed responses; for example, having replied to the word "cave" with the adequate word "shelter," the patient responded to the next stimulus "moon" with "hut."

The inert character of the patient's associations was also revealed by the results of an experiment using the method of free association. In response to the suggestion to name the word springing to his mind, the patient produced the following series: "house, roof, chimney, house, fireplace, porch, roof.... I have said that before....pigeon, bird, house again, high, low, leaf, tree, green, standing by the house, porch, path."

Comparison of the results obtained by means of the different methods of psychological investigation shows that the dynamics of thinking were disturbed because of the extreme inertia of the associations of previous experience; the associations formed both in previous experience and in the present experimental situation could not be changed. Comparison of the results of our experiments with clinical observations suggests that in this case we have to deal with a disturbance of the mobility of the cortical neurodynamics with a tendency toward inertia. Pavlov [220] characterizes the loss of mobility of the nervous processes, tending toward inertia, as an inability to yield quickly to the demands of the external conditions and to give preference to one stimulus over another. The delayed reactions and the subjection to the aftereffect of the stimulus may in fact be evidence of the inability to keep up with the newly applied stimuli.

Pavlov repeatedly stressed that mobility is one of the fundamental characteristics of the neurodynamics of the healthy cortex. This is also demonstrated by the animal experiments of Petrova, Narbutovich, Rozental', and others. Many researches by Soviet physiologists and psychiatrists have been devoted to this problem. Kaminskii and Savchuk [125], for example, discovered a disturbance of the mobility of the nervous processes in patients with essential hypertension, Melekhov and Kamenskaya [193] found similar disturbances in brain injuries, as did Remezova and Seredina [283] in epilepsy.

In these investigations, of especial interest because of their clinical and physiological findings, no attempt was made to describe the intellectual disturbances of the patients. However, in an analysis of the working capacity of these patients, an evaluation of their intellectual activity is of great practical importance.

In an experimental situation, as in any situation in life, new aspects of objects are constantly revealed, and the conditions of the environment change constantly. In order to understand these different relationships correctly and to act in accordance with the changing conditions, man must be able to change over from one mode of action to another, he must not be chained to a fixed, automatic mode of behavior.

The perfection of intellectual activity is determined not only by the fact that a person is able to perform a particular intellectual operation, to analyze and integrate material, and to distinguish that which is essential, but also by the fact that this capacity for correct operations has established itself as a stable method of reaction. On the other hand, the method of solving the problem must vary with the changing conditions. Synthesis and generalization can attain a high level of efficiency only when a change in conditions gives rise to a concomitant change in reaction. If thinking is to reflect the objective world of reality, it is essential that a person's reasoning be adequately stable, yet at the same time possess the power of variability. The psychological experiment makes it possible to create the conditions which allow the investigation of these properties.

Hence, the psychological examination of patients with "sluggishness" of thinking points to a disturbance which is apparently the antithesis of the disturbance which we described in the preceding section—the "flight of ideas." Whereas the sequence of thought of patients in a hypomanic state was disturbed because of the multiplicity of overflowing associations, the logical course of thinking in the patients whom we have just described was disturbed because their associations did not replace one another.

3. ILLOGICAL REASONING

A characteristic feature of this disturbance is the inability to maintain a stable method of task performance. The general level of generalization was not lowered; the patients correctly grasped the instruction, analyzed and integrated the material well, and understood the figurative meaning of proverbs and metaphors. However, the patients' reasoning was not always adequate: the correct methods of performing the test were frequently replaced by incorrect methods.

For example, the results of an experiment using the classification method showed that in certain groups of patients the generalized type of solution of the problem was interrupted by incorrect combinations based on concrete situations. Table XIV shows that fluctuations of this sort were found in 81.6% of patients with cerebrovascular diseases, in 68.2% of patients following trauma, and in 66.7% of patients with manic-depressive psychosis.* They were also seen in 14.2% of patients with schizophrenia in a state of remission. This instability in the use of a particular mode of action was thus observed in several different disease categories.

The condition of the patients forming this group (apart from the schizophrenics, whose condition will be examined later) was described as asthenic. They showed increased fatigability, excitatory weakness, and intolerance of strong stimuli (bright light, loud noise, etc.). The case records mention disturbances of sleep, headaches, and fluctuations of mood. While conversing, they often began to cry without reason, and they usually found it impossible to endure long periods of mental stress. When given a job to do, the patients soon abandoned it, exclaiming that they were tired and that the work bored them. They easily tired of reading, saying that they could not understand what was written. Nearly all the patients

---

*Although statistical analysis of the types of solution to the object-classification test compels us to include patients with manic-depressive psychosis in this group, we thought it would be more accurate to include these patients in the group described in the section on the "flight of ideas."

TABLE XIV

Performance in the Object-Classification Test Using
Associations Based on Concrete Situations

Diagnosis	Number of patients examined	Number of patients making mistakes
Schizophrenia	155	22 (14.2)*
Epilepsy	50	2 (4.0)
Cerebrovascular diseases	125	102 (81.6)
Brain trauma	170	116 (68.2)
Oligophrenia	40	—
Encephalitis	20	—
General paresis	30	1 (3.3)
Manic-depressive psychosis	15	10 (66.7)
Psychopathy	30	6 (20.0)

*The corresponding figures expressed as percentages are given in parentheses.

had been classified as disabled in categories II or III. Although a high proportion of the patients had continued to work up to the time they were admitted to the hospital, most of them had already lost some of their professional skill.

We will examine in some detail these patients' patterns of behavior in performing the object classification test. They had no difficulty in grasping the instruction, they used a method adequate to the solution of the problem, and they began to sort the cards in accordance with generic signs; but after a short time they abandoned the correct method of solution. Having in some cases attained a high level of generalization, the patients periodically wandered off into incorrect, random associations. There were several types of variations.

1. Very often the principle of classification alternated between that of generalization and that of concrete situations. A few examples may be given.

Patient Sh-v (closed brain injury) began to sort the cards in accordance with a generic sign, forming groups of plants, animals, etc., and then suddenly began to have doubts about where to put a toadstool: "It is harmful; let us leave it alone." In the same way, he could not decide where to place a beetle: "Put it with the textbook and the exercise book; they study it at school." After the experimenter had asked the patient to pay more attention to the work, he replied somewhat confusedly: "Wait, here I have dishes, furniture, and plants..... Of course, and the fungus belongs here, regardless of whether it is poisonous or not; the beetle should go with the animals." Eventually the patient obtained the following groups: people, animals, plants, dishes, furniture, school articles, housekeeping equipment. The experimenter asked the patient to combine several groups. The patient replied: "People with animals, perhaps? Plants...and then what? Surely the rest cannot be put together: how can you combine things used in a house with things used in an office?" The patient was obviously tiring; he developed a mild tremor of the hands and began to perspire. The experimenter began to talk about something unrelated to the test. Five minutes later, at the experimenter's request, the patient resumed the work and at once produced without help a correct, generalized solution.

Patient Sh. (cerebral arteriosclerosis), having correctly separated a group of tools (saw, broom, spade), included a blacksmith in this group, "because he is drawn with a hammer in his hand, and he works with different tools." When the experimenter asked: "And what have you in this group?" (charwoman, sailor, child, doctor) the patient replied: "These are people," and she then transferred the blacksmith to the group of people of her own accord.

Patient P. (cerebral arteriosclerosis), having correctly picked out groups of people, animals, furniture, clothing, and so on, added a fur hat and boots to the picture of a skier lying on the top of the pile, explaining that the skier needed these objects. When the experimenter asked the patient what this group should be called, he took the hat and boots away from the group of "people" and transferred them to the "clothing" group.

The fluctuations in the mental activity of these patients took the form of vacillation between generalizations and concrete situations as a basis for their decisions. The solution of problems by these patients at the level of generalized decisions had not become a stable modus operandi.

2. The mistakes made by another group of patients were the result of the replacement of logical associations by random combinations. For instance, they spoiled their performance in an object classification test by combining objects inattentively into one group: they tossed the cards carelessly into a group next to the one which

they intended to form; they placed cards in a certain group simply because it lay nearby.

For example, patient Sh. picked out groups representing "transport," "furniture," and "animals." Having started to form a group of plants, he added the card of a tumbler which happened to be lying nearby. He noticed the mistake himself, and explained it by saying: "I was not paying attention." Another patient, having formed a group of "furniture," included with it the card showing a thermometer which was lying nearby, immediately realized his mistake, and corrected it.

3. The mistakes made by still another group of patients took the form of combining objects into similar groups: they often selected objects in accordance with the correct general sign, and then immediately began to form another almost identical group. For example, patient O-v picked out a group of plants which contained vegetables, flowers, and fruit, after which she proceeded to form an analogous group of plants which included bushes and trees.

This instability in the mode of solution was also revealed in experiments using the exclusion method. The patient was given a card on which were drawn a purse, a briefcase, a book, and a bag. Patient Sh. said: "The purse must go in the pocket.... No, the briefcase is the odd one. The book can go in the briefcase.... Let me think.... The book is the odd one, for things can be put inside the others." The same patient, when given a card showing a clock, a pair of spectacles, scales, and a thermometer, said: "The spectacles are the odd one. All the others are for measuring. You cannot measure with spectacles." When given a card with "the sun, a candle, a kerosene lamp, and an electric flashlight," the patient said: "The sun must be left out, it is a natural light....If it is daylight the rest are not needed."

Another patient correctly solved the problem of excluding the odd item from the group, clock, thermometer, scales, spectacles, but became confused when given the group, cupboard, chest of drawers, bookcase, bed. The patient's inclusion–exclusion decisions were sometimes adequate and sometimes clearly mistaken.

Hence, comparison of the results of experiments using different methods (classification, exclusion, etc.) revealed this instability in the mode of solution of a problem—which we may define as "illogicality of reasoning."

If the disease was of mild severity, this illogicality of reasoning could be quickly corrected. Often, as soon as the experimenter asked the patient what he was doing, or simply expressed surprise at his actions, (i.e., drew the patient's attention to his mistakes), the patient himself readily corrected his mistakes himself.

It should be noted that fluctuations in the patients' achievements were noted with the slightest changes in the conditions of work. This is illustrated by the following facts, revealed during analysis of the results of an experiment using the method of "relating phrases to proverbs." Several patients, although they had described the figurative meaning of proverbs without difficulty, made glaring mistakes when they were required to match them with phrases of similar meaning (we have drawn attention to this fact in an article devoted especially to the understanding of metaphorical values [102]). For example, one of the patients who understood the proverb, "All that glitters is not gold," and explained it correctly, matched it with the unsuitable phrase, "Gold is heavier than iron," but then immediately corrected his mistake and was embarrassed at having made it. Another patient, having correctly explained the proverb, "It is no use crying over spilled milk," matched it with the phrase, "Things must not be put off until tomorrow."

Particularly sharp fluctuations in the level of attainment were found during the performance of tests requiring the prolonged retention of a particular trend of thought and the constant inhibition of irrelevant associations. This was seen when variant III of the association experiment was performed with the patients of this group, when the instruction determines the response reactions beforehand (the patient must answer with a word opposite in meaning to the word stimulus). The answers given by our patients often lost this directed character. For example, one of the patients responded to the word "miser" with the name "Plyushkin," and to the word "forget" with "absent-mindedness," and so on; a verbal association was reproduced here which, although formed in the patient's previous experience, was inappropriate to the present instruction.

As we pointed out in the first section of this chapter, the presence of such a large number of undirected responses is a deviation from the normal course of the association process.

It may also be mentioned that variant III of the association experiment did not cause much difficulty in patients characterized by a lowered level of generalization or "sluggishness" of thinking, although these patients sometimes could not find the suitable word because of their limited range of knowledge. In some cases no response reaction was present at all, and in others the patients contented themselves with a negation: "healthy"—"unhealthy," "kind"—"unkind." As we have stated above, although such replies may have indicated a poor store of words or a slowness in finding the required association, the associative behavior nevertheless remained directed; no associations irrelevant to the conditions of the test appeared. On the other hand, in the patients of the present group (with illogicality of reasoning) it was the directed character of the associations that was inadequate.

To illustrate this lack of directedness we give extracts from the case history and the results of experimental psychological examinations of one of the patients of this group.

Patient S., female (case report of Dr. V. V. Gromova), born 1907. Diagnosis: cerebral arteriosclerosis, astheno-depressive state. Early development normal. A good pupil. She began to feel ill in 1950: she could not sleep, was increasingly irritable, and had attacks of vertigo. She remained at work, but was soon tired, and she became "absent-minded and confused."

Neurological State. Slight ptosis of the right eyelid. Anisocoria (L>R). Reaction to light and convergence satisfactory. Tendon and periosteal reflexes equal, patellar reflexes increased (R>L); no pathological reflexes present. Slight swaying during Romberg's test. The EEG showed no gross changes in the brain.

Mental State. The patient was fully oriented but complained of tiredness, headaches, loss of memory, and inability to sleep. She could not stand noise, her moods were unstable, and she was in low spirits.

In the object classification experiment the patient had no difficulty in starting to solve the problem. She picked out groups representing transport, furniture, and dishes, but she suddenly had doubts when she saw the card with the picture of an airplane: "All the other forms of transport move along the ground, but this is in the air. But perhaps it is a military plane?" The patient stopped sorting, but she put the airplane among the transport group. After a short time she had correctly sorted three groups: "animals," "plants," and "inanimate nature." During the sorting process she did not know where to put the thermometer: "Surely there aren't any patients here," and after a short pause she again put it in the group "inanimate nature."

Similar fluctuations were also revealed in the experiment on the exclusion of objects. The patient was given a picture showing a clock, thermometer, scales, and spectacles. She correctly excluded the spectacles, following the principle: "The rest are used for measuring." When she was given the next picture (candle, kerosene lamp, electric flashlight, sun), she attempted to exclude the kerosene lamp, because "nowadays there is electricity everywhere in our country." Hence the patient performed the same test sometimes on the plane of generalization and sometimes on a concrete and elementary level. The association experiment (variant III) demonstrated the presence of undirected responses (see Table XV).

The fluctuations in our patients' mental attainment observed in the course of the same experiment were particularly noticeable at its end. In some cases these fluctuations disappeared as the patient's condition improved. In an analysis of the nature of the fluctuations in the level of mental attainment, the first problem to be considered is that of their relationship to the complexity of the test.

The opinion has often been expressed in the literature that the lowering of the level of mental attainment in patients with cerebral arteriosclerosis may be attributed to their inability to organize and systematize their activity. Petrova [229], for instance, points to the weakening of the active attention of these patients. In an

TABLE XV

Patient S. Results of an Association Experiment (Variant III)

Stimulus word	Latency period (in sec)	Response reaction
blunt	2	sharp
thin	2.5	thick
dirty	2.5	clean
belonging to someone else	2.5	one's own
down	3	up
large	3	fruit
enemy	1.5	will be beaten
young	3	old
high	1.5	low
hard	2.5	nut
dry	2	wet
pretty	1.5	charming
restfulness	4.5	restlessness
similarity	3.5	difference
minority	2.5	submits to the majority
forget	3	absent-mindedness
miser	2	knight
light	1.5	heavy
victory	2	defeat
truth	2	honesty

*Wide-spaced words represent incorrect answers.

article by Sagalova [274], of interest because of its wealth of data, it is stated that mistakes in the work of patients with cerebral arteriosclerosis may be explained by their "inability to organize structurally the process of the reinforcement of perception and reproduction." In this writer's opinion, patients attain lower levels of mental performance as greater demands are made upon them to classify and organize the material.

The results of our investigation demonstrate that the disturbance of mental activity of these patients has a different mechanism from that postulated by Sagalova. The fluctuations in their psychological performance were not caused solely by the complexity of the material or by difficulties in its organization, for these fluctuations were also frequently observed during the performance of the most elementary tasks, such as the retention and reproduction of ten words. After the first reproduction the experimenter asked the subject to listen once again and to repeat all the words he could remember. The experiment was repeated from 8 to 10 times. Experiments conducted on healthy subjects showed that the number of retained words increases with the number of repetitions. If this process is shown graphically it is represented by a rising curve (Fig. 1A).

The word reproduction curves obtained from tests on our patients differed from the "normal" curve (Fig. 1B, C, D) they showed marked variations in the number of reproduced words. Attention is drawn to the fact that sometimes quite considerable numbers of words were reproduced (patient S.—7 at the fourth repetition; patient V.—6 at the third and eighth repetitions; patient L.—7 at the third repetition). On the other hand, the graphs show that a reduction in the number of reproduced words does not necessarily occur at the end of the experiment (see, for example, Fig. 1C). A characteristic feature here is the irregular character of the process of reproduction.

A similar picture of the fluctuations in performance level is shown by the results obtained with the "proofreading test" of Burton. The patient is given a sheet of paper on which are printed continuous rows of letters (not in alphabetical order), two of which he has to cross out. The number of rows scrutinized by the subject and the number of mistakes he makes are counted. The graphs in Fig. 2 show the number of mistakes in each minute period during performance of this test. They should be compared with the graphs in Fig. 1 which indicate the fluctuations in performance results

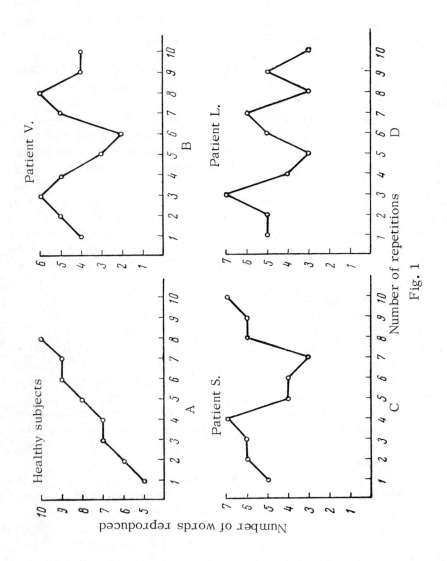

Fig. 1

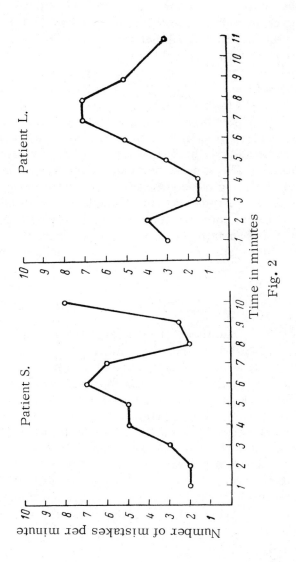

Fig. 2

revealed in the same patients in the experiment involving the reproduction of words.

Vasil'eva [43], working in our laboratory, showed that these fluctuations may be detected in patients with cerebrovascular diseases even in such elementary activities as seeking a number in Schulte's tables. She found that the speed of the search reactions in these patients may be highly variable.

All these findings demonstrate that the fluctuations in the mental performance of the patients in the present group does not depend on the difficulty of the task, nor on their attitude toward the task, nor on their ability to systematize. It is possible for a form of activity to be well within a patient's capability for a certain period of time, when the same task a short time later can be performed only with great difficulty. The same experiment reveals a similar fluctuation in the level of the logical course of the patient's thoughts.

These facts are important in principle. They demonstrate that the fluctuations of mental attainment in different forms of mental activity are the manifestation of a more general disturbance— instability of the capacity for mental work. Because of these fluc- tuations in the capacity for mental work the same patients some- times appear to be perfectly normal, with adequate thoughts and actions, and at other times may appear to have lost all sense of purposeful action.

It is evident that these fluctuations are a manifestation of the rapid fatigability of the patient's mental processes. This rapid fatigability is of a special nature and should be distinguished from the common fatigability of the healthy person. In the latter case the tempo of work is slowed, and the number of mistakes increases toward the end of the experiment. In experiments carried out on normal subjects (adults and children), fatigability was mani- fested as a retardation in working tempo and an increase in the number of mistakes toward the end of the experiment. If the healthy subject tires, however, although he will classify objects more slowly he will still do so on an adequate level. The fatig- ability of the mental processes of our patients, on the other hand, was characterized by temporary changes in the actual quality of their mental performance.

This fatigability is very likely based on the process of protective inhibition, which was seen to develop rapidly in our patients. Pavlov often stated that when the level of cortical activity is lowered, any task causing concentrated stimulation of a certain point induces inhibition of the rest of the cortex. Pathophysiological investigation of these patients revealed a weakness of excitation and inhibition, resulting in the rapid extinction of the conditioned reflexes which were formed (Kaminskii and Savchuk [125]). This is a further demonstration of the role in pathological fatigability of a lowered reactivity of the cortical process.

The series of clinical symptoms which appear as disturbances of individual, isolated mental processes are essentially different manifestations of this spreading inhibition. For instance, when the patients complain that they forget what they have read, or forget to do jobs entrusted to them, this often appears to be a disturbance of memory; when the patients remark that insignificant and irrelevant factors (conversation of neighbors, a quietly tuned radio) prevent them from working, this is apparently a "scattering" of attention. In fact, all these symptoms are manifestations of a single disturbance—the excessively easy development of external inhibition.

The thinking of the patients of this group appeared to be disturbed because their reasoning had not attained a stable mode of reaction. The patients could generalize and synthesize material correctly and had no trouble in adapting to the specific conditions of the problem, but they could not maintain the correct method of solution throughout the entire test period. The almost inevitable development of inhibition interrupted the correct course of the patient's thoughts, thus temporarily depressing his level of generalization and undermining his reasoning. Disturbances in the dynamic, or "process" aspects of thinking also led to a degradation in the quality of intellectual activity.

4. "HYPERRESPONSIVENESS"

In one group of patients the instability both in the method of performing the test and in the associated fluctuations in level of mental attainment was at times manifested in an extremely exaggerated and grotesque manner. For example, one patient classified objects correctly for a time and then began to act absurdly, treating the pictures as if they were real objects (e.g., he placed the picture of a ship horizontally: "Otherwise it will sink," and arranged the cards "fanwise," like playing cards. Another patient, having sorted some of the cards in correct consecutive order, suddenly began to fixate upon an incidental detail of one of the pictures (the cause of the breakdown of a cart) and proceeded

no further in the solution of the problem. Having descended to
such low levels of performance, it was only after much time had
elapsed that the patients could resume adequate test behavior.

We call these disturbances of thinking "hyperresponsiveness."
It was observed mainly in patients suffering from severe forms of
cerebrovascular disease (more often with essential hypertension).
This phenomenon was also observed in patients with severe head
injuries complicated by suppurative processes (abscesses or severe
meningo-encephalitis).

In most cases the case records indicated that the patients were
at times severely disoriented in time and place. At times they
would say that they were in their own home, sometimes they might
say they were at the factory, adding immediately afterward, however, that "this is a hospital" and that they were having treatment.
Many patients exhibited behavior proper to a hospital, but in
response to questioning as to where they were, they answered
differently every time: "This is a hospital...a workers' hostel...
a station...a school...people in white overalls — these are teachers
and the doctors are senior engineers. Perhaps it is a theater —
these are actors lying here, they are ill too...," and so on.

The patients reproduced with difficulty facts and dates having to
do with either past or present events, gave confused information
concerning themselves, and could not remember the names of their
friends and neighbors or of the doctors who had treated them.
They possessed uncritical attitudes toward their conditions, taking
little notice of the mistakes in their own actions and statements.
They often followed answers to correct the doctor's questions by
meaningless ramblings.

In these patients speech was disturbed. During longer conver-
sations they often became incoherent. For example, in reply to a
question concerning the difference between error and deception,
one patient said: "You can make mistakes in different ways. You
can be mistaken in understanding a person.... Man has become
truly mixed up in this. You may say one thing or another, but
fundamentally it is all bad.... This is something which just happens by itself." The patients lose the thread of their thoughts and
become fixated upon individual words.

At times the patients behave absurdly. Their relatives often
mention the patients' foolish behavior before admission to the hospital—leaving the gas turned on, putting on their coats inside out, etc.
Left to themselves, they rarely asked questions, made requests,

or initiated any type of spontaneous conversation. Some of them were fastidious; others lay in bed all day, wanting nothing and complaining of nothing, all were essentially passive.

These disturbances are dynamic in nature. In the course of a short period of time the character of the patients' reasoning and behavior might exhibit sharp variations. Patients at first considered to be mentally deficient showed comparatively normal behavior after a short interval of time, answering questions correctly, reacting to situations, etc. Other patients almost totally forgot and then later recalled their names, ages, friends' names, and other pertinent details of their lives and their present circumstances.

The particular features and the general dynamic character of these patients' psychic disturbances often complicate the analysis of their mental state, so that different writers have variously interpreted the problem of mental disturbances in hypertension. Whereas Averbukh [9] mentions the "flattening" of the personality, Zvereva [100] evaluates these disturbances in terms of a lowering of the "intellectual functions," particularly of memory. Fridman [327] points out that the mental disturbances in hypertension have the character of a severe organic dementia with transient fluctuations of consciousness. Ozeretskii [213] describes the poverty of intellectual activity and the narrowing in interests and in the critical faculty.

We consider that the intellectual changes in our patients, because of their instability, variety, and fluctuation, do not fit into the ordinary pattern of organic dementia. We shall therefore discuss them in some detail.

Observations on these patients in an experimental situation revealed their hyperresponsiveness to the most varied and irrelevant environmental stimuli. Upon hearing a conversation between a doctor and another nearby patient, one hyperresponsive patient, apparently so indifferent to everything, began to take part in the conversation. Likewise, any noise which chanced to come up from the street would become the subject of some new remarks. Having heard the people in the next ward singing the song "Kalinka-malinka," one patient suddenly turned to the nurse with the request: "Bring me some raspberry (malinovogo) and bilberry jam."

Often the patients' hyperresponsiveness took a different form: the patient interspersed his speech with the names of objects which were in his field of vision but which bore no relationship to what he was saying. For instance, when asked how he felt, one patient replied: "Quite well, thank you, there is a little knocking here." (In the next room somebody was hammering.) Another patient, in the midst of copying a story from a book, suddenly wrote the words, "yellow lampshade," which had nothing to do with the story. (A yellow lampshade stood on a table in front of the patient.) The patients seemed to develop a compulsive tendency to reflect in their speech everything that they perceived. As with other manifestations of hyperresponsiveness, this compulsive reflection also displayed a dynamic character, at times becoming prevalent and at others almost disappearing.

The phenomenon of hyperresponsiveness was manifested especially clearly in an association experiment (variant I, see p. 111) which we carried out with 30 such patients. As responses they often gave the names of random objects which happened to be located within their range of vision (this phenomenon is known as interweaving): in response to the word, "singing," one patient gave the word, "table"; in response to the word "wheel," the word "spectacles," etc. This tendency was sometimes observed in other groups of patients, although it disappeared as soon as the experimenter pointed out the error. In the case of hyperresponsive patients, however, verbal correction could only curb this tendency for a very short time. Reactions of this type accounted for 22.4% of the total number of responses (altogether 550 stimulus words were presented). The percentage of responses of the perseveration type was also high (19.6%), and adequate responses were given only in 30.7% of cases.

The hyperresponsive patients also exhibited this tendency in the variant of the association experiment in which the instruction stipulated an added qualification to the responses, for instance, when the subject was told to name a number of objects of a particular color (e.g., red or green). This test can sometimes give rise to considerable difficulty in healthy subjects since it requires the active discarding of words which do not correspond to the meaning of the instruction. In such cases the subjects use various methods as aids in recalling the required words (such as observing the surrounding objects), but they do not use them in their answers if they do not correspond to the instruction (that is, they will not name the surrounding objects if none are of the required color). The experimenter's instruction acquires the value of a determinant stimulus; the responses of a normal person in the experimental situation depend on the conditions of the task and the demands of the experimenter.

On the other hand, in this experiment our hyperresponsive patients at times named objects which were in their field of vision but which were not necessarily of the required color. The experimenter's instruction evoked purposive behavior only for a limited time. The relationship between the direction of our patients' associations and the conditions of the problem was extremely unstable. Any object observed or words overheard could distort the course of their reasoning. We attributed their absurd thoughts and actions to the syndrome we have described as hyperresponsiveness.

It is possible that our patients' characteristic fluctuating disorientation in time and space was also closely associated with this hyperresponsiveness. For instance, one of them at first said that he was in a restaurant and then immediately declared he was in a watchmaker's shop instead. (It turned out that the watchmaker repaired watches at this time.) Five minutes later he correctly stated that he was in the hospital. Another patient, when asked by the experimenter where he was, replied: "I am in the paper laboratory, busy with the analysis of these a and b, b and a." (A small cupboard hung in front of the patient, bearing the letters B and A for groups of drugs.) Some hours later he had evolved a new interpretation of the situation: he declared that he was with an army unit. (He had noticed a soldier going past the window.) This type of two-fold orientation was also present in a patient described by Zvereva [100]; this patient maintained that he was at the same time in a railroad car and in a hospital.

It should be noted that rapid hyperresponsiveness to external, random stimuli was combined in these patients with difficulty in switching from one association to another. The results of the association experiment contained a large proportion of responses characterized by perseveration.

As an illustration of the foregoing remarks, we present an extract from the case history and the results of an experimental psychological examination of one patient of this group.

Patient L–v (case notes of Dr. D. B. Golant), male, born 1880. Registered disabled person. High-school education. Clinical diagnosis: malignant arteriosclerosis with multiple foci of softening, mainly in the left hemisphere; hypertensive syndrome. Pathological diagnosis: malignant cerebral arteriosclerosis with old and recent foci of softening; generalized arteriosclerosis.

History. Normal birth and early development; a bright pupil. Having graduated from an agricultural institute, he worked as a senior scientific worker. The first pathological manifestations occurred in 1939, when he began to feel weak and suffered headaches and attacks of dizziness. His blood pressure was found to be high. In 1947 his fellow workers began to notice his strange behavior: talking to himself and appearing always to be intoxicated. He soon showed speech disorders of the type of amnestic aphasia and could no longer manage to do his work. Because of his irregular behavior he was admitted to the hospital.

Neurological State. Pupils equal, reaction to light slightly sluggish. Convergence impaired. Periosteal and tendon reflexes much increased. Muscle tone slightly raised. No pathological reflexes present.

Mental State. The patient was oriented in time, but inadequately in space. He was extremely sluggish, apathetic and confused. He did not grasp immediately what was said to him and answered only after a short pause. At times he sat idly, indifferent to his surroundings and at others he wandered confusedly about the ward, seeking the door, being unable to find his bed. He quickly lost the thread of a conversation and could not give the dates of the more important events of both his own life and that of the community. Yet at the same time, quite unexpectedly, he correctly stated his age, the name of his high school and the date of his graduation, and the names of his teachers. In fact, he recited chronologically the more important events of his childhood, adolescence, and first years at work. However, when asked: "What did they do to you on Thursday?" he replied: "Fraternity." (Later he correctly stated that a lumbar puncture had been performed.) He considered that he was in a railroad car; he called the doctors "meteorologists" and the head doctor "Napoleon." A short time later he stated that he was in a hospital and was surrounded by patients, and he asked to be sent home.

In an experiment on the classification of objects, the patient began to sort the cards correctly, but soon abandoned the task and glanced confusedly at the cards, saying: "Where shall I put them so as not to leave them in disorder on the table?" Soon afterward he resumed sorting them properly, forming groups of animals, plants, and inanimate objects.

Determination of the sequence of events. The patient examined the individual cards for a long time, started to do the test correctly, but then, taking card No. 3 in his hand, he exclaimed: "Where are they going? Probably a woodcutter.... And where is he...that is, no, where is the saw? They have lost it and they will have to find it" (tried to look under the table). After a short pause he arranged the cards in the proper order.

Interpretation of proverbs. The patient correctly explained the proverb, "Strike the iron while it is hot," saying: "Work quickly...". He then continued confusedly: "Here is this pen (points to a pen lying on the table), this has to be done, and here we have to hoe the leaves." (looks through the window at a tree).

Association experiment (variant IV). The patient was asked to name 5 red objects. He answered: "Cherry, poppy, *lamp*, carrot, *wall*, blood." When asked to name 7 green objects, he replied: "Grass, cabbage, *pencil, paper, watch, tumbler,* water may be green if it is slimy, a green tree." (The words in italics repre-

TABLE XVI

Patient L-v. Results of an Association Experiment (Variant I)

Stimulus word	Latency period (in sec)	Response reaction
bread	5	house
lamp	5	roof
singing	2	t a b l e *
wheel	2	s p e c t a c l e s
beauty	5	c u p b o a r d
war	2	t a b l e
air	2	sun
development	6	eye
bell	4	c i g a r e t
cave	2	b o o k
endlessness	5	s u i t c a s e
moon	2	sky
brother	4	sister
treatment	6	illness
ax	4	saw
fall	5	h a n d l e
deception	6	w a l l
head	5	s o f a
doubt	6	child
game	5	football
purpose	7	health
depth	12	i n k s t a n d
hardness	15	h a n d l e
conscience	15	patient

*The wide-spaced words denote objects lying within the patient's field of vision.

sent objects which the patient saw in front of him and which were neither red nor green.)

When instructed to name 7 sharp objects, the patient answered: "Knife, razor, pen, it isn't sharp, ruler, scythe, pencil, wire." The patient's response was often determined by his field of vision. Similar results were obtained in variant I of the association experiment (see Table XVI).

The patient's speech was disturbed; signs of amnestic aphasia and perseveration were present. At times, however, the patient named objects correctly and gave the right answers to questions. Several examples follow.

Patient's replies when shown pictures:

Ashtray—"Ashtray."

Button—"It is an ordinary common frame."

Coil—"Probably a needle case or simply a frame under simple needles."

Collar—"A tie from a simple needle, that is a collar."

Cigaret case—"Under the paper there is probably a cigaret. You can get as many as ten cigarets at a time in it. I always have these things under 10 cigarets."

Tie—"Things under 10 cigarets the same. I don't know what this is. An ordinary small cigaret case for 10 cigarets, things under 10 cigarets."

Stud—"This is a small cigaret case for fastening 10 cigaret cases. Or a flare, a stud."

A 20-kopek coin—"This is 20 kopeks, of course."

Carrot—"I don't know whether there were some or not at home, it is a carrot, 20 kopeks."

Hairpins—"A universal attachment for threads."

A chair—"This is the physical of sitting. I sit on the seat of the chair. This is a wooden chair."

Character of the patient's speech in dialogue:

Character of the patient's speech in dialogue:
Experimenter. Were you in the war?
Patient. Yes. In Austria-Hungary.
E. Where are you?
P. Home away from home is a military unit.
E. Where have we seen each other before?
P. Frankly speaking, I don't remember, evidently at home.
E. What did you have for breakfast?
P. Boiled fish and nothing else. (This was true.)
E. Have you had dinner yet? (The conversation took place shortly after breakfast.)
P. Yes.
E. What did you have for dinner?
P. Not the whole of that cut-up fish.
E. Where are you?
P. Austro-German territory, conditions in Austro-German territory — this will be the conditions.
E. What are you doing here?
P. As I am telling you, I am fully occupied here with conditions. I am busy.
E. What am I asking you about?
P. I now understand the solution of the problem confronting me.
E. What are you doing here?
P. They brought me here for treatment.
E. Are you healthy or ill?
P. Healthy, of course.
E. With whom do I work here, in your opinion?
P. You have the specialty of a physician. You treat patients.
E. Are you healthy or ill?
P. Ill, of course.

E. Why did they bring you here?
P. I don't understand, you see, it is difficult for me to answer, because they brought me to be treated.

The hyperresponsiveness in our patients was manifested by a gross abnormality of the course of the thinking process. In the healthy person, every object lying in the field of vision does not necessarily act as the source of ideas, thoughts, or actions. The normal thinking process demands the ability to inhibit irrelevant stimuli which might otherwise disturb the smooth course of thought. With our hyperresponsive patients, on the other hand, any object at all could serve as a stimulus to direct their thoughts and actions.

When we described this phenomenon in our earlier writings, we defined it as the phenomenon of "field behavior," since we wished to stress its lack of purpose and its random nature. We were unable, however, to formulate an explanation of this syndrome in terms of the concepts of Gestalt psychology. It can, however, be explained in terms of Pavlov's theory of hypnotic phases.

The hyperresponsive syndrome indicates the loss of that accuracy of analysis which characterizes the cortical activity of the healthy person. It may be suggested that rapid hyperresponsiveness in patients, diffuseness of reasoning, and sharp fluctuations in the level of mental performance are associated with those changes in higher nervous activity which Pavlov described as hypnotic phasic states. In his account of the hypnoid phases, Pavlov pointed out that "When it is a question of more complex forms of the hypnotic state, it is clear that it is difficult to draw a complete parallel between animals and man." [217; IV]. Stimulus strength for man is dependent on the social importance of the stimulus. Hence, in the situation of a psychological experiment, a word or a request from the experimenter—or the instructions themselves—must needs have a greater effect on the patient than a neutral object (such as a lampshade) or words accidentally overheard. In our patients, on the other hand, an apparent equalization of the value of the stimuli had taken place.

It is pertinent to mention that the investigations of Kaminskii and Savchuk [125], who studied the conditioned reflex activity of hypertensive patients (some of whom we have already described), revealed the presence of phasic states in these patients. The presence of hypnotic phases may also account for some of the disturbances in the mental activity of these patients, disturbances which at first glance appeared to be but isolated memory disturbances.

We have noted that hyperresponsive patients often cannot relate events in their lives, cannot remember their neighbors, and cannot evaluate time relationships. The clinical assessment of these patients is nearly always given in terms of the concepts of an amnestic symptom complex or of amnestic dementia. If, however, the processes involved in acquiring new material are analyzed into the classical triad: "grasping, retaining, reproducing," it becomes clear that the last of these is most severely impaired in these patients. All their images, ideas, and impressions of the new material may sooner or later be found in their flow of thought. One patient, for example, was unable to repeat a fable, stating he had "forgotten" it; in the course of a subsequent conversation in a different context, several days later, he was able not only to trace it but to do so in the most detailed manner. In exactly the same way, when patient Shch. had read a fable, she was unable to repeat it; she was then told another, easier story and asked to repeat it, and in response, she unexpectedly related the first fable. Thus, no marked disturbance of the grasping process was present in these patients. Evidently the concentration of effort on reproduction led to the inhibition of the grasping or understanding activity.

The same considerations apply to the speech disorders of the patients of this group—amnestic defects (and paraphasias). Often the patients cannot find the required word while seeking it intensively, while they unexpectedly utter it after they have stopped looking for it. This phenomenon was previously reported by Gal'perin and Golubova [57] in 1938. Using the method of transfer of effort, these workers established experimentally the role of protective inhibition as the basic mechanism of paraphasia. Apparently the forgetfulness of these patients may be explained in the same way. They often lose and are unable to find things which lie literally before their eyes; subsequently these objects "find themselves" when the patient is no longer looking for them.

In connection with the paraphasias, it should be noted that in our cases it was not only individual words or names of objects that were mistaken. Together with S. Ya. Rubinshtein [116], in experiments with patients with severe cerebrovascular diseases, we found that the speech of these patients was characterized by such an incomprehensible, mutilated style, and in some cases the absurdity of the replies was carried to such a degree, that suspicions were aroused as to the possible presence of schizophrenic dissociation or Ganser's syndrome.

One of these patients, for example, when asked what 3 × 4 makes, replied: "It is an infected thing." The patient was shown a picture of the driver of a cart who was upset because the wheel had broken off the axle. The patient said: "A beet may be pressed, but in any case this is not a liquid. . . ." The patient was shown a cock, and he said that it was an apple. Immediately afterward he was given a pair of spectacles, which he described as the stalk of the apple. The interweaving was obvious here: "apple" was perseverated, and the word "stalk" was prompted by seeing the bridge of the spectacles.

While giving these replies, the patient neither noticed nor corrected his mistakes, although he was upset by his general incompetence. He reproached the doctors for laughing at him, and told them that they should have shouted, "hurrah!" He later explained that what he had wanted to say was that the doctors ought not to upset the patient by laughing, but should rather encourage him by their optimism and cheerfulness. What gave rise to the words "shout hurrah!"? Possibly this was a paraphasia caused by the fact that the affective need to express his thoughts was impeded by his inert speech function, so that, unable to find the precise word he needed, he used a diffuse and vague expression.

Examples of the spontaneous expressions or descriptions given by these patients are especially interesting. During direct perception they seemed to be characterized by a general deautomatization of psychomotor acts, but during the isolated repetition of a text they nevertheless did not seem to be exhibiting schizophrenic sterility and incoherence. Patient M, for example, explained the proverb, "Don't spit in the well, it's drinking water," as follows: "Don't spit in the well. . . . He heard, he heard, but he only drinks so that. . . . Whoever he is, he doesn't realize that it isn't necessary, really isn't necessary, and let me say it here and now, quite openly, it isn't necessary(?). . . . You see that what I say is absolutely true and as it should be. It should be at that particular moment. . . . Where do you want to spit, and if whoever spits and a good man and what is he doing, well no matter, there is no difference, no difference. . . . It is a general principle, when you are alone you do nothing, and there is power which is. . .only harnessed. Where does a certain organ work, and not what(?). . . . It is quite true, this man is discussing something quite different. . .quite different. . . . There is a man who is discussing differently(?). . . . Well, one way or the other, it's a mere trifle, not worth a straw, I consider that the trifle is not that whatever it is, but it is a trifle to the man who is looking here and there. On the other hand, you have to look and, anyhow there must be a man...something must I live...and it doesn't pay to live for today, it doesn't pay anywhere, and there are people who live hither and thither, wherever you wish...."

The patient explained the proverb, "All that glitters is not gold," as follows: "Gold glitters but the rest does not. Now, there is artificial gold. It glitters, but not all the time. When it is dropped in the mud or rubbish somehow. And if an artificial thing is dropped it glitters while you are holding it, but when it has dropped into the mud it loses its shine. (Can this be applied to man?) He paints and makes himself up, he glitters...but it passes, it changes, the glitter goes."

Of course, these gross disturbances of memory and speech are not observed in every patient with hyperresponsiveness. However, even when these massive disturbances are not present, their intellectual activity is characterized by diffuseness and by the alternation of different levels of organization.* If the hypothesis is correct that the pathophysiological basis of these disturbances is the presence of limiting inhibition, it may be accepted that in the patients of this group inhibition has for the time being lost its protective importance.

Pavlov repeatedly stated that the process of inhibition not only arrests activity, but also facilitates its restoration; in the words of Fol'bort [324], "inhibition promotes restoration." Fol'bort's work showed that during the development of pathological phenomena, dissociation may develop between the processes of exhaustion and recovery, when "the process of exhaustion does not give rise to a process of recovery, and the process of inhibition ceases to evoke restoration." [324].

Our patients' hyperresponsiveness must not be confused with the phenomenon of distractibility found in young children. Any object or any sound will divert the attention of small children; this distractibility may often seem superficially to have much in common with the pathological phenomenon we have been describing. The supporters of the view that pathological behavioral symptoms represent reversions to phylogenetically earlier modes of reaction would here appear to find confirmation of their opinions. In fact,

---

*Clinically, the syndrome we have described is closest to the protracted, "stunned" state of consciousness described by Ravkin [247], differing from it in the former's absence of an increase in the thresholds of perception and by the greater lability of the symptomatology. Birenbaum and Shekhanova (unpublished investigation) observed similar clinical states in schizophrenic patients in the form of complications after convulsion therapy, and Gol'dovskaya [73] also observed it in patients in a postinfective state.

however, the genesis of the distractibility of the child is quite different. It is based on an increase in the strength of the orienting reflex, i.e., on a high degree of cortical activity. The child's distractibility allows him to form a large number of temporary associations, on the basis of which its goal-directed activity may be stimulated. The hyperresponsiveness of our patients, however, was the result of a lowering of the level of cortical activity, and it contributed rather to the impairment of the purposiveness of their mental activity.

This example of the superficial similarity between distractibility and hyperresponsiveness also illustrates the general principle that psychopathological phenomena externally identical with certain forms of child behavior differ from them genetically.

5. SLIDING*

In clinical descriptions of disorders of thought in schizophrenia the term "sliding" is often encountered although, so far as we are aware, no special investigation of this phenomenon has been made. This symptom of thought disturbance can only be distinguished in comparatively mild cases, for otherwise the "sliding" is overshadowed by other, more serious disturbances. In this form of disturbance, while they may be performing a task correctly or reasoning adequately about an object, the patients unexpectedly slide from the correct course of thought into a spurious, inadequate association, after which they resume their logical course of reasoning, tending neither to repeat their mistake nor to correct the one they have already made.

One of our patients, for example, had mastered the principle of classification and was using it logically in the course of a lengthy chain of reasoning, when he unexpectedly became sidetracked into forming the absurd combination of a lily of the valley and a ship: "They should be put together because the diameter of the mast is equal to the diameter of the stem of the lily of the valley." Another patient, in the course of his correct performance on the systematic memorization test, when given the word "dinner" chose a card on which a hoop was drawn: "Both (in Russian) begin with the letter 'o'." He later resumed his adequate performance of the test.

---

*This is an exact translation of the Russian soskal'zyvaniya, but a common English term for the symptom is "displacement." Ed.

   Such incorrect actions are not manifestations of hastiness or inattentiveness. In response to specific questioning by the experimenter, the same patient quietly explained his actions. These explanations only serve to emphasize the absurdity of his behavior, since they were often given concomitantly with correct, logical arguments. The patient himself is unaware of this absurdity, however, and he does not correct his mistakes.

   A characteristic feature of this sliding is the sudden and episodic nature of its appearance: the logicality of the patient's judgments is disturbed only for a short time. The patients' intellectual activity may remain for the most part undisturbed.

   The associations of patients with the sliding syndrome are distinctive in character. In association experiments they frequently display chance association ("moon"—"honey," "bell"—"rose," etc.). To illustrate these points we present an extract from the case notes and results of the experimental psychological investigation of patient Shch.

   Patient Shch. (case notes of Dr. Avrutskii), male, born 1932. Diagnosis: schizophrenia. History: the patient's uncle and aunt had succumbed to schizophrenia. He was quiet and reserved as he grew up, and was an erratic pupil. He became a tramp and was addicted to alcohol. He last worked as a fitter in a factory, during which time he also attended evening classes. His fellow workers described him as taciturn but a disciplined and good worker. The first signs of mental disorder appeared in 1953: it seemed to him that he was being watched, that people were saying things about him and had "found out something about him"; perhaps he was being hypnotized. Confused thoughts appeared in his head. Things around him seemed to have changed, and he had lost all sense of reality. He abandoned his work and his evening classes, and looked for a hypnotist; it appeared that only that way could he be saved. He was admitted to the Gannushkin Psychiatric Hospital. (Insulin therapy gave good results. The patient regained his critical attitude toward his illness and returned to work, which he subsequently performed with success.)

   No significant abnormality was found in the internal organs and nervous system.

   Mental State. He was properly oriented. On the ward he remained aloof from the other patients, wandered about aimlessly, was unapproachable, and remained suspicious of his surroundings. Everything seemed to have changed, he could not understand what was happening to him, he had become another person: "I don't seem to be living my own life...everything has changed, both on the inside and on the outside of me." He felt that something "strange" must have taken place in him. He mulled these things over and over: "I am thinking about myself and other people...about problems of life." He considered that he was under the hypnotic influence of the doctors or of "black strangers."

   In classifying a group of objects, the patient followed the correct principle of generalization. Having formed a group of plants, he suddenly included a streetcar bearing the route indicator "Garden Circle" with the vegetables, "because Garden Circle is written on it." He immediately resumed his classification and completed it correctly, although he did group together the lily of the valley with the ship.

When the task involved the exclusion of the odd article, the patient performed the test correctly. When shown the card with "sun, candle, electric flashlight, kerosene lamp," he eliminated the sun, because it is a "natural light" while the others are artificial. When next he was shown a card on which were drawn a clock, scales, thermometer, and spectacles, he unexpectedly declared that "the scales and spectacles should be placed in the same group because they are bent here." (The patient pointed to the respective places at which the scales and the spectacles were bent.)

In the experiment involving systematic memorization, the patient mastered the problem very easily: to memorize the word "parting," he chose a card on which an envelope was drawn; for the word "road," the picture of a tree; for the word "game," an airplane ("children like to play at pilots"); and then for the word "fire" (pozhar), he chose a drawing of a pen (pero): "Their first letter is 'p'."

When composing pictograms, the patient formed adequate generalized associations: to memorize the expression "a happy holiday," he drew an accordion, and to memorize the word "doubt," he drew a question mark. Yet at the same time, to memorize the word "grief" (pechal'), he drew a press (pechat'); to memorize "a clever action" (smelyi postupok), he drew a piece of chalk (kusok mela); and to memorize the expression "tasty supper," he drew two squares ("Two words....").

The association experiment revealed a short latency period (1.5–2.5 sec) and a high proportion of phonic response reactions ("topor"—"motor," "more"—"gore," etc.). The patient correctly explained the metaphorical meaning of proverbs and was able to match them with the appropriate phrases.

Hence the processes of generalization and abstraction were not disturbed in the patients with the sliding syndrome. They correctly integrated the material and easily distinguished the important sign. At the same time, for short periods the course of their thinking was disturbed and their reasoning was temporarily influenced by random signs, irrelevant to the actual situation.

* * *

The disturbances of thinking described in this chapter were observed, as we have seen, in patients with various diseases; these disturbances differ in their character and in their severity.

At first glance, to unite such varied forms of disturbances of thinking as flights of ideas, hyperresponsiveness, sluggishness of thinking, illogicality of reasoning, and the sliding syndrome under one heading appears to be unconvincing, especially in the light of clinical studies aimed at the discovery of types of disturbances of thinking characteristic of individual forms of a disease. It must be remembered, however, that the perfection of the act of thinking depends not only on the level of generalization, but also on the logicality and interconnection of the judgments, i.e., on the character of the dynamics of the thinking process. The thinking of our patients is characterized by the fact that the single line of reasoning and its logical course were disturbed.

Although individual intellectual operations (comparing and distinguishing, generalization and abstraction, etc.) were relatively intact, these dynamic disturbances of thinking had a negative influence on the patients' mental attainment. The purposiveness of thinking, undisturbed initially, was later lost (or periodically weakened), and the thought processes ceased to be adequate to the task.

In the cases we have described, the disturbances of purposiveness appeared to result to some extent from disturbances in the dynamics of thinking. Clinical practice does in fact show that purposiveness may be lost as a result of an independent and persistent disturbance of thinking. Such a disturbance of thinking may also, however, be found in patients in whom a mental disease has led to disturbances of the personality as a whole and in whom the intellect has ceased to regulate behavior.

Chapter 6

Disturbances of the Purposiveness of Thinking

In order to probe the deeper meanings of objects and events or phenomena, in order to reflect their nature and the relationships between them, the human thinking process must be continuously active, directed toward objective reality and the solution of problems—it must be purposive. Without its purposiveness, thinking remains superficial and incomplete and ceases to regulate human actions.

Sechenov, in discussing the role of thinking as a regulator of actions, wrote: "Thinking begins to be reasonable only when it becomes the director of action, that is, when perceptual relationships become the basis for action. Only in thus acquiring a goal and a meaning can actions become purposive; their guide then assumes the character of their director." [286; 348].

The view of thinking as a regulator of actions should not, of course, be understood as implying that thinking may be regarded as the source or the moving force of behavior. Engels says: "People have been accustomed to explain their actions by their thoughts, instead of explaining them by their needs (which are, of course, reflected in their brains, in their consciousnesses), and hence in the course of time the idealistic doctrine has developed which has dominated men's minds, especially since the end of antiquity." [2; 139].

Consequently, the source of human actions lies in the emergence into consciousness of man's needs which arise as a result of social intercourse and work. The needs he recognizes present him with a number of concrete goals and problems in life. Man's real activity, which is directed toward the achievement of these goals and the solution of these problems, is regulated and corrected by thinking. First aroused by need, thought becomes the regulator of action; in order to regulate behavior thinking must be purposive and critical.

Thus, thinking cannot exist apart from needs, desires, expectations, and feelings, i.e., apart from the human personality as a whole. In severe forms of those mental diseases that disturb the personality, those aspects of behavior, such as intellectual activity, which are primarily responsible for the regulation of human behavior, are the first to be disordered (i.e., the impairment of the critical faculty and loss of purposiveness are among the first signs of a mental disease). In the most severe disturbances of thinking, both purposiveness and critical appraisal may be disturbed at the same time.

1. DISTURBANCES OF THE REGULATING FUNCTION OF THINKING IN NORMAL PERSONS

Perfectly healthy people are known to perform incorrect actions under the influence of passion, or even of less intense emotions. Examples could be cited without limit to show that people may lose their self-control, become uncritical, carry out absurd and purposeless acts, make inadequate decisions, and form incorrect assessments of other people and situations.

In some cases human judgments become mistaken under the influence of emotions, so that they inadequately reflect reality. The affectively based errors of thinking described by Bleuler [32] may arise. In other cases human thoughts and value judgments may remain correct, but they cease to regulate behavior. The "reasonableness of thought" described by Sechenov is lost, In both cases thinking as such becomes inadequate. The words of Gannushkin apply here: "If feelings can triumph over reason, then reason must be weak." [64].

These disorders of thinking may arise episodically and selectively in relation to a particular range of phenomena. Human thinking in such cases does not lose its regulating function as a whole, but it merely proves inadequate in the presence of strong passion or in a particularly acute situation. The change is only of the moment, in relation to a specific situation; no major change in either the thought processes, the basic personality, or the basic world view or philosophy of the individual is involved. Herein lies the distinction between this form of disturbance of purposiveness and the disturbances to be examined below.

Mistakes caused by the influence of passion or deviations from the purposiveness of thinking constitute a very large and complex problem, which unfortunately has not received its proper share of study in modern psychology. Gruhle pointed out many years ago that a state akin to "confusion" may arise in healthy persons under the influence of strong emotion [411]. Disturbances of perceptual activity in healthy persons in a traumatic situation were described by Shubert [348]; he noted the similarity between certain forms of behavior and thinking in healthy persons overcome by despair, and the actions and thoughts of patients in a reactive state. We shall now discuss our own findings in relation to disturbances of critical appraisal and of the purposiveness of thinking in mental patients.

2. DISTURBANCES OF THE CRITICAL ASPECT OF THINKING

The problem of the critical aspect of thinking has been the subject of special study in psychology, although it has been resolved only on the general plane. S. L. Rubinshtein [257] stresses that it is only in the process of thinking, when the subject more or less consciously relates the results of the thinking process to the objective data, that a mistake is possible, and that "the possibility of recognizing the mistake is the privilege of thought." In characterizing the properties of the mind, Teplov mentions the critical faculty and assesses it as "the ability to evaluate strictly the work of thought, to weigh carefully all the arguments for and against suggested hypotheses, and to subject these hypotheses to comprehensive testing." [311].

The problem of the critical aspect of thinking becomes particularly acute in the analysis of various psychopathological phenomena. In all the textbooks and monographs dealing with dementia, disturbance of the critical faculty is given a foremost place (Gilyarovskii [68], Gurevich and Sereiskii [77], Korsakov [144], Kraepelin [432], Osipov [216], and Sukhareva [308]). The concept of critical appraisal is fundamental in psychopathological analysis, as may be readily seen from the fact that the evaluation of the patient's condition and the diagnosis of the disease are often based chiefly on the presence or the absence of the critical aspect of thinking.

The concept of critical appraisal does not always refer to the same phenomenon in psychopathology. For instance, it also often implies a critical attitude on the part of the patient toward delirium, hallucinations, and other abnormal experiences. However, we propose to analyze that form of critical attitude which consists of the ability to act deliberately—to check and correct one's actions in relation to the objective conditions.

* * *

A group of patients involved in solving the object-classification problem exhibited a special group of mistakes, which could be described as the thoughtless manipulation of objects. Having paid no attention to the instructions, the patients glanced quickly over the cards and immediately began to sort the objects into groups, without any form of check. For example, one such patient began to put in the same group cards which lay side by side: "bear," "thermometer," "spade," and "cupboard"; in another group were included cards found around the edges: "fungus," "bird," and "bicycle." It is clear that the patients had no real comprehension of the nature of the problem. Table XVII reveals performances of this type in 60% of the patients with progressive paresis, 20% of the brain-injured patients, and 11.2% of the cerebrovascular patients. (When the experimenter repeated the instructions, emphasizing the rational principles involved in the classification procedure,

TABLE XVII

Thoughtless, Purposeless Sorting of Cards (Manipulation of Objects) in the Object-Classification Test

Diagnosis	Number of patients investigated	Number of patients making mistakes
Schizophrenia	155	3 (1.9)*
Epilepsy	50	1 (2.0)
Cerebrovascular diseases	125	14 (11.2)
Brain trauma	170	34 (20.0)
Oligophrenia	40	2 (5.0)
Postencephalitis	20	—
Progressive paresis	30	18 (60.0)
Manic-depressive psychosis	15	1 (6.7)
Psychopathy	30	—

*The results in parentheses are expressed as percentages.

the above-mentioned patient sorted the cards correctly and selected the groups by a generic sign [animals, furniture, people, plants].) *

The disease patterns in these patients showed an absence of acute psychotic symptoms. In fact, they appeared to be relatively normal upon superficial observation. They understood and responded to questions, were oriented in time and place, they took part in social and work activities, carried out various assignments, read books and remembered what they had read, and listened to the radio. Closer observation revealed, however, the inadequacy of their behavior. In conversation with their families, for instance, although they might reply correctly to questions, they themselves never asked questions, showed no interest in the lives of their friends and relatives, and never spoke of their plans for the future. Having begun to read a book, they would quickly put it down to take another—whichever happened to catch the eye. According to S. Ya. Rubinshtein [268], who investigated the behavior of such patients while they worked in the occupational therapy workshops, these patients made mistakes without noticing them. When the instructor in the workshops pointed out their errors to them, they were unconcerned and made no attempt to correct them: "It will pass," or "Never mind, leave it that way"—such were their usual replies.

This indifferent attitude toward their errors at times reached particularly absurd degrees. One patient, for example, although still capable of calculating, made such a gross blunder in calculating his daughter's age that she turned out to be only two years younger than he. When the experimenter drew the patient's attention to the absurdity of his answer, the latter replied, without a sign of embarrassment: "Anything can happen."

These patients readily concurred with any judgment proffered, however ridiculous, and they readily and unthinkingly obeyed any

---

*Since the mistakes in the patients' actions and solutions are random in character, a detailed description and analysis of them does not seem justifiable: the grouping of these random responses would of necessity be arbitrary. For instance, Table XVII shows that only 20% of the patients with head injuries actually misplaced the objects in the classification test. At the same time, relatively few of the patients whom we described in Section 1 reached this degree of thoughtless behavior. However, the study of the clinical pattern of the patients' behavior on the ward and in the occupational therapy workshops, together with an analysis of the experimental facts as a whole, revealed the existence of elements of a basic lack in the critical aspect of thinking in many more patients.

We therefore decided, in describing the thinking processes of these patients, to give a fuller account of the patients' behavior in general, to describe several representative examples of their behavior in experimental situations, and, in relation to the classification experiment, to cite only the results in quantitative form.

suggestion made by another person. (One of these patients, for example, willingly agreed on the day before a serious operation to the suggestion of a fellow-patient that he leave the surgical ward and go out into the cold, rainy weather for a swim in the lake.) They never noticed any defects or disturbances in their own mental capacities, they never complained about anything, they were not put out by having to stay in the hospital, and they did not ask to be discharged. For the most part, they remained in good spirits and gave no thought whatsoever to their futures.

This thoughtless behavior was particularly noticeable in their performance in psychological experiments. As already mentioned, the patients started to work immediately without really taking a good look at the material. For example, a patient who was shown a series of pictures of wolves attacking a boy walking to school, replied after hardly having glanced at them: "The boy is climbing a tree; he probably wants to pick an apple." —Experimenter: "Look more carefully." —Patient: "The boy is saving himself from the wolves." Another patient scarcely listened to the experimenter's request to explain the proverb, "Strike the iron while it is hot," replying instead: "Yes, of course, the iron must be hot; otherwise it couldn't be shaped." However, he immediately followed this with the correct explanation: "Things must not be put off until later."

The patients could grasp the theme of a fable, the conventional meanings of instructions, and the metaphorical meanings of proverbs. Although they could pick out generic signs, they persistently made the most glaring mistakes, acted contrary to the instructions, and matched phrases and proverbs wrongly. Thus, although they usually possessed an adequate understanding of the conditions of a test, they frequently acted contrary to this understanding. Since their errors appeared most frequently at the beginning of the experiment rather than at the end, we must conclude that they are caused chiefly by a rapid onset of inhibition, rather than by fatigability. Not only did the patients not notice their mistakes, but when they were pointed out to them, they made no effort either to comprehend the real meaning of the problem or to correct their errors. It was found, however, that if the experimenter frequently asked control questions and aided the patient in the external organization of his work, he could understand even complicated problems. The errors of these patients were obviously caused chiefly by an absence of self-control and an indifferent attitude toward the material. To illustrate these points we present case-history extracts together with the results of the experimental psychological examination of several of these patients.

Patient M., male, born 1890. Diagnosis: progressive paresis. His development was normal. He graduated from the medical faculty and worked as a surgeon. At the age of 26 he contracted syphilis. At the age of 47 the first signs of mental illness appeared: while performing an operation he made a gross blunder (he anastomosed the large intestine to the stomach) which cost the patient her life. Psychiatric examination in connection with the criminal proceedings established a diagnosis of general paresis. After treatment, he attempted without success to resume his work as a doctor.

Mental State. The patient was properly oriented, accessible, talkative, and inclined to gossip with the patients. He realized that he was suffering from general paresis, but regarded the matter with considerable levity. He constantly repeated that he had "residual manifestations following progressive paresis," but "they were negligible," a "trifle" which would not prevent his return to work as a surgeon. When reminded of his lamentable surgical blunder, he said with a smile, quite casually, that he had "made a slight mistake, but we all have accidents." He now considers that he is well ("as fit as a bull" in his own words). He is confident that he will be able to work as a surgeon and to be the medical chief of a hospital. At the same time, he gives the most inept advice to the patients in the department. Without any embarrassment he told them that he had met his wife in a saloon and that at that time she was a prostitute.

In performing the simplest tasks, the patient made gross mistakes and did not try to correct them. For example, he understood correctly the meaning of a proverb, but then matched it with an unsuitable phrase: "I have made a slight mistake, now what shall I do?" The object-classification test was started without listening to the complete instruction. He exclaimed: "Why, this is like dominoes," and tried to begin the test as if playing at dominoes. He then asked: "Now tell me, which one shall I play? We can't play for money, because I haven't any." Having heard the instructions a second time, he performed the test correctly.

In the course of the test on "establishing the sequence of events" he first tried to explain each picture, and then to invent the theme which was not evident from the material on the cards. Having glanced at picture No. 2, he said: "Here somebody has gone for a walk. He has gone to meet somebody.... Where could he have gone? Evidently he is waiting for somebody, probably a woman.... Or perhaps it is a business meeting. And here (picture No. 5) the uncle has gone away. This one is left alone; he is expecting somebody, of course, but whom? Perhaps the one he was hurrying to meet? What have we here? The wheel has broken? That is bad management."

The experimenter interrupted the patient's reasoning and asked him to arrange the pictures in the proper order of the development of the theme. The patient did the test correctly. When matching phrases and proverbs the patient correctly explained the proverbs,

"All that glitters is not gold" and "Measure seven times, cut once,"* but matched them with the wrong phrases: "Gold is heavier than iron," and "If it is cut wrongly, it is no use blaming the scissors."

An experiment involving systematic memorization with the aid of pictograms gave the following results: The patient did not listen to the instructions for the test: "You want me to put your words into a picture? I'm not an artist, you know." The experimenter again explained the meaning of the test and asked the patient to listen carefully to the instructions. The patient replied: "Oh, is that what has to be done, just draw a sketch? That's easy." He formed associations of a fairly general order: to signify the expression "a happy holiday" he drew a flag; for the words "a dark night," a shaded square; and to signify the expression "a starving man," he drew a very lean man. The patient constantly let himself be distracted from his task and tried to start a conversation with the doctor on a completely extraneous topic.

Although the experimenter continued to stress that the problem was being given in order to test his memory, the patient was not in the least surprised when the experimenter, having apparently finished the experiment, excused himself from the patient without asking him to reproduce the suggested words. Neither was the patient embarrassed when, in the next test, it turned out that he had memorized only an insignificant number of words (only 5 of 14). When the experimenter remarked that he had not remembered many, the patient replied with a smile: "Next time I shall remember more."

Patient T. (case notes of Dr. Rommel'), male, born 1934. Category 2 disabled person. Diagnosis: traumatic dementia. This patient grew and developed normally, completed 6 classes at school, and worked as a fitter. He was active and sociable. In 1950 he was knocked down by an automobile in the street, and was unconscious for a long time. He lay for two months in a serious condition in the Sklifasovskii Institute. He was off work during the next 6 months on account of headaches, fatigue; and general malaise. Subsequently he became increasingly apathetic and drowsy; he lay down for long periods, was addicted to alcohol, became involved in fights, and behaved aggressively toward his companions. He was frequently admitted to mental hospitals.

Neurological State. Slight facial asymmetry, tremor of the eyelids and of the outstretched fingers. The tendon and periosteal reflexes were brisk: R>L in the upper limbs and L>R in the lower.

Mental State. He thought that he was of sound mind and that "only the cartilage of his nose was affected." He was not at all upset by having to stay in the hospital: "Its all the same to me; it's somewhere to live." He had no interest in his surroundings, nor in his family when they came to visit him. He was not at all worried about his ailing

*Roughly equivalent to the English proverb, "Look before you leap."—Tr.

mother and he never asked about his child. In the ward he appeared happy and placid.
He behaved familiarly with the doctors; when he saw while conversing with the doctor
that the patients had begun to play some sort of game, he immediately broke off the
conversation in the middle of a word and followed the others. He could be persuaded
to play dominoes but usually left the game unconcernedly after a few moments. He was
very imitative and suggestible and complied with all the requests of his companions; as
a result of their entreaties he often performed quite tactless and silly acts: Whatever
the time of day, he was always willing to dance and sing; at the instigation of one patient
he removed a chair from a visitor without a touch of embarrassment. Although the doctor
persuaded him to begin working in the occupational therapy workshops his own work soon
bored him and he gave it up and tended to join in any activity being carried on by the
other patients. Although he had no difficulty in sleeping, when he heard the other patients
ask for sedatives, he also demanded "medicine to make me sleep."
     The results of a pathophysiological investigation (unconditioned vascular reactions
and an electroencephalogram) conducted by V.M. Kamenskaya revealed lability of the
cortical processes with signs of pathological excitation in the basal portions of the brain.

The specific features of the intellectual activity of patient T.
were revealed even in his performance of the simplest tasks, such
as describing the subject of a picture. When asked to describe the
theme of Yaroshenko's picture, "The Prisoner," he replied: "A
man is drawn here." When asked what sort of man, he replied:
"I don't know, perhaps some sort of employee." — Experimenter:
"Where is he?" — Patient: "How should I know? In his own apart-
ment, or perhaps in some institution." The experimenter tried to
direct the patient's attention to the characteristic details of the
picture: "Look carefully, is this an ordinary window?" "It is
barred," replied the patient in the same tone of voice, taking no note
of his previous mistake.

The next picture to be presented ("The Skating Rink") showed
a man who has fallen through a hole in the ice, and a crowd of
people with fright expressed on their faces. The patient gave the
following description: "Here are some people, going somewhere
or taking a stroll." He did not notice that the facial expressions
were not at all appropriate for people merely taking a stroll.
However, no sooner had the experimenter drawn the patient's attention to the problem than he explained the theme of the picture correctly. The patient's unthinking actions assumed a still more obvious form during the object-classification tests. At times he grouped
cards together merely because they lay next to each other; or else
he would take pains to create groups by making piles which were
numerically exactly equivalent; and at other times, he tried to
use the cards to play dominoes.

Patient K. (hospital case No. 3120), male, born 1922, developed normally and
completed 4 classes at a rural school, after which he trained as a crane operator; he
subsequently practiced this occupation in a factory. On March 23, 1943, he received a

perforating bullet wound of both frontal lobes. Some loss of brain substance at the entry and exit wounds was observed. The day after he was wounded an operation was performed to remove the numerous splinters of bone embedded in the brain substance of the left frontal pole. Postoperative recovery was smooth. The neurological findings six weeks after the operation were as follows: disturbance of convergence, especially on the left side, spontaneous nystagmus during divergence of the eyes, and obliteration of the right nasolabial fold. The tendon reflexes were increased on the right side, but no pathological reflexes were present. All forms of sensation were within normal limits. Coordination was normal.

Mental State. The patient was oriented in space and time, and fully recognized his environmental situation. He was able to recall the events of his past life and was aware that he had been wounded, but he thought that the wound was slight and was unaware of any resulting defects in his physical or mental condition. He assumed that he would return to his military unit. He was accessible, talkative, and serenely happy. He obeyed the hospital rules without protest, but if his fellow patients suggested he do something that infringed upon the rules, he followed their suggestion equally unprotestingly. At their request, for example, he would often play the balalaika and sing, but if left to himself, he would sit inactively and silently for long periods.

At the doctor's suggestion the patient began working in the occupational therapy workshops. He proved so eager to undertake any form of work, even the heaviest jobs, that he had to be watched constantly, frequently prevented from doing some types of work, and told when O.T. period was over. However, when performing some task at the instructor's request, patient K. was never interested in the result of the work as a whole or concerned with the quality of his work. Often, having started a job, he would go outside for a smoke, and then forget to go back to the workshops. Every now and then he would spoil the material or damage the tools, not because he did not know how to use them, but because of his unthinking, irresponsible attitude toward the work; he never became angry or embarrassed when the instructor or his fellow patients remonstrated with him because of his behavior. One day, he used a sewing machine to stitch the front of a garment to the back; when this was pointed out to him he merely laughed and said: "It will do!"

After examination by a medical board, the patient was discharged from the armed forces and graded as a category 3 disabled person; he was about to leave to stay with his uncle when he decided to visit one of his former neighbors in the ward. He was then asked to stay in the hospital and to work as an orderly, to which he agreed without hesitation. From the time of his discharge from the hospital the irregularity of his behavior became quite obvious. When he had been subjected to the rigid code of conduct of the hospital routine, he did not stand out among his fellows. Now his behavior appeared grossly inadequate to his new situation. Whereas wounded patients on the day of their discharge from the hospital almost invariably display an active concern about their plans for the future, K. remained completely indifferent.

K's duties as an orderly involved assisting others to move patients from one hospital area to another. He performed these duties competently and tirelessly under supervision, but as soon as something happened to distract his attention or someone called him, he would put the stretcher down "for a minute," go away, and not return. He was transferred to the job of stoker, but on his first day in his new job he went out to the movies at the invitation of a fellow patient, returned to the hospital, and went to sleep, leaving the work undone. For several months he worked satisfactorily while under supervision, arousing the sympathy of those around him by his invariably good-natured, willing behavior. When allowed the slightest independence, however, he became irresponsible and behaved incorrectly, adversely affecting both his own and his comrades' work: he forgot to collect the invoices, he stored things in the wrong boxes, and he would leave his work during working hours to do some absurd errand for a mental patient. When in the company and under the observation of his family, however, his behavior was comparatively normal. (Results of an investigation by S. Ya. Rubinshtein.)

We now present some of the results of an experimental examination of this patient. In the classification experiment, K. began to sort the cards into neat piles and to examine them even before he had heard the end of the instructions. However, he did perform the test correctly after the instructions had been emphatically repeated several times. The peculiarities of his behavior were particularly evident in tests involving the determination of the chronological order of events. In one such test K. was presented with a series of pictures representing the breaking and the repair of a cartwheel. The patient described the first picture that came into his hand and then arranged the cards in random order; when the experimenter admonished him to be more attentive to his work, however, he performed the test correctly within a relatively short period of time. If the patient's attention could be directed toward the problem he could solve it, even if it required fairly complex analysis and synthesis (the patient understood the metaphorical meaning of proverbs, could establish analogy of associations, etc.).

The patient also made mistakes when putting Link's cube together. The nature of this test is as follows: the subject has to assemble a large wooden cube from 27 cubes by arranging them in three layers, each of 9 cubes. The sides of each small cube are painted yellow, red, or green. The large cube must be constructed in such a way that all its sides are painted red. The color combinations determine the place of each small cube in the large cube. This test requires planning of actions, careful and constant checking, and immediate correction of any mistakes made. Our patient was unable to perform this test. Although he grasped the meaning of the instructions, he chose the small bricks to give the correct color only on the sides of the large cube facing him and did not bother about the other sides.

Patient Ch-v, male, born 1906, developed normally and worked as a bookkeeper. After finishing his studies at a technical school he worked as foreman in a factory. During the war he studied for and attained the rank of lieutenant.

From a brief case report compiled at the various stages of evacuation only the following information is available: In January 1943, he received a splinter wound in the frontal region. He was unconscious for an unknown period. Extrusion of brain substance was observed from the wound, and both his eyelids were edematous. Aseptic meningoencephalitis was diagnosed. An operation was performed to remove bone sequestra and an extradural abscess cavity.

Neurological State. The reaction to light and convergence was brisk. Full range of movement of the eyeballs present. Tongue deviated slightly to the right on protrusion. Amimia. All forms of sensation intact. Tendon reflexes brisk and increased on the right. No pathological reflexes nor clonus present. He performed well on tests of coordination. Slight unsteadiness during Romberg's test.

Mental State. He was correctly oriented in time and space and had full cognizance of his environmental situation. He spoke well and with animation. At the doctor's request he gave a coherent written account of his medical history, corresponding to the true facts. He knew the date when he was wounded and knew why he was in the hospital. Nevertheless, he was quite unaware of any change in his condition or mental state after being wounded. He was aware of no headaches, or losses of strength, and he considered that he was in good health (even after a second operation).

The patient retained his stock of general knowledge and ideas. He had no difficulty with figures and could describe in writing books he had read some time ago or stories heard for the first time. His previous skill at his job and his level of ability were maintained. At first glance his behavior in the department was correct: he obeyed the rules fully and carried out all the instructions of the doctor and the staff. However, in whatever he did, the patient showed no interest in either the quality or the results of his behavior.

He was unconcerned about evaluating his mental powers and was neither pleased when praised nor upset when criticized. Although he retained his skill and knowledge, when working in the workshops he frequently made mistakes simply because he did not plan his actions ahead nor check them. When the instructor drew his attention to the mistakes, however, the patient soon realized what he had done and put the matter right. One day, however, when he was told that an article he had made was useless, he nevertheless continued working at it for a long time to finish it off.

He was interested neither in the state of his health nor in the prospect of having to remain in the hospital, and he never wrote to his family. He never once raised any questions as to the reasons for a forthcoming operation. When asked why he had never written to his family (his wife, mother, and child), he replied that he had no paper. When he was given paper, he still did not write; when requested to do so by the doctor, however, he immediately wrote a short letter, which, although on the whole sensible, was of little impact.

The patient treated all people with the same attitude. He was friendly with nobody and never turned to anybody with a request, but he always answered questions and carried out errands and instructions. He also had a uniform attitude toward all events, regardless of their degree of importance. An hour before he was to be operated upon, for example, despite the fact that he had already been prepared for surgery, he left to go to the O. T. workshop, since it also happened to be the regularly scheduled hour for this activity. His stay in the hospital did not perturb him and he made no plans for the future. He was just as content to stay in the hospital as to go home or back to his army unit. (From an investigation by S. Ya. Rubinshtein.)

Experimental psychological examination of patient Ch-v also showed that he lacked control over his actions. He chose the correct sign to use in classifying objects, and in the pictogram experiment he formed adequate associations for memorizing words. Yet, although he was capable of the fairly complex synthesis and generalization which these problems required, he was unable to do certain simpler tasks. For instance, he could not arrange in the proper order a series of pictures having to do with the repairing of a wheel. He formed instead the following series: picture No. 4—"Here they are mending the wheel," No. 2—"The man has gone for a walk," No. 1—"He is vexed because the axle has broken and he has had an accident," No. 3—"Here two of them are going for a walk," No. 5—"Here they are on their way." After the experimenter asked him to look more carefully and repeated the instruction, indicating that the first picture represented the beginning of the series, the patient immediately performed the test correctly.

Although he understood the correct meaning of proverbs, the patient could not match them with the appropriate phrases.

In simple tests which required that he check his performance not merely at the end of the operation, but after each successive stage, patient Ch-v made many obvious and seemingly inexplicable errors. This type of behavior was illustrated in an investigation carried out as part of her diploma program by V. I. Urusova-Belozertseva under our direction at the Department of Psychology, Moscow State University. We now present some of the results of the investigation.

A group of 18 patients was given short stories from which individual words had been omitted; they were instructed to fill in the blanks (a variant of Ebbinghaus' method). The following stories were given:

1. A lion had become...and could not go out.... He decided to live on his wits: he lay in his lair and pretended to be.... Thereupon the other wild animals began to come near the sick...to see what was happening. But when they were within range he pounced on them and.... A fox came up, but did not go into the lair, and stopped at the.... The lion asked it: "Why don't you come inside to see me?" But the...replied: "I can see many tracks leading into your... but I can't see...coming out again."
2. An...wanted a drink and walked down to a stream. A wave...him away and he began to.... A pigeon flying nearby saw this and threw a twig onto the water. The ant climbed upon this...and was saved. The next day the ant saw that a hunter was trying to catch this...in a net. He crawled up to him and bit...on his foot. The hunter cried with pain and let go of the net. The pigeon escaped from the net and flew away.
3. A man ordered some fine...from a spinner. The spinner spun some fine thread, but the man said that it was...and that he must have it thinner. The spinner said: "If this is not thin enough for you, here is some which may do," and pointed to... place. The man said he could see nothing. "Of course, you can't see it, because it is so thin. I can't see it myself." The stupid man was content with this, ordered some...like it, and paid the spinner his money.

Only 4 of the patients read through the complete story initially; the remaining 14 immediately interjected words into each gap as they went along, without paying attention to the subsequent phrases. Control experiments, using as subjects patients with depressed levels of generalization, revealed a different picture: even those patients who achieved poor levels of performance always read the whole story first and then filled in the gaps with words which at least were in context, even if they were not correct.

We now present examples of the performance of these tests by patients of this group.*

Patient T. (Test No. 3, above) A man ordered some fine h a n d s (thread) from a spinner. The spinner spun some fine thread, but the man said that it was not (thick) and that he must have it thinner. The spinner said: "If this is not thin enough for you, here is some which may do," and pointed to a n o t h e r (an empty) place. The man said he could

*The words which should have been inserted are given in parentheses.

see nothing. "Of course you can't see it, because it is so thin. I can't see it myself." The stupid man was content with this, ordered some t w o h a n d s (thread) like it, and paid the spinner his money.

Patient Ch. (same test) A man ordered some fine s o c k s from a spinner. The spinner spun some fine thread, but the man said that it was t h i n and that he must have it thinner. The spinner said: "If this is not thin enough for you, here is some which may do," and pointed to the t h r e a d s place. The man said he could see nothing. "Of course you can't see it, because it is so thin. I can't see it myself." The stupid man was content with this, ordered some thread like it, and paid the spinner his money.

Patient T. (Test No. 1) A lion had become a g r o w l e r (old) and could not go out h u n t i n g. He decided to live on his wits: he lay in his lair and pretended to be a s l e e p (ill). Thereupon the other wild animals began to come near the sick d e e r (lion) to see what was happening. But when they were within range he pounced on them and a t e t h e m....

Urusova-Belozertseva differentiated the incorrect inserted words as follows: (a) those which make sense in the immediate context—the surrounding words or phrases—but which make no sense in the larger context; (b) those selected arbitrarily, at random; (c) those taken from other stories; and (d) those which have suitable contextual meaning but which are grammatically or syntactically discordant.

As in other situations in which they have made numerous mistakes during the performance of tasks, the patients fail to notice the inconsistencies in their versions of the stories and make no attempts to analyze the material. If they do notice the inconsistencies or contradictions, they usually make no effort to understand the real meanings and to isolate and correct their mistakes. When the experimenter pointed out one of his mistakes to Patient T. the latter replied: "Something different was needed here. But let it stay as it is!"

The patients never asked the experimenter for help in solving the problem. When the experimenter asked the subjects if they had done the test correctly, some of them replied: "I don't know if it is right," or "How should I know? You know more; what can I know!" Other patients replied confidently: "It's right!" or "Absolutely correct." Not one subject said that he was unable to do the test.

The patients' absurd answers on the tests were due neither to a lowering of their levels of generalization or to a disintegration of their mental operations. If the patients were told to reflect carefully, they were able to fill in the blanks correctly. Thus their mistakes were most often a manifestation merely of their general lack of control over their behavior.

Comparison between these experimental findings and the results of clinical evaluations of these patients reveals unified characteristics in the disturbances of their mental activity. The gross mistakes and random, arbitrary answers which characterized their performance during the tests; their inability to utilize their past experience and their capabilities in the experiments; and their unthinking behavior both in the hospital and in work situations—in fact the complete absence of any self-appraisal of their work: all these factors demonstrate that the actions of these patients are neither regulated by their intellect nor guided by personal interests. Neither was their behavior influenced by adequate social attitudes. In sum, their behavior was completely random in character.

We observed the patients in the clinic and in the O. T. workshops, and frequently engaged them in conversation; we were everywhere struck by their absence of a personal attitude to the situation of the moment. For instance, it did not seem strange to them that, although they understood the instructions of a psychological investigation, they could not solve the problem; it never struck them as odd that, "being able to sew," they nevertheless were unable to do the simplest job in the sewing room; although they knew how to calculate, they could not solve the simplest arithmetical problem. They were not upset by the fact that they could not remember errands on which they had been sent.

This abnormal attitude radically transformed their patterns of behavior, primarily by depriving it of its purposiveness. They thus continued to work at obviously purposeless tasks, stopping work at the slightest distraction. They could not become skilled in work operations, not because they were unable to understand the explanation of the investigator or instructor, but because they could not fix their attention on their work, because they had no definite attitude toward it, and could not grasp its purpose.

This disturbance of their attitude toward their environment and toward their own "egos" not only caused a change in their behavior but also seemed to effect a fundamental character transformation. Their carelessness, light-heartedness, and indifference were manifestations of a gross "flattening" of their personality. This absence of attitudes had the result, for example, that patient K. could leave a patient on a stretcher in the snow simply to go after some almost total stranger who beckoned to him. This absence of attitudes also explains why the patients were neither upset by their own deficiencies nor concerned over the quality of their work and never bothered to verify and check their behavior. The mistakes made by the patients during the solving of mental problems; the superficial, random character of their judgments; their lack of control over their behavior and their inability to evaluate it: all these factors demonstrate the uncritical nature of the thinking of this group of patients.

In some of our earlier writings on the subject of the disturbance of mental activity in patients with brain injuries we described a disturbance of critical appraisal which we associated with a lesion of the frontal lobes. This conclusion was based on the views of many eminent neurologists and psychiatrists who attach particular importance to the function of the frontal lobes (Goldstein [407], Korsakov [144], Khoroshko [330], Shmar'yan [343], Yudin [351], etc.).

Many Soviet psychologists also have described similar disturbances of thinking in patients with lesions of the frontal lobes. Luria [180] observed disturbances of the purposiveness of thinking in such patients. He noted that the behavior of such patients was not guided by internal motives, and that "dissociation between an action and its motive" took place. S. Ya.Rubinshtein [268], who investigated the recovery of working capacity in patients after wounds of the brain during the war, observed a deficiency of self-perception in a certain group of patients with lesions of the frontal lobes; she speaks of the "autagnosia" of these patients, of a disturbance of their "perception of themselves as personalities." Gadzhiev [55] analyzed the constructive activity in patients with lesions of the frontal region of the brain and described the unplanned nature of their actions in contrast to those of normal persons. In any action, according to Gadzhiev, these patients start out simply from a direct contemplation of one particular element, rather than from a conceived plan. The disturbances in perception and in the purposiveness of thinking in patients with frontal-lobe lesions have also been described by other authors (Evlakhova [86], Kartsovnik [127], and others).

All these facts have become clear in the light of Pavlov's theories of the activity of the cerebral hemispheres. Pavlov concluded from the results of experimental investigations by Krasnogorskii that the frontal cortex is a motor analyzer responsible for the analysis and synthesis of stimuli arriving from the internal and external environments of the organism.

This does not mean, of course, as the supporters of the psychomorphological doctrine believed, that such important functions of human mental activity as consciousness, critical awareness, and the activation of the thinking process, etc., are localized in the frontal cortex.   The symptoms of the disturbance of functions are not equivalent and do not necessarily possess a unique relationship to the localization of functions; this has been emphasized repeatedly by neurologists and psychologists.   The disturbance of the critical aspect of thinking is associated with a local brain lesion only to the extent to which the analysis and synthesis carried on by the frontal cortex create the basic conditions for critical self-evaluation. The importance of this self-evaluation is very great.

The performance of any task (including an experimental problem) assumes an understanding of the significance of the task in the concrete, situational context, as well as a knowledge of the means employed to do the work.   Another factor is no less important: the subject must be able to evaluate the degree to which his action conforms to the requirements of the problem.

Pavlov characterized this evaluative factor as follows: "Mental power is manifested to a far greater degree by the correct interpretation of reality than by a mass of scholarly knowledge, which can be collected and passed on in any way you like—intelligence of the lowest order.   A much truer indication of intelligence lies in the correct attitude toward reality, or correct orientation..." (cited by Chistovich [334; 40]).   For this, a person must not only understand his goal, but must also be able to predict the result of his action, to adjust his behavior to the conditions of the situation, to correctly evaluate his capabilities, and to check himself.

To attain this self-verification, a person must conceive of himself in relation to the object toward which he is now directing his thoughts.   His attitude toward his task must become that of an individual personality solving a problem.   Only in the presence of such a conscious personality attitude may thinking assume the role of a regulator of behavior. Purposiveness of thinking demands realization of oneself.   Only in the presence of this self-realization is it possible to consider one's actions and thoughts critically.

This particular relationship was mentioned by Sechenov. Having examined in his "Elements of Thought" the genesis of self-awareness and its development from the feeling of well-being in the child, Sechenov says that self-awareness gives man "the ability to form a critical attitude toward the acts of his own consciousness, or, in other words, to distinguish between his own internal sphere and everything taking place outside it, to analyze it, and to compare it with that which is external—in brief, to achieve the level of self-awareness." [286; 389—390].

Without the capacity to evaluate and to objectively perceive one's actions, correct thinking is impossible; only when there is a critical attitude toward the external environment and toward the self (that is, only if self-awareness has developed), can thinking assume its proper role as the regulator of behavior. As Pavlov says: "Man, of course, is a system (or, less delicately, a machine), which, as in any other natural system, must obey nature!s inviolable laws. However, as far as we may discern in the plane of our present scientific vision, this system is self-regulating to the highest, most complex degree.... I still can, and therefore I must, know myself and, using this knowledge, maintain myself at the height of my means...." [217; Vol. II, part 2, pp. 187—188].

Ability to perceive objectively and evaluate one's behavior is a distinguishing feature of human purposive thinking. Critical behavior is the highest and most perfect form of behavior. It demands a genuine understanding of the environment, a purposiveness of action, the possibility of self-regulation, and a generally rational progression toward the attainment of these goals.

The analysis of disturbances in this aspect of thinking is of considerable practical interest. The inability to evaluate one's actions is found in many intellectually backward patients. Naturally, if the level of a patient's judgments is lowered, if he has no correct understanding of facts, if he does not remember the task he has performed, then he will not be able to evaluate it correctly and adopt a correct attitude toward it. Figuratively speaking, the patient has nothing with which to measure, to compare, and to assess. If, however, his mistakes are pointed out to him, such a patient will try, albeit imperfectly, to correct his actions.

The inability to regulate their actions also develops in patients who cannot orient themselves in their environment because of a disturbance of consciousness. Random associations direct their thinking and random perceptions control their actions, so that their behavior loses its voluntary character. These states, however, are dynamic: we have often observed how such patients, although at first uncritical of all that is taking place around them, after a certain interval of time may assess their actions correctly. Uncritical behavior may also develop because of affective changes. Frequently patients with high intellectual powers and lucid states of consciousness are unable to evaluate a situation correctly simply because they are emotionally fixated upon certain specific experiences or desires.

Uncritical behavior may also be exhibited by a disinhibited patient. In a state of excitation the patient (as well as a healthy person) may be unable to regulate his behavior or actions. The patient's reactions in such a state will be inadequate, inept, elementary, and even grotesque. With the loss of disinhibition, however, the normal pattern of reaction reappears. However, as we have already said, there is a different genesis of the disturbances of critical appraisal in our patients from those we have just cited. They had no gross disturbance of the process of generalization, their state of consciousness was normal, and their unregulated behavior was not accountable for by disinhibition. It was due instead to the fact that these patients had no self-regard for their work, toward their capabilities, and toward the evaluation of the results of their actions—i.e., the disturbance of critical appraisal was a manifestation of a profound disturbance of the personality.

The diagnosis of this type of thinking disturbance is of practical importance in determining the type of work situation for which each patient is suited. If his intellectual impairment takes the form of a narrowing of the range of associations, or of inadequate analysis, he must be provided with lighter work. If his mental inadequacy makes prolonged adaptation to a task impossible, he must be advised to do work requiring shorter periods of time for completion. Patients with uncritical thinking should be placed in a working environment which provides constant, unremitting supervision.

It is very important to be able to diagnose this latter type of intellectual disability in childhood. Investigations by Pevzner [223], working in Sukhareva's clinic, have indicated the existence of a group of mentally retarded children who, although they can do arithmetical operations and speak relatively well, cannot be educated in an ordinary school because of their "uncritical" behavior. Special methods of training and education are required for these children.

Familiarity with breakdowns in critical thinking reveals how all the more important is the development of the critical aspect of thinking and of self-evaluation in healthy children. Unfortunately, few psychological studies of this problem have been made (see, for example, [331]). Psychologists studying the structure of the personality of children and adolescents, the moral foundations of the personality, and the principles of its formation must pay particular attention to the formation of a critical attitude.

3. MULTILEVEL THINKING

The disturbance of the purposiveness of that type of intellectual activity which we describe as "multilevel thinking" is one in which the patient's judgments take place on different levels. Despite the fact that he may grasp the instructions, and that such mental operations as comparison and distinction and generalization and abstraction are not disturbed, he does not bring the task properly to fruition: his judgments follow devious routes.

We do not refer to that faculty of comprehensive, exhaustive analysis that characterizes the thinking of the normal person—the act of approaching a problem from various aspects, in the course of which his actions and judgments are purposively determined both by the conditions of the task and by the orientation of the personality. Nor do we refer to the illogicality of judgments which we discussed in Chapter 4, in which the performance of a task takes place at different levels of generalization. The alternation of generalized and nongeneralized methods of solution in patients with disturbances of the dynamics of thinking means that for a certain period of time the patients are unable to reason adequately and correctly; however, they have not lost the purposiveness of intellectual activity as such. For example, if while performing the object-classification test a patient in whom fluctuations of the activity of the cerebral cortex have been noted ceases temporarily to be guided by the generic criterion, his actions nevertheless remain adequate for the purpose and for the conditions set by the experimenter, that is, he classifies objects on the basis of an objective sign which, although more elementary, is still adequate for the purpose.

The actions of a patient with multilevel thinking, on the other hand, are not purposive in nature. Their multilevel thinking is especially prominent in experiments in which there is only one correct method of performing a task—such as in the object-classification test, in which the selection of groups demands the choice of only one particular sign.

Table XVIII gives a few typical examples which show how patients with multilevel thinking fared in the object-classification test. We see that the patients frequently attempted to perform the test according to principles unrelated to the conditions of the experiment. For instance, although patient O-v was initially guided by the objects' actual, functional significance (in terms of furniture,

TABLE XVIII

Performance on an Object-Classification Test by Patients with Multilevel Thinking

Objects placed in same group by patient	Patient's explanation
Patient O-v (schizophrenia, paranoid type)	
Horse, elephant, bear	"They are animals."
Cherry, apple, pear, plum	"They are fruits."
Sheep, mushroom	"Sheep like mushrooms."
Charwoman, saw, dog	At first the patient put the charwoman and saw in one group: "A housewife with a saw and a broom." She then added the dog: "It is a friend of man."
Melon, carrot, onion	At first the melon alone was picked, with the explanation: "There is a custom among the Kazakhs: when marriage is proposed, if the woman places a melon on the table it means she refuses." The carrot was added: "It is a diuretic." Then the onion was added: "Vegetables."
Blacksmith, doctor, calipers, dress, skier, child	"The worker needs the doctor if he is ill." Then he added the calipers: "A tool for the worker." He added the dress: "This is his special clothing." After adding the skier and child: This is what God created for them."
Hat, boots	"This is up and down in space. The hat means up and the shoe down."
Fish, swan, fox	"The swan steps backward; no, it seems the opposite direction." He added the fox: "Surely a pike, it attacks other fish."
Table, cupboard, bed, sofa, etc.	"Furniture."
Tumbler, spoon, saucepan, etc.	"Dishes."
Clock, thermometer, globe, book	"For the scientific basis of rocket construction. It is all divine force."
Patient Gap-n (schizophrenia, paranoid type)	
Elephant, horse, bear, butterfly, beetle, and other animals	"Animals."
•Aeroplane, butterfly	"A group of flying objects" (the patient had taken the butterfly from the group of animals).
Spade, bed, spoon	"Ironwork."
Automobile, airplane, ship	"Objects indicating the strength of the human intellect" (the airplane had been taken from the group of flying objects).

TABLE XVIII (cont'd)

Objects placed in same group by patient	Patient's explanation
Patient Gap-n (schizophrenia, paranoid type) (cont'd)	
Flower, saucepan, bed, charwoman, saw, cherry	"Objects painted red and blue."
Elephant, skier	"Object for a circus. People want bread and circuses; the ancient Romans knew that."
Cupboard, table, bookcase	"Furniture."
Charwoman, spade	"A group of things for sweeping what is bad out of life. The spade is an emblem of work, and work is incompatible with corruption."
Flower, bushes, trees, vegetables, fruits	"Plants."
Tumbler, cup, saucepan	"Dishes."
Patient L-v (schizophrenia, paranoid type)	
Cupboard, table, sofa, etc.	"Furniture."
Cherry, apple, plum, pear	"Fruit."
Melon, onion, carrot	"Vegetables."
Doctor, thermometer, blacksmith, skier	"The doctor with his instrument and the black-smith with his tool: they are working." He then added the skier to this group: "After working they relax on skis."
He places all the objects in three groups	"There are 3 people in this room—it works out so that each receives a pile."

dishes, fruit, animals, etc.), certain objects evoked subjective or incidental associations (i.e., the melon as the symbol of the refusal of marriage; also the onion reminded him of the tower in the well-known Krylov fable) and determined the character of the classification (hence, "fish," and "swan"). Their performance is also influenced by elements of their delirious and/or religious experiences (hence, a group of people—"God created them in his own image")

Patient Gap-n distinguished groups at times on the basis of a generic sign (animals, dishes, furniture), and at others on the basis of material ("ironwork") or color (objects painted red and blue). Some objects were grouped together on the basis of the patient's moral outlook and general world view (a group "for sweeping what is bad out of life," a group "bearing witness to the power of the human intellect," and so on).

In exactly the same way, in the course of the object-classification test, patient L-v began by conforming to the plan required by the instructions but soon changed over to considering people from the point of view of their degree of activity or relaxation ("after working they must relax"). This patient also showed a third approach to the problem: he divided the cards into 3 groups in accordance with the number of people in the room. All these three aspects were exhibited simultaneously, disturbing the purposiveness of his judgments and actions.

Some patients were guided in their performance of the test by personal tastes or by fragmentary reminiscences. Patient S-v (schizophrenic, paranoid type), for instance attempted in the object-classification test at first to form groups of animals and plants, but then added at once: "But if I approach it from the point of view of my personal taste, I don't like mushrooms, and I shall reject this card. Once I was poisoned by mushrooms and even had to be admitted to the hospital.... No, not mushrooms.... And I don't like this dress, either, it isn't smart and I shall put it aside. But I like the sailor and I shall acknowledge sport." He then placed the sailor and the skier in the same group.

So that this patient, too, had lost his purposiveness of action and began to classify from the point of view of personal taste —the remembrance of having been poisoned by mushrooms, etc., he had lost control of his reasoning and his answers became more and more ridiculous.

Patient K-n (schizophrenia), whom we described jointly with Gal'perin [115], could not agree in the same test that the dog should be placed in the group of domestic animals: "I am not going to eat dog meat." His actions were no longer governed by objective reality, and his judgments clearly assumed a multilevel character.

We now present two examples of patients' multilevel judgments during the performance of the test involving the explanation of proverbs.

Patient M. was asked to explain the proverb, "Don't count your chickens until they are hatched." The patient's speech was tape-recorded: "Yes, this is quite clear. The results are always assessed at the end, when they are all available. When the job is finished. Not before then can you say that a particular thing has been a success or not. That is how we worked. Then you can make as much noise as you like. Much ado about nothing, as Shakespeare puts it, remember?... They made a noise, spoke, ran, chased about, spent all their money, and all over what? What was the result? It all goes up the chimney. Al show and no work. Therefore let's have less noise and more work, more preparation and more organization, and then we can say, 'Now comrades, at all events the job is done. Your health. Let's drink to the success of your work; those are our results.' For example, suppose we build something or other — that is our duty. Or suppose we are examiners — this is our evaluation, our marking: five is excellent, or roughly four, if the worst comes to the worst, I say. Four, that is bearable, I consider, but in general you ought to have excellent, to get five. That's how it is. That is what they call it ... much ado about nothing, or, as you said, this proverb: 'Don't count your hens, or chickens, until they are hatched.' The chickens can still walk. To speak directly on this matter, chickens may walk very much, but cats may steal them, as they say. They must be looked after for a year, protected, watched, or even tended with loving care, like a gardener and his plants or trees or what have you...."

This extract shows that the patient understood the meaning of the proverb ("The results are counted at the end..."), although when defining it he thought it also necessary to discuss unnecessarily ostentatious and boisterous activity during work. He also defined his own attitude toward his studies ("You ought to have excellent, to get five."). With all this, however, he did manage to include a literal interpretation of the proverb.

Patient K-n explained the proverb, "All that glitters is not gold," as follows: "This means that everything is not good that looks good. An apple, for example, may look good yet be rotten inside. Now gold, a precious metal, which is generally regarded as the best—but surely this is wrong, this proverb is wrong. In general we ought to speak of gold as a 'sacred idol,' as they sing in 'Faust.'" This patient also understood the meaning of the proverb, but because he approached the problem from different points of view, to all intents and purposes he ceased solving it.

In this connection, it is pertinent to remenber Gruhle's [411] claim that to the schizophrenic, words do not necessarily correspond to objects, phenomena, etc. Gruhle speaks of the many-sidedness of objects ("die Vielseitigkeit eines Gegenstandes"), analogous to the way that the word "Napoleon," for example, may have different meanings: hero, enemy of the motherland, monster, etc.

As a result of the simultaneous coexistence and the interweaving of all these various aspects of the patient's reasoning, his definitions and conclusions are not directed toward the correct interpretation of the proverb, and he does not keep to the straightforward purpose. The patient's statements are interspersed with random associations, fragments of ideas, elements of reminiscences, and desires.

Similar disturbances of thinking were observed by Birenbaum during an investigation of schizophrenic patients.* In her patients she found that thinking "apparently runs in different streams simultaneously," so that in a single judgment the patient might slide off into the paths of phonic association, of syncretic impression, of intertwining of subjective sensations, and of syntactic reversal. Birenbaum defined this symptom as "the eluding of the essential," in which the patients tend to reveal their subjective attitudes to the problem instead of solving it. For instance, a patient performed an "odd-one-out" test rather satisfactorily; when shown pictures of

*Unfortunately the author's untimely death prevented the continuation of these investigations. The data given here are taken from a lecture which she gave.

a lamp, a chair, a table, and a sofa, however, he left out the chair, with the explanation: "I don't need the chair, I don't like sitting on chairs, I like sitting on the sofa." Another patient, in an experiment involving the variant of the association experiment involving the naming of antonyms, when given the word "rich," declared: "I don't need riches, I don't want to be rich."

This simultaneous coexistence of different aspects in the form which we have described them here is a manifestation of a profound disturbance of intellectual activity. Of course, any phenomenon or object also represents various values and meanings to the normal person. Normal people also tend to approach their work and their judgments from a variety of aspects, although the objective significance of reality remains consistent throughout.

In the patients we are describing, this objective significance was lost. Even in performing such simple tasks as classifying objects, defining concepts, etc., they were guided not by the concrete situation, but rather by abnormal attitudes, modified orientations toward life, and delirious ideas, although in these circumstances there was no simple undeviating application of the psychopathological symptom to the experimental situation (the patient did not simply interweave the elements of delirium into the performance of the task).

The thought processes of a certain group of schizophrenic patients were characterized by multilevel thinking in conjunction with an affectively saturated symbolism. Commonplace objects and occurrences began to assume the form of symbols. For example, one patient (with a delirium characterized by self-accusation), having been given biscuits for breakfast, came to the conclusion that on that day he was to be cremated ("pechen'e"—biscuits, "pech'"—stove). Biscuits appeared to him as the symbol of a stove, in which he was to be burned.

Such an absurd association between things bearing no relationship to each other occurred because this patient tended to regard the simplest, most commonplace objects from aspects totally irrelevant to the situation. The multiplane thinking of such patients is particularly conspicuous because of the complete subjection of their judgments to their emotions. Without affective saturation, multilevel thinking takes on a simpler, more rudimentary form, and may pass unnoticed as such. Even in such cases, however, it nevertheless disturbs the purposiveness of thinking. In an experimental situation which calls for the definite regulation of the thinking processes, this multiplane property of thinking may be observed if it is present at all, thus clearly demonstrating the existence of a disturbance of the unity of the personality.

In some cases the disturbance of the unity of the personality attains considerable intensity, to the point of disorganizing the whole of the patient's behavior. We consider that such a disturbance of the unity of the personality is related to that form of disturbance of thinking known in the clinical field as the dissociation of thinking and speech.

4. DISSOCIATION OF THINKING

The concept of the dissociation of thinking is one of the most widespread and firmly rooted concepts in clinical psychiatry. It is used most frequently to characterize the thinking of patients with schizophrenia (Gilyarovskii [68], Gurevich and Sereiskii [77], Kerbikov [129], etc.). Dissociation is regarded as such a specific symptom in this disease that any assessment of a patient's thinking as dissociated has become almost synonymous with the diagnosis of schizophrenia.

In a paper by Vrono [49] an attempt is made to limit the definition of the concept of dissociation of thinking and to distinguish it from schizophasia. Vrono points out that schizophasia is characterized by the relative integrity of the grammatical flow of speech. Although schizophasic speech is capable of reflecting delirious experiences, the patient's behavior usually remains relatively adequate. Dissociation of speech, on the other hand, is combined, in Vrono's opinion, with absurd behavior on the part of the patient; the grammatical structure of the sentence is more severely disturbed than in schizophasia, and delirious experiences are reflected to a lesser degree in the patients' speech. In the basic psychiatric literature, however, this differentiation between schizophasia and dissociation of thinking and speech has not achieved popularity. When describing the characteristics of thinking in schizophrenia, most writers use the term "dissociation."

S. Ya. Rubinshtein [270], who studied the disturbances of speech and thinking in reactive states, indicated that dissociation of thinking is also observed in certain very severe reactive psychoses. In our experiments we discovered dissociation and its elements in patients with schizophrenia. In cases of well-marked dissociation this evaluation does not cause difficulty; the problem of evaluation of thinking arises more often in cases of uncertain diagnosis, when it is possible to speak only of the presence of elements of dissociation. In these cases the dissociation of the patient's thinking is assessed in accordance with the sign of absence of associations between individual elements of the patient's expressions which the examiner can understand. This criterion of "understandability" of the patient's statements is frankly inadequate; it therefore becomes necessary to make a more detailed examination of the objective signs of dissociation.

We may begin with the more severe cases. We now present a verbatim report (tape-recording) of a conversation with patient Ch-n. (The patient is holding the experimenter's watch in his hand.)

Experimenter. Well, Yu. S. [patient's initials], are you going to give me back my watch?
Patient. No, no, no.
E. Surely it doesn't belong to you, this thing.
P. Thing, not a thing, man, not a man. (He then responded to the next few questions simply by inadequate facial movements and gestures.)
E. Why are you moving your lips?
P. My lips are always the same.
E. The same?
P. Yes. And where do my teeth grow from, or don't they? You see, you won't tell me....
E. Teeth grow?
P. I have teeth, but I can't play with you.
E. With teeth?
P. No, you mustn't laugh, your highness.... I have sold the flag, then I shall sell the arms, and on the arms of these...(unintelligibly, softly).
E. What? I couldn't hear.
P. Nothing more.... But light is light. But what is darkness.... This means you want to say that we mustn't meet any more.
E. Why?
P. For example, man depends on mankind. In general, let it be that way. Mankind sleeps, he speaks to it alone. My father has it, but here there is none.
E. None of what?
P. Well, what were they promised. Before nationality there was simply people.
E. What was there before nationality?
P. Your highness, you don't look, simply not showing what it is like, red, pale, white. None of this...(unintelligibly).
E. I can't understand what you are saying.
P. Aren't you selling this! You are telling me what I am thinking? Really, Mr. Chief of Police! You need psychology.
E. Am I truly a chief of police?
P. That is in what sense? What are they eating?.... It isn't good, it leaves a bad taste. Just look at them, who can this...(unintelligibly). You wanted to hurt me...and I might have been, but my money has all gone.
E. Is this a sign of something?
P. It isn't important...(omission). Today you aren't leaving your office, and you aren't letting anybody come into your office. I am always ready.
E. Ready for what?
P. It isn't important. For a son of the state...(unintelligibly).
E. I can't understand what is important.
P. I don't know either (laughs).... Let me have a smoke and don't talk any longer to me in here.

E. But you came here yourself.
P. I was an honest man, I wanted to have a look at the kitchen. I have a watch which
    has a regulator. I have a little brother, he is just a simple workman. And if
    everybody thought that way about himself, everything would... (unintelligible).
E. Will you give me back my watch?
P. I have only just eaten the watch. But if I do eat it, generally speaking... (speaks
    unintelligibly and softly).
E. Well, what?
P. I have nothing at all. And this isn't good for me. I am economical. All humanity
    economizes... and I want to do it credit.
E. Why, Yu. S.?
P. Don't laugh, father.... I am simply saying....
E. Why, for what purpose?
P. Father, eat this thing (hands an ashtray).
E. Do you think it is edible?
P. How many times have they broken...(unintelligibly). Broken, look, father,
    broken.
E. It certainly isn't edible.
P. You are right, it isn't edible.
E. That means you can't eat it. (He gives the patient a cigarette.)
P. If he takes it, you buy, but they, if he sells it, don't drink. (He points to the
    water bottle.)

Frequently such patients will conduct a conversation even if
there is nobody to listen to them (the monologue symptom). We
shall now present an example of the monologue speech of patient N.
(schizophrenia, state of mental deficiency), as recorded on tape.
While the patient's behavior was outwardly adequate and he was
properly oriented in relation to his environment, he would speak
for hours on end in a monotonous and quiet voice and would be
unconcerned as to whether anyone was listening to him.

Why, why I say, has nobody told me, of course, about this, and where I didn't read
it? It wasn't shown to me anywhere. I think and I know, certainly of course, that this
is the matter of movement, the whole terrestrial globe (incomprehensible). I still think,
and I have thought for a long time, about this affair, but I can see that it means — living
matter, that is what living matter means, well I think that then I think, formerly I studied,
how long did I study, nevertheless I studied air — not living, oxygen, hydrogen, all dead
substances, and now it seems to me that all the greenery inhabiting the surrounding
atmosphere is, in fact, enveloping living matter, absolutely living matter, absolutely
living, and it consists, by giving its color, or so I imagine it, of a smoke, only not at once,
so it seems, see how it has disappeared already, hardly visible and consists of tiny
beings, simply difficult to distinguish, and they have a strange power, of course they move
where they like, through the pores in any substance. All this is in motion at the same
time, I consider, as it originated. Why is there woman, to my mind the substance from
which the whole of mankind on earth has originated. By definition, for example, of man, the
form of man in the woman's womb was its body, it is said that somehow this artist, yes
definitely an artist, yes, yes. In my opinion the genesis that is in this little book, I saw
that people are descended from monkeys, which isn't true. There is all manner of fish
there, the sea-bed as Brehm described it. There, as Brehm wrote, you find so many, you
understand, species on the sea-bed, all manner of these starfish, infusorians, fishes, and
I imagine which artist and which grandiose forms, and he cites the correct features, he
is all of it. (Who is "he"?—Au.) This is matter, yes. And you yourself think that man
was descended from monkeys, but with every human birth everything appears afresh, do
you think that my blood. The artist the red blood corpuscles have an artistic side, they
fall, so to speak, into the uterus, and such tricks appear there and can be photographed.
No, with each birth they reappear again and again, and with each appearance this is the
material.

Analysis of these examples of dissociated speech leads to several conclusions.

First, in the long statements made by these patients there was no continuous thread of reasoning; they uttered a series of phrases which were quite meaningless, and they included no relationships, even of a spurious nature, between objects and phenomena.

The example of patient Ch-n has a superficial resemblance to conversation between two people: some of the patient's replies actually refer in part to the experimenter's question. Even in dialogue form, however, the patient's speech does not serve the function of communication: the patient communicated nothing to the experimenter, nor did he attempt to find out anything from him. In calling the experimenter the "Chief of Police" or "father," the patient showed no hint of the appropriate attitude. The experimenter's attempt to direct the patient's speech to a particular theme was unsuccessful; although the patient reacted to the experimenter's question, it was only to use it as a stimulus for the emission of a new, incomprehensible stream of words. As Artemov [18] rightly points out, the ability to keep strictly to the theme is one of the characteristic features of the perception of speech. In our patients this feature was absent.

Second, the speech of these patients revealed no particular object of thought. For example, patient N. named a number of objects— air, matter, artist, origin of man, red blood corpuscles—but there was no logical object of his thought; there is no other explanation for these peculiarities.

Third, the patients were not concerned as to whether anybody was listening to them, and they expressed no attitude to other people in their speech. Their "dissociated" speech had none of the basic characteristics of human speech: it was neither an instrument of thought nor a means of communication with other people.

These two features—absence of the function of communication and incomprehensibility to others—make this dissociated speech similar to the egocentric speech of the child, as defined and described by Piaget [234]. Piaget regarded egocentric speech as based on two circumstances: the asocial character of the child and the egocentric nature of its activity. The egocentric speech of early childhood subserves no behavioral function and disappears when the child enters school. In a paper criticizing Piaget, Vygotskii [50] comes to the opposite conclusion: the egocentric speech of the child becomes a means of intellectual activity, it assumes the role of the instigating action, reflects the practical intellectual operations of the child, and regulates its actions. The egocentric speech of the child is an intermediate stage between external and internal speech.

The dissociated speech of our patients, on the other hand, in no way regulated their behavior. The similarity between the dissociated speech of the patient and the egocentric speech of the child is thus seen to be purely external in character.

It is difficult to analyze the structure of the dissociation of thinking in severe cases. Examinations of patients in whom the dissociation was not so well marked, however, revealed several distinctive features in their thinking processes.

The first point to be mentioned is the prolific and multidimensional character of their associations. The many and various "slips" of thought disturb its course, deprive it of a controlled direction, and lead to diffuseness of thinking. These "slips" include those due to similarly sounding words, to objects of similar external appearance, and to similarity of experiences, which are interwoven to form the pattern of affective symbolism of intellectual activity.

The dissociation of the patients' speech was frequently dynamic in character, and sometimes almost disappeared with a change in their condition. In these cases it was possible to perform experimental tests with the patients, and these disclosed the multilevel structure of their thinking.

The second special feature of the thinking processes of these patients is the weakening of the ordinary, habitual associations, characteristic of normal people, formed as a result of life experiences. For example, when the normal subject is asked to respond to a word given to him by any word which crosses his mind, as we mentioned above, he usually responds with a word which bears some logical connection to the stimulus-word. On the other hand, a patient with elements of dissociation of thinking will respond with words which bear no relationship to the stimulus-word ("moon"— "poison," "singing"—"wheel," etc.). The patient's associations are incomprehensible and unexpected, so that they do not reflect the objective (external or internal) associations between objects.

In exactly the same way, in another variant of the association experiment, in which the subject is asked to name any 30 words at random, the responses of the normal person reflect objectively existing associations. For example, a healthy subject may give the following series of words: "lily of the valley," "cornflower," "flowers," "trees," "forest," "field," etc. In an analogous experiment a patient with dissociation of thinking produced the following series of words: "salad," "radish," "airship," "love," "frying pan," "despite," etc. The subjectivity, incomprehensibility and unexpectedness of these associations may be attributable to the fact that they reflect the multidimensional, multilevel associations between objects.

From the above discussion it seems that the dissociation of thinking may rightly be regarded as an extreme instance of the multilevel phenomenon which was mentioned earlier (Section 3). However, the nature of the disturbance is not thereby fully explained. One further aspect of it must still be considered: the simultaneous presence in speech of both a lack of conceptual content and an intact grammatical form.

The development of grammatically correct, coherent speech takes place in early childhood; certain dynamic stereotypes are developed, as a result of which the pronunciation of words and the construction of complex sentences is converted into a skill, i.e., into an automatized process. The skills of reading and writing are formed in the same way. During normal mental development these skills do not, however, become important on their own account, as in the case of such skills as walking and running, but are instead always firmly associated with complex forms of mental activity or, more accurately, with thinking. The automatic skill of reading a text rapidly is always associated with an understanding of its meaning; the skill of writing usually is concerned with the reproduction or development of thought. Grammatically coherent speech occurs only in the presence of that complex activity which comprises the interchange of thoughts between persons.

The speech of patients N and Ch-n, however, involved no such interchange of thoughts. It seems to have fallen to the level of a simple automatism, devoid of meaning (similar to the dissociation observed, for example, in their stereotyped, meaningless grimaces).

Whereas difficulties of thinking in other types of patients lead to a slower tempo of speech, to a superficiality and illogicality of judgments, etc., in the present group of patients there occurs a compensation for the defect: the replacement of thought by fragmentary, automatized speech movements. In the early psychiatric literature, this disorder was described as the ataxia, or dissociation, of thinking.

It is now clear that "dissociation" is a complex disorder of thinking arising in patients in whom a "multilevel" quality of thinking is combined with signs of the appearance of fragmentary stereotyped speech movements. This problem requires further experimental investigation.

In the present chapter, which has been devoted to the disturbance of the purposiveness of thinking, we have lumped together several forms of disturbance of thinking which differ as to symptomatology and nosological classification. Whereas in some patients disturbances of thinking (manifested as the lack of critical appraisal) were found because of their total unconcern over the recognition of objective reality, in other patients (with "multilevel" "dissociated" thinking) the disturbances were associated with a dualistic, distorted attitude toward reality.

In disturbances of thinking such as the multilevel and dissociation phenomena, the dynamics of the thinking processes are also affected. For this reason, in the book, "Disturbances of Thinking in Mental Patients" [112], we regarded these disturbances as disturbances of the logical course of thinking. Nevertheless the decisive feature of these forms of disturbance of thinking is not the change in the dynamics of the thinking process, but rather the changed attitude of the patient to his environment. It is for this reason that the purposiveness of thinking is so severely disturbed and thinking itself loses its regulatory function.

Despite the fact that the individual skills and habits and the stores of previously acquired knowledge remain relatively intact in these patients, their behavior in general becomes inept and inadequate. The disorder of the intellectual activity of these patients essentially indicates a profound disturbance of the unity of the personality. For this reason the patients of this category form the hard core of the mentally ill.

Conclusion

Investigations in the field of the psychopathology of thinking have a two-fold purpose: on the one hand, their results may be used for the needs of psychiatric practice, and on the other, they are of interest to the theory of general psychology.

We have analyzed not only the forms of disturbance of thinking which have already become part of the stock-in-trade of clinical investigation (the "sluggishness" of thinking, "reasoning," and "dissociation"), but also forms which had been hitherto inadequately described, such as, for example, the illogicality of judgment, the "multilevel" character of thinking, "hyperresponsiveness," and lack of critical appraisal. The forms of the disturbances of thinking we have distinguished are more varied than those described in accounts of clinical and experimental psychological investigations. One of the most vital problems in clinical psychiatry is the establishment of a diagnosis, so that the foremost problem with which pathopsychological research is confronted is that of determining the specificity of these thought disturbances for the various disease categories.

It has been found that there is no direct, absolutely necessary correlation between a particular type of disturbance of thinking and a particular form of disease. The experimental facts reveal no single disorder of thinking specific, for example, to all forms and types of schizophrenia. On the contrary, they show that there is no unique pattern of experimental test behavior which can be regarded as characteristic of patients with any one form of disease. Even such symptoms as the distortion of generalization or the "dissociation" of thinking, which is apparently characteristic of schizophrenics in general, may also be encountered in other diseases, such as psychopathies and reactive states.

Table XIX indicates the frequency of various types of error in the object-classification test according to disease category. We thus find that errors involving meaningless or sterile combinations are found in most patients with schizophrenia (67.1%), but are also rather frequent in psychopaths (33.3%) and are present in many patients who had encephalitis (20.0%). On the other hand, errors due to excessively concrete associations are found in oligophrenics (95.0%) as well as in epileptics (86.0%), and patients with post-encephalitis (70.0%).

Instability in test behavior, in which correct solutions alternate with incorrect ones (excessive concreteness, duplication in forming groups, etc.) was found to be typical for cerebrovascular patients (81.6%), as well as many brain-injured patients (68.2%). Finally,

TABLE XIX

Character of Performance of the Object-Classification Test by Patients

Diseases	Number of patients tested	Correctly generalized solution	Solution characterized by generalization but disturbed by occasional instances of excessive concreteness	Solution solely by means of concrete-situation combinations (including excessive attention to detail)	Incorrect solutions as a result of many incorrect formal combinations	Aimless sorting of the simple manipulation type
				Methods of solution and character of mistakes (percent)		
Schizophrenia	155	7.8	14.2	9.0	67.1	1.9
Epilepsy	50	4.0	4.0	86.0	4.0	2.0
Cerebrovascular diseases	125	3.2	81.6	4.0	—	11.2
Posttraumatic psychosis	170	5.3	68.2	4.1	2.4	20.0
Oligophrenia	40	—	—	95.0	—	5.0
Postencephalitis	30	10.0	—	70.0	20.0	—
Progressive paresis	30	—	3.3	36.7	—	60.0
Manic-depressive psychosis (hypo-manic phase)	15	13.3	66.7	13.3	—	6.7
Psychopathy	30	46.7	20.0	—	33.3	—

the substitution of simple manipulation in place of the regular performance of the test was found in patients with progressive paresis (60.0%) and in postraumatic cases (20.0%).

Hence, the distribution of mistakes in the performance of the classification test gives no evidence of the presence of strict specificity of the individual symptoms of disturbances of thinking in relation to patients with particular groups of diseases.

In our view it is more correct to speak of a particular form of disturbance of thinking as typical only of a certain group of patients or, more correctly still, of a certain state, as is brought out by Table XIX. For example, although solutions involving concrete-situation combinations are not specific to any particular group of patients, they are not frequent in schizophrenics (9.0%), while incorrect solutions due to a multiplicity of formal combinations are never seen in oligophrenics and hardly ever in posttraumatic patients (2.0%) or in epileptics (4.0%).

A further conclusion may be drawn from a more detailed analysis of the material: the incorrect methods of solution seem to represent behavior which is characteristic of those diseases which (perhaps because of some common pathogenetic factor) give rise to similar mental states. For example, performance of the object-classification test by concrete-situation combinations is a dominant feature of oligophrenics, epileptics, and some postencephalitics— i.e., of all those patients whose mental state is characterized by inertia.

The high proportion of concrete-situation solutions given by patients with epilepsy and encephalitis (Economo) was the result of the tendency of the patients of both groups to pay too much attention to detail. The same high percentage of incorrect combinations was found in those psychopaths whose clinical picture was dominated by elements of ratiocination or "mental rumination," and in relation to whom doubts were expressed concerning the differential diagnosis of schizophrenia.

On the other hand, performance in the tests in which the correct solution was interrupted by incorrect concrete-situation combinations was found to be characteristic of patients with cerebrovascular diseases, and also was fairly well marked in patients with brain injuries, whose mental state was described as asthenic with manifestations of fatigability and emotional lability. On these grounds it seems more correct to speak of individual forms of disturbances of thinking as typical rather than specific.

The fact that a particular type of disturbance of thinking was typical or characteristic was often determined by a combination of the variants of such disturbances described above. A characteristic feature of the patients with schizophrenia, for example, was the ease with which formed their sterile verbal-logical associations, combined with an inertia of these associations related to the inadequate level of critical appraisal in these patients. The combination of these qualities of thinking provided a basis for the schizophrenic ratiocination. The distinctive variety of ratiocination sometimes found in epilepsy has a different origin: it is based on difficulty in abstraction from concrete details, on a tendency to include all the concrete elements of the situation, and on a meticulousness of reasoning. In other words, whereas schizophrenic ratiocination is characterized by a combination of distortion of generalization, illogicality of reasoning, and lack of critical appraisal, epileptic ratiocination results from a combination of "sluggishness" of thinking and a lowering of the level of generalization.

Combinations of one or more types of disturbance of thinking with other pathological symptoms and personality changes may also be characteristic of these patients. The types of disturbances of thinking which we have distinguished coincide only partially with the total manifestation of disease in each individual case.

The various disturbances of thinking that were found were sometimes characteristic of a particular system of lesions. For example, inadequacy of the critical aspect of thinking, which leads (as shown in Chapter 6) to the substitution of crude solutions in the test performance, was mainly found in patients with general paresis; it was also seen frequently in patients with Pick's disease (this material is not summarized in the present book). Table XVII also indicates the occasional appearance of this type of error in brain-injured patients (20%) and oligophrenics (5%). Clinical investigation showed that the former were patients who had received gunshot wounds in the frontobasal regions of the brain. (Extracts from the case records and results of tests on two of these patients—K. and Ch-v—appeared in Chapter 6.) As for the oligophrenics who uncharacteristically performed the test in this manner, a diagnosis of oligophrenia associated with hydrocephalus was made [227].

Hence, the types of disorder of thinking we have distinguished may be characteristic at once of the nosological group, of the patient's condition, and of the system affected by the lesion; they may thus be used as criteria of a wide range of clinical designations. The results of experimental psychological investigations should not be used universally and/or indiscriminately for diagnostic purpose. Only in conjunction with the specific clinical data can they be of any value in the solution of various problems in psychiatric practice.

*   *   *

We consider that the use of data relating to the disturbance of thinking may also be of value in the solution of theoretical problems in general psychology. The results of a psychopathological investigation contribute to the overthrow of functionalism in the interpretation of human perceptual activity.

From the point of view of the traditional division of mental activity into individual processes, generally accepted in psychology, it may be objected that the various types of disturbances of thinking that we have distinguished as disturbances of the logical course of thinking or of its purposiveness, are not in fact disturbances of thinking at all. When describing the patients with disturbances of the critical aspect of thinking, we pointed out that these patients are capable of performing tasks requiring generalization and abstraction, and that their mistakes are due to an attitude of indifference toward what they are doing and to the absence of self-regulation. In other words, disturbances of thinking such as lack of critical appraisal, "multilevel" thinking, etc., could be described as secondary, caused by a disturbance of the personality as a whole—by disintegration of the system of the patient's needs which is not related strictly to a disturbance of thinking (in the true meaning of the word).

A similar statement may be made concerning the group of disturbances of thinking which we called disturbances of the logical course of thinking. It might have been pointed out that such forms of disturbance of thinking as illogicality of reasoning or "hyper-responsiveness" also are merely an expression of a disturbance of the general dynamic of mental activity, and not a disturbance of the process of thinking as such. It is not by accident that many authors have attempted to uphold the concept of "extraintellectual" dementia (Fridman and others).

However, the clinical material cannot explain the disintegration of mental activity in terms of a disintegration of individual processes. A more profound analysis of the disturbances of thinking shows that they always take the form of the disturbance and disintegration of complex activity.

For an example of this we may turn to some of the forms of disturbance of thinking which we have described and which are apparently specific symptoms of the disintegration of thinking as such (distortion of the process of generalization, "dissociation," "sluggishness," etc.). Distortion of the process of generalization implies that the patients' judgments are not determined by actual relationships between objects, that the concrete links between them are not taken into account. The ratiocination of such patients is caused by the dominance of random, sterile associations. At the same time it must be stressed that this pseudoabstract ratiocination becomes possible because real relationships—the situation as it really is—lose their significance for these patients, living as they do, in a world of pathological ideas and experiences. The sterility of their associations is inseparable from their abnormal attitude toward life.

The clinical material thus shows that the disintegration of intellectual activity is always complex and multidimensional in nature. Thinking breaks down, not as an individual process, but as an activity, and it is what characterizes it as an activity that is primarily disturbed. The very possibility that varieties of disturbances of thinking—such as a disturbance of its purposiveness or a disturbance of its dynamics—may be distinguished, suggests that thinking cannot be reduced to an isolated function.

Clinical practice shows that the disintegration of purposive, generalizing, synthesizing, systematizing, emotionally saturated activity, possessing a definite dynamics, involves the disintegration of a higher form of cognition—the disintegration of thinking. Thinking cannot exist apart from man's needs, his desires, and his aspirations.

It should be noted that this conclusion that thinking cannot be separated from the emotional-volitional sphere was reached in the 1930's by two eminent Soviet authorities—Vygotskii and Gannushkin.

Vygotskii, polemicizing with Lewin on the subject of mental retardation, defended the point of view that it is essential to rise above the "isolated metaphysical view of the intellect and affect as separate, self-satisfying entities, and to recognize their internal association and unity. . . ." [52]. From the results of experimental investigations, conducted with his co-workers on mentally retarded children, Vygotskii concluded that unmotivated thinking is just as impossible as action for no reason. "As soon as we dissociate thinking from life, from dynamics and needs, deprive it of reality, we shut all the doors leading to the elucidation of the properties and the principal purpose of thinking: to determine the pattern of life and behavior, to modify and control our actions, and to free them from the power of the concrete situation." [52].

Gannushkin, who was not particularly concerned with the theoretical investigation of the disintegration of thinking, concluded from his clinical findings that a disintegration of thinking cannot be examined in isolation from a disturbance of affect. He expressed this hypothesis as follows: "For the senses to take precedence over the intellect, the intellect must be weak." [64].

We consider that the facts we have cited are pertinent to the solution of certain problems in general psychology; they may help to overcome the functional approach in the search for the principles governing mental activity.

In real life, when solving concrete problems, man's mental activity is exhibited not as an integrated group of processes but as an activity. During the analysis of the formation of the child's mental activity; when it is necessary to distinguish certain forms of influence on human behavior; during the analysis of work processes; and in the selection of methods of psychotherapy—in short, during the application of the results of psychological science to the solution of any practical problem, it is found that consideration must be paid not so much to the principles of individual processes (perception, attention, memory) as to the general principles of mental activity as a whole; moreover, these processes themselves may be regarded as activity.

During recent years Soviet psychologists have demonstrated on the general theoretical level that this division into individual processes is conventional. However, when describing their own methodological principles, psychologists have paid too little attention to the results of concrete investigations. We consider that the facts we have reported from the field of study of the disintegration of thinking could be used by these psychologists to their advantage.

Finally, psychopathological research may also be of importance to the solution of the problem of the relationship between the disintegration and development of thinking. The question arises whether this problem can be solved in psychology as it is in morphology. Numerous investigations in the field of cytoarchitectonics and histology have shown that in diseases of the central nervous system the (phylogenetically) younger formations of the cerebral cortex are the first to be affected. Similar conclusions were reached by Vogt, Snesarev, Miscolci, and Gerstmann. After comparing his clinical investigations in the field of schizophrenia with pathological and cytoarchitectonic findings, Gurevich remarks: "It may be regarded as established that the changes in schizophrenia are selective, and that the new (human) fields are affected more severely, while the phylogenetically older fields are almost unaffected." [78]. Gurevich makes a similar claim in respect of the cytoarchitectonic changes in atrophic diseases of the brain (Pick's disease). Several workers who have studied the pathophysiology of higher nervous activity have shown that in brain lesions the regulation of the subjacent brain centers by the cortex is weakened. A lesion of these phylogenetically more recent structures, and a weakening of their regulatory influence, leads to strengthening, and to "liberation" of the activity of the more primitive formations.

The experimental investigations of Pavlov and his co-workers, carried out on animals, confirmed the view that in pathology that which was acquired last is soonest disturbed. For instance, artificially produced conditioned reflexes are much more easily disturbed in brain diseases than are unconditioned reflexes; the activity of the second signal system is disturbed to a greater degree than the activity of the first.

Clinicians have illustrated this view by clinical observations. Kerbikov [129], for instance, points out that when schizophrenic patients develop emotional dullness, it is the more recently developed emotions (for example, those which are social in origin) that are disturbed first. The phylogenetically most primitive emotions of anger and fear remain intact for a longer time. In just the same way, in disturbances of consciousness it is orientation in time that is disturbed soonest, followed by orientation in space; orientation in personality, based on a complex of the most stable associations, is preserved the longest of all.

A further conclusion was made from these hypotheses: in certain brain diseases, man descends to a lower behavioral level which corresponds, as it were, to a particular stage of development of the child. For instance, the American writers Pinkerton and Kelly point out that the loss of the ability to abstract in cerebro-vascular patients is reminiscent of the picture of the development of this ability in children, but in the reverse order. In like manner, as Ozeretskii pointed out in his survey, the hebephrenic behavior of the schizophrenic patient has been equated by certain American psychiatrists with the behavior of the child of preschool age. He cites the fact that in a Mexican hospital a bizarre patient exhibiting hebephrenic behavior was treated by being placed in surroundings resembling a kindergarten.

The conception of the regression of the mental activity of the mentally defective person to a phylo- and ontogenetically lower level of development underlies the views of those authors who have compared the thinking of schizophrenics with archaic thinking (Storch, Schilder, Sumbaev, and others). These views are incor-rect. On theoretical grounds we consider that it is justifiable to expect that the forms of disintegration of any mental activity, including thinking, may repeat in reverse order the principles of its development, for mental processes arise by a reflex mechanism on the basis of associations formed during life. Our concrete investigations have demonstrated the correctness of this hypo-thesis.

Let us now examine some of the disorders of thinking we have described, which may resemble certain stages of childhood, dis-turbances which we have described by the terms "lowering of the level of generalization" and "illogicality of reasoning."

The characteristic features of the disturbance which we call a lowering of the level of generalization are as follows: inability to go beyond the limits of habitual, concrete associations when forming judgments, inability to abstract from a group of concrete signs, and limitation of knowledge concerning objects. These features may at first glance seem analogous to the special features of the thinking process of the preschool child who, having no abstract concepts at his command, when performing a mental action also relies upon concrete, sensory signs.

Psychological analysis reveals the qualitative difference be-tween the thinking of the mentally defective patient and the thinking of the child. The defective adult patient cannot grasp a system of new associations and cannot establish unaccustomed relationships between objects when performing mental tasks; at the same time he does possess a store of previous knowledge and skills which he can use. The child, on the other hand, while not possessing a store of knowledge or a wide range of associations, readily forms a new system of knowledge. The child's range of associations widens rapidly in the process of education, and his knowledge of the outside world gradually enlarges and develops. Although the child's thinking also is imperfect and embraces only a small proportion of phenomena, in the course of his practical activity it is gradually perfected. Because of his powerful orienting reflex, and by dint of contact with surroundings, the child rapidly obtains a wide range of information and accumulates and integrates his knowledge. Despite the external similarity with the thinking of the mentally defective adult patient, there is a qualitative difference between the two.

Let us now turn to the examination of that form of disturbance of thinking which we called a disturbance of the logical course of reasoning. The characteristic features of this disturbance of intellectual activity are inadequate purposiveness of associations, fluctuations in the level of attainment, hyperresponsiveness to extraneous stimuli, and a possible resemblance to the distractibility of the child. However, a more careful examination of this disturbance leads to the rejection of this suggestion. As we showed in Chapter 4, the symptoms of this disturbance of thinking are a manifestation of the depressed activity of the cortex, a manifestation of protective inhibition. It is not by accident that these features of thinking we have just described are combined in these patients with a weakness of memory and with verbal paraphasias, i.e., with other manifestations of the rapid inhibition of cortical activity. The increased distractibility of the child, on the other hand, together with the illogicality of its judgments, are largely a manifestation of increased orienting activity, and demonstrate the existence of a high level of cortical activity.

The purposeless, unthinking actions of the patient with general paresis are often reminiscent of the carefree behavior of the small child. In both cases there may be absence of control over the individual's actions. In this case, too, however, we can detect only an external similarity. The behavior of the small child in this respect is unthinking by virtue of the fact that because of his small range of knowledge, he cannot foresee the result of his actions. Relations of cause and effect between phenomena cannot arise, and his actions therefore appear purposeless. In fact they are not. The aims pursued by the child are limited; they are not included in a more general, complex chain of attitudes. However, this limited aim in the small child exists, and all his actions are directed toward a need (albeit elementary, or purely biological), so that in this sense they are always motivated and goal-directed. Because of his powerful orienting reflex, these chains change rapidly, so that the child's actions may appear to be transient manipulations.

It is a different matter with the patients with defects of the critical aspects of their thinking. Our experimental findings and clinical observations show that the actions of these patients were not evoked by the orientation of their personality, by their attitudes. Consequently, these forms of disturbance of thinking also show only an external resemblance to the structure of the thinking of the child at a certain stage of his development.

Meanwhile, investigation of the disintegration of intellectual activity reveals forms which, even in their external manifestation, have nothing in common with the thinking pattern of the child. Aspects of thinking such as "dissociation" or distortion of the process of generalization are never encountered at any stage of childhood. As we mentioned above, in "dissociation" of thinking it is difficult to find an object of the patient's thoughts. By means of their speech, the patients communicate virtually nothing to the listener, and do not reveal their attitudes toward other people. Speech is no longer an instrument of thought, or a means of communication.

Features such as these are not characteristic of the thinking of the child. However incoherent the child's speech, it is always directed toward some object. However distractible the child, his babble is always addressed to some object, and his speech always reveals his attitude toward his environment; it is addressed to people around him. The investigations of Soviet psychologists have shown that in his so-called egocentric speech, the child expresses his desires; his speech is always directed toward something and somebody.

Hence, the psychological analysis of the clinical material shows that the structure of the thinking of the adult patient does not correspond to the structure of the child's thinking. Thinking as a mental process arises by a reflex mechanism on the basis of socially formed associations developing during life, as a result of training and education. Even when the disease affects the youngest, specifically human regions of the nervous system, the behavior of the human patient does not resemble the behavior of man in the early stages of phylo- or ontogenesis. If we turn to the principles of development of thinking at the stages of childhood (infancy, preschool age, etc.), on the one hand, and the forms of disintegration of thinking, on the other, it is easily seen that no disease leads to a repetition of the course of development of thinking as found at these stages. Their similarity, as we have pointed out, is purely external. The disintegration of mental activity is not the antithesis of its development.

* * *

Any form of cognition, in its development and formation, is, of course, a single process; its individual aspects can be analyzed only artificially. Meanwhile, as Pavlov pointed out, during disintegration that which is normally hidden may come to light particularly clearly. Disease disturbs mental activity differently: sometimes it affects elementary synthesis; sometimes only the highest manifestations of synthetic activity are affected; sometimes, again, the whole human personality may be disturbed. In this way disturbances of different aspects of human mental activity may be manifested.

Knowledge of the "parameters" qualifying the disturbance of the process of thinking, and knowledge of the psychological facts obtained from that rich field, clinical psychiatry, may promote the theory and practice of psychological science.

Bibliography

A. RUSSIAN

1. Marx, K., and Engels, F. Works, Vol. 3.
2. Engels, F. The Dialectics of Nature. Gospolitizdat (1955).
3. Lenin, V. I. Materialism and Empiriocriticism. Works, Vol. 14.
4. Lenin, V. I. Philosophical Notes (Filosofskie tetradi). Works, Vol. 38.
5. Abashev-Konstantinovskii, A. L. "The psychopathology of frontal lesions." Nevropatologiya i psikhiatriya, Vol. 18, No. 4 (1949).
6. Abashev-Konstantinovskii, A. L. "The problem of consciousness in the light of clinical psychopathology." Voprosy psikhologii, No. 4 (1958).
7. Abramovich, G. B. "The clinical psychological experiment." Sovetskaya psikhonevrologiya, No. 1 (1939).
8. Averbukh, E. S. "The clinical psychopathological analysis of amentive states." Nevropatologiya i psikhiatriya, Vol. 15, No. 6 (1946).
9. Averbukh, E. S. "Acute vascular psychoses." In: Mental Disturbances in Hypertension (Leningrad, 1946).
10. Akkerman, V. I. Mechanisms of Schizophrenic Primary Delirium (Irkutsk, 1936).
11. Anan'ev, B. G. Essays in Psychology (Lenizdat, 1946).
12. Anan'ev, B. G. "The problem of the idea in Soviet psychological science." Filosofskie zapiski, Vol. 5 (1950).
13. Anan'ev, B. G. "Man as a general problem in modern science." Vestnik Leningradskogo universiteta, No. 11/2 (1957).
14. Anikina, A. M. "The differential features of the work processes of patients with idiopathic and traumatic epilepsy." Collection: Epilepsy and Clinical Aspects of Working Capacity (Medgiz, Moscow, 1939).
15. Anokhin, P. K. "General principles of the compensation of disturbed functions and their physiological basis." Collection: Reports of a Conference on Problems in Defectology (Izd. APN RSFSR, Moscow, 1956).
16. Anokhin, P. K. "The physiological substrate of spinal reactions." Zhurnal vysshei nervnoi deyatel'nosti im. I. P. Pavlova, Vol. 7, No. 1 (1957).
17. Anfimov, V. Ya. "Concentration of attention and capacity for mental work in epilepsy." Obozrenie psikhiatrii, nevrologii i eksperimental'noi psikhologii, Nos. 11-12 (1908).
18. Artemov, V. A. "The perception and understanding of speech." Collection: Reports of a Conference on Problems in Psychology (Izd. APN RSFSR, Moscow, 1954).
19. Astvatsaturov, M. I. Clinical and Experimental Psychological Investigations of the Speech Function (St. Petersburg, 1909).
20. Balashova, L. N. "Some types of remission and defect in schizophrenia with a favorable course (in relation to occupational resettlement)." Collection: Problems in the Clinical Course, Pathogenesis, and Treatment of Schizophrenia (Medgiz, Moscow, 1958).
21. Balonov, L. Ya., Kaufman, D. Ya., Lichko, A. E., and Traugott, N. N. "On Professor I. F. Sluchevskii's article 'Some current problems in psychiatry.'" Zhurnal nevropatologii i psikhiatrii im. S. S. Korsakova, Vol. 52, No. 12 (1952).
22. Banshchikov, V. M. "The role and importance of S. S. Korsakov in the development of Russian psychiatry." In book: Selected Works, by S. S. Korsakov (Medgiz, Moscow, 1954).

23. Banshchikov, V. M. "Dynamic observations on patients with mental disturbances associated with circulatory disorders in the brain." Collection: Current Problems in Neuropathology and Psychiatry (Kuibyshev, 1957).
24. Bassin, F. V. "The disturbance of word values in schizophrenia." Candidate dissertation (Khar'kov, 1936).
25. Belousova, M. T. "The pseudoparalytic syndrome in closed brain injuries." Trudy Tsentral'nogo instituta psikhiatrii, Vol. 4 (1949).
26. Bernshtein, A. N. Clinical Methods of Psychological Investigation of Mental Patients (Moscow, 1911).
27. Bernshtein, G. I. "Clinical features of epilepsy." Doctorate dissertation (Moscow, 1947).
28. Bzhalava, I. T. "The psychopathology of the fixed idea in epilepsy." Collection: Proceedings of a Conference on Psychology (Izd, APN RSFSR, Moscow, 1957).
29. Bekhterev, V. M. "The objective investigation of neuro-psychic activity." Obozrenie psikhiatrii, nevrologii i eksperimental'noi psikhologii, No. 7 (1907).
30. Birenbaum, G. V. "The formation of metaphors and conventional word meanings in the presence of pathological changes in intelligence." Collection: Advances in the Study of Apraxia, Agnosia, and Aphasia (Moscow—Leningrad, 1934).
31. Birenbaum, G. V., and Zeigarnik, B. V. "The dynamic analysis of intellectual disorders." Sovetskaya nevropatologiya, psikhiatriya i psikhogigiena, Vol. 4, No. 6 (1935).
32. Bleuler, E. A. Autistic Intelligence (Odessa, 1928).
33. Bozhovich, L. I. "Attitude of schoolchildren to learning as a psychological problem." Izvestiya APN RSFSR, No. 38 (1951).
34. Bozhovich, L. I. "Peculiarities of self-awareness in adolescents." Voprosy psikhologii, No. 1 (1955).
35. Boiko, E. I., Vlasova, M. M., Kostomarova, N. M., and Chuprikova, N. I. "The experimental analysis of the process of mental comparison." In book: Proceedings of a Conference on Psychology (Izd. APN RSFSR, Moscow, 1957).
36. Boiko, E. I. "The problem of the conditioned-reflex basis of higher mental processes." Collection: Psychological Science in the USSR, Vol. 1 (Izd. APN RSFSR, Moscow, 1959).
37. Brainina, M. Ya. "Psychopathological features of severe organic dementias in minors." Problems in Forensic Psychiatry, Collection II (Yurizdat, Moscow, 1940).
38. Budilova, E. A. I. M. Sechenov's Theory of Perception and Intelligence (Izd. AN SSSR, Moscow, 1954).
39. Bykov, K. M. Selected Works, Vol. II (Medgiz, Moscow, 1954).
40. Valitskaya, M. K. "Psychophysical changes in mental patients." Vestnik klinicheskoi i sudebnoi psikhiatrii, Vol. 6, No. 1 (1898).
41. Wallon, A. From Action to Thought [Russian translation], (IL, 1956).
42. Vasilevskaya, V. Ya., and Krasnyanskaya, I. M. "Special features of the perceptual activity of pupils at a special school during work with visual material." Izv. APN RSFSR, No. 68 (1955).
43. Vasil'eva, V. A. "Disturbances of the tempo of sensorimotor reactions in patients with vascular diseases of the brain." Collection: Mental Disturbances Associated with Atherosclerosis of the Cerebral Vessels (Medgiz, Moscow, 1960).
44. Vvedenskii, I. N. "Psychogenic puerilism." Problems in Forensic Psychiatry, Collection V (Yurizdat, Moscow, 1946).
45. Veisfel'd, M. "Primary delirium or delirium in the strict sense in schizophrenics." Trudy instituta im. Gannushkina, Vol. 1 (1936).
46. Vladychko, S. D. "Attention, mental working capacity, and free associations in patients with dementia praecox." Obozrenie psikhiatrii, nevropatologii i eksperimental'noi psikhologii, No. 6 (1908).
47. Vladychko, S. D. The Character of Associations in Patients with Chronic Primary Dementia (St. Petersburg, 1909).
48. Voprosy filosofii i psikhologii, Book 4/24 (1894).
49. Vrono, M. S. "Special features of the final period of schizophrenia with incoherence of speech." Zhurnal nevropatologii i psikhiatrii im. S. S. Korsakova, Vol. 57, No. 5 (1957).
50. Vygotskii, L. S. "Intelligence and speech." In book: Selected Psychological Investigations (Izd. APN RSFSR, Moscow, 1956).

51. Vygotskii, L. S. "The disturbance of concepts in schizophrenia." In book: Selected Psychological Investigations (Izd. APN SSSR, Moscow, 1956).
52. Vygotskii, L. S. "The problem of mental retardation." In book: Selected Psychological Investigations (Izd. APN RSFSR, Moscow, 1956).
53. Vyrubov, N. A. The Pathology of Associations (Moscow, 1914).
54. Gakkel', L. B. "A comparative study of the disturbances of higher nervous activity in patients with oligophrenia and senile dementia." Zhurnal vysshei nervnoi deyatel' nosti im. I. P. Pavlova, Vol. 3, No. 1 (1953).
55. Gadzhiev, S. G. "Analysis of the disturbance of intellectual activity in lesions of the frontal areas of the brain." Candidate dissertation (Moscow, 1947).
56. Gakkel', L. B. "The role of the phenomena of induction in the interaction between the signal systems." Zhurnal vysshei nervnoi deyatel'nosti im. I. P. Pavlova, No. 6 (1955).
57. Gal'perin, P. Ya., and Golubova, R. A. "Mechanism of paraphasias of the complex type." Sovetskaya psikhonevrologiya, No. 6 (1939).
58. Gal'perin, P. Ya. "Experimental study of the formation of intellectual actions." Collection: Reports of a Conference on Problems in Psychology (Izd. APN RSFSR, Moscow, 1954).
59. Gal'perin, P. Ya. "The problem of internal speech.".Dokl. APN RSFSR, No. 4 (1954).
60. Gal'perin, P. Ya. "The intellectual action as the basis of formation of thought and image." Voprosy psikhologii, No. 6 (1957).
61. Gal'perin, P. Ya. "The development of investigations on the formation of intellectual actions." In: Psychological Science in the USSR, Vol. I (Izd. APN RSFSR, Moscow, 1959).
62. Gal'perina, R. I. "Special features of the working capacity and compensatory powers of schizophrenics." Collection: Assessment of Working Capacity and Resettlement of Schizophrenic Patients (Moscow, 1940).
63. Gannushkin, P. B. "Dementia of reasoning and overreasoning." Zhurnal nevropatologii i psikhiatrii im. S. S. Korsakova, Books 3 and 4 (1905).
64. Gannushkin, P. B. Clinical Features of the Psychopathies, Their Statics, Dynamics, and Systematics (Sever Press, Moscow, 1933).
65. Geier, T. A. "The differential diagnosis between schizophrenia and organic diseases in the narrow meaning of this term." Collection: Transactions of the Psychiatric Clinic, 1st Moscow Medical Institute, No. 3 (Medgiz, Moscow, 1929).
66. Geier, T. A., and Kholzakova, N. G. "Schizophrenia and essential hypertension." Collection: Transactions of the Psychiatric Clinic, 1st Moscow Medical Institute, No. 4 (in memory of P. B. Gannushkin), (Medgiz, Moscow, 1934).
67. Gilyarovskii, V. A. Old and New Problems in Psychiatry (Medgiz, Moscow, 1946).
68. Gilyarovskii, V. A. Psychiatry, 4th edition (Medgiz, Moscow, 1954).
69. Gritsenko, I. M. "Repetition in the process of development." Voprosy filosofii, No. 8 (1958).
70. Golant, R. Ya., and Yankovskii, A. E. "Some experimental data relating to the problem of the disintegration of intelligence in schizophrenia." Sovetskaya nevropatollogiya, psikhiatriya i psikhogigiena, Vol. 3, Nos. 2–3 (1934).
71. Gol'dblatt, O. O. "On dementia." Klinicheskaya meditsina, No. 8 (1925).
72. Gol'denberg, S. I., and Golodets, R. G. "Psychopathological syndromes in the clinical picture of gunshot wounds of the brain." Trudy Tsentral'nogo instituta psikhiatrii, Vol. 4 (1949).
73. Gol'dovskaya, T. I. "Clinical features and pathogenesis of protracted postinfective asthenic states." Trudy Tsentral'nogo instituta psikhiatrii, Vol. 1 (1940).
74. Gromova, V. V. "Late mental disturbances (with predominance of the picture of asthenia) after influenza." Collection: Neuropsychic Disturbances in Traumatic and Infectious Lesions of the Central Nervous System (Medgiz, Moscow, 1957).
75. Gurvich, B. R. "Some special features of the defect after a series of acute schizophrenic attacks and the influence of postacute protracted asthenic states on the course of the process." Nevropatologiya i psikhiatriya, Vol. 8, Nos. 9–10 (1939).
76. Gurevich, M. O. "The nature of the schizophrenic process." Nevropatologiya i psikhiatriya, Vol. 14, No. 5 (1945).
77. Gurevich, M. O., and Sereiskii, M. Ya. Textbook of Psychiatry, 5th edition (Medgiz, Moscow, 1946).
78. Gurevich, M. O. "Importance of the architectonics of the cerebral cortex in psychiatry." Collection: Cytoarchitectonics of the Human Brain (Medgiz, Moscow, 1949).

79. Gutman, L. G. Experimental psychological investigations of manic-melancholic psychosis (the state of concentration in respect to attention, capacity for mental work, and association). (St. Petersburg, 1909.)
80. Dobrynin, N. F. "Activity of personality and activity of consciousness." Uchenye zapiski Moskovskogo gorodskogo pedagogicheskogo instituta, Vol. 36, No. 2 (1954).
81. Dobrynin, N. F. "Significance in psychology." Collection: Proceedings of a Conference on Psychology (Izd. APN RSFSR, Moscow, 1957).
82. Dovbnya, D. N. "An associative experiment on mentally healthy persons." Psikho-terapiya, No. 2 (1914).
83. Dubinin, A. M. "The problem of endocrine dementia." Transactions of the Psychiatric Clinic, 1st Moscow Medical Institute, No. 4 (in memory of P. B. Gannushkin), (Medgiz, Moscow, 1934).
84. Dubinin, A. M., and Zeigarnik, B. V. "The problem of traumatic dementia." Nevropatologiya i psikhiatriya, Vol. 9, Nos. 7–8 (1940).
85. Dukel'skaya, I. N., and Korobkova, E. A. Medical Assessment of Working Capacity and Resettlement of Schizophrenic Patients (Medgiz, Moscow, 1958).
86. Evlakhova, É. A. "Types of intelligence in schizophrenia." Collection: 50th Anniversary of the S. S. Korsakov Psychiatric Clinic (Moscow, 1940).
87. Zhislin, S. G. "General clinical patterns in mental diseases in the elderly." Trudy Tsentral'nogo instituta psikhiatrii, Vol. 4 (1949).
88. Zhislin, S. G. "Some problems in the diagnosis and definition of schizophrenia." Collection: Clinical Features, Pathogenesis, and Treatment of Schizophrenia (Medgiz, Moscow, 1958).
89. Zavadovskii, K. I. "The character of associations in patients with chronic primary dementia." Izvestiya imperatorskoi voenno-meditsinskoi akademii, Vol. 19, No. 2 (1909).
90. Zalkind, É. M. "Mental disorders after head injury." Trudy Tsentral'nogo instituta psikhiatrii, Vol. 1 (1940).
91. Zalmanzon, A. N., and Skornyakova, S. I. "The structure of epileptic and schizophrenic thinking." Transactions of the Psychiatric Clinic, 1st Moscow Medical Institute, No. 4 (in memory of P. B. Gannushkin), (Medgiz, Moscow, 1934).
92. Zalmanzon, A. N. "The basic disorder in schizophrenia." Transactions of the Psychiatric Clinic, 1st Moscow Medical Institute, No. 5 (Medgiz, Moscow, 1934).
93. Zalmanzon, A. N. "The structure of schizophrenia." Collection: 50th Anniversary of the S. S. Korsakov Psychiatric Clinic (Moscow, 1940).
94. Zalmanzon, A. N. "The structure of the schizophrenic defect." Collection: 50th Anniversary of the Psychiatric Clinic, 1st Moscow Medical Institute (Moscow, 1950).
95. Zankov, L. V. The Psychology of the Mentally Retarded Child (Uchpedgiz, Moscow, 1939).
96. Zankov, L. V. (editor). The Psychology of Pupils of Special Schools. Izv. APN RSFSR, No. 57 (Moscow, 1954).
97. Zankov, L. V., and Petrova, V. G. "The comparative investigation of the differentiation of similar material in mentally retarded and normal schoolchildren." Izv. APN RSFSR, No. 57 (1954).
98. Zaporozhets, A. V. "The development of voluntary movements," (paper read to the 14th International Congress on Psychology). Voprosy psikhologii, No. 1 (1955).
99. Zaporozhets, A. V. The Development of Voluntary Movements (Izd. APN RSFSR, Moscow, 1960).
100. Zvereva, V. D. "Dementia in hypertension." Trudy Moskovskoi oblastnoi nevro-psikhiatricheskoi kliniki, Vol. 10 (1950).
101. Zvereva, M. V., and Lipkina, A. I. "Comparison of objects by mentally retarded schoolchildren." Collection: Special Features of the Perceptual Activity of Pupils at a Special School (Izd. APN RSFSR, Moscow, 1953).
102. Zeigarnik, B. V. "The understanding of metaphors or sentences in the presence of pathological changes in intelligence." Collection: Advances in the Study of Apraxia, Agnosia, and Aphasia (Medgiz, Moscow, 1934).
103. Zeigarnik, B. V. "Psychological analysis of the structure of posttraumatic dementia." Trudy Tsentral'nogo instituta psikhiatrii, Vol. 1 (1940).
104. Zeigarnik, B. V. "Psychological analysis of posttraumatic dementia." Nevropatologiya i psikhiatriya, Vol. 10 (1941).
105. Zeigarnik, B. V. "Local and general cerebral factors in frontal lesions of the brain." Nevropatologiya i psikhiatriya, Vol. 12, No. 6 (1943).

106. Zeigarnik, B. V. "Psychological analysis of postconcussional disturbances of hearing and speech." In: L. B. Perelman: Reactive Postconcussional Deaf-Mutism (Medgiz, Moscow, 1943).
107. Zeigarnik, B. V. "Experimental psychological findings in relation to frontal-lobe injuries." Trudy Tsentral'nogo instituta psikhiatrii, Vol. 3 (1947).
108. Zeigarnik, B. V. "The experimental psychological investigation of patients with brain injuries." Collection: Nervous and Mental Diseases in Wartime (Medgiz, Moscow, 1948).
109. Zeigarnik, B. V. "The disturbance of spontaneity in patients with war injuries of the frontal lobes." Collection: Neurology in Wartime, Vol. 1 (Izd. AMN SSSR, Moscow, 1949).
110. Zeigarnik, B. V. "Types of disturbances of intelligence." Proceedings of a Conference on Psychology (Izd. APN RSFSR, Moscow, 1957).
111. Zeigarnik, B. V. "One type of disturbance of intelligence." Voprosy psikhologii, No. 6 (1956).
112. Zeigarnik, B. V. Intellectual Disturbances in Mental Patients (Medgiz, Moscow, 1958).
113. Zeigarnik, B. V. "Special features of intellectual disturbances in initial cerebral arteriosclerosis with mental disturbances." Abstracts of Proceedings of the Annual Scientific Conference of the State Research Institute of Psychiatry (Moscow, 1957).
114. Zeigarnik, B. V., and Birenbaum, G. V. "The problem of conceptual perception." Sovetskaya nevropatologiya, psikhiatriya i psikhogigiena, Vol. 4, No. 6 (1935).
115. Zeigarnik, B. V., and Gal'perin, P. Ya. "Psychological changes after leucotomy in schizophrenics." Nevropatologiya i psikhiatriya, Vol. 17, No. 4 (1948).
116. Zeigarnik, B. V., and Rubinshtein, S. Ya. "The experimental psychological investigation of patients in psychoneurological institutions." Technical Letter (Moscow, 1956).
117. Zeigarnik, B. V., and Rubinshtein, S. Ya. "Experimental psychological laboratories in the psychiatric clinics of the Soviet Union." Collection: Psychological Science in the USSR, Vol. II (Izd. APN RSFSR, Moscow, 1960).
118. Ivanov-Smolenskii, A. G. Essays on the Pathophysiology of Higher Nervous Activity (Medgiz, Moscow, 1950).
119. Ivanov-Smolenskii, A. G. "The pathophysiological investigation of the phenomena of incoherence of speech in schizophrenia." Arkhiv biologicheskikh nauk, Vol. 36, Series B, No. 1 (1934).
120. Ivanov-Smolenskii, A. G. "Pathological changes in the combined activity of the 1st and 2nd signal systems of the brain." Voenno-meditsinskii zhurnal, No. 2 (1952).
121. Il'in, A. V. "The processes of concentration (attention) in patients with dementia." Izvestiya imperatorskoi voenno-meditsinskoi akademii, No. 3 (1909).
122. Il'in, A. V. "Mental peculiarities of the epileptic." Sovetskaya nevropatologiya, psikhiatriya i psikhogigiena, Vol. 1, No. 8 (1932).
123. Kaganovskaya, É. L., and Zeigarnik, B. V. "The psychopathology of negativism in epidemic encephalitis." Sovetskaya nevropatologiya, psikhiatriya i psikhogigiena, Vol. 4, No. 8 (1935).
124. Kalashnik, Ya. M. "Some psychological principles during simulation of dementia." Collection: Problems in Forensic Psychiatry (Yurizdat, Moscow, 1938).
125. Kaminskii, S. D., and Savchuk, V. I. "Role of the cerebral cortex in the pathogenesis of hypertension." Byulleten' eksperimental'noi biologii i meditsiny, No. 10 (1951).
126. Kandinskii, V. Kh. The Problem of Irresponsibility (Moscow, 1890).
127. Kartsovnik, I. I. The Frontal Syndrome and Its Clinical Variants in Penetrating Wounds of the Brain (Novosibirsk, 1949).
128. Kaufman, D. A. "The pathophysiology of the schizophrenic defect." Zhurnal nevropatologii i psikhiatrii im. S. S. Korsakova, No. 4 (1953).
129. Kerbikov, O. V. Acute Schizophrenia (Medgiz, Moscow, 1955).
130. Kogan, V. M. "Occupational resettlement of mental patients." Collection: Technical Instructions in Relation to Industrial Medical Boards (Moscow, 1940).
131. Kogan, V. M. "Special features of the working capacity of mental patients (with schizophrenia and epilepsy) and measures of organization of their work." Abstracts of Proceedings of a Scientific Session of TsIÉTIN (Moscow, 1941).
132. Kogan, V. M., and Kostomarova, N. M. "Special features of the working capacity and resettlement of schizophrenics." Collection: Assessment of Working Capacity and Resettlement of Patients with Schizophrenia (Moscow, 1940).

133. Kononova, M. P. "Psychological data from the study of one form of slowly progressive schizophrenia in childhood." Sovetskaya nevropatologiya, psikhiatriya i psikhogigiena, Vol. 4, No. 11 (1953).
134. Kononova, M. P. "Psychological data from the study of various forms of schizophrenia." In book: Clinical Features and Treatment of Mental Diseases, Collection 2 (Moscow, 1938).
135. Kononova, M. P. "The psychological analysis of the asthenic state during exhaustion (in children and adolescents)." Trudy bol'nitsy im. Kashchenko, No. 4 (1945).
136. Kononyachenko, V. A. "Cyclic states in hypertension." Zhurnal vysshei nervnoi deyatel'nosti im. I. P. Pavlova, Vol. 5, No. 6 (1955).
137. Kopnin, P. V. "Forms of thinking and their interconnection." Voprosy filosofii, No. 3 (1956).
138. Korobkova, É. A. "Psychological characteristics of the working capacity of patients following trauma." Abstracts of Proceedings of a Scientific Session of TsIÉTIN (Moscow, 1936).
139. Korobkova, É. A., and Savich, M. G. "Psychological characteristics of the working capacity of neurotics." Abstracts of Proceedings of a Scientific Session of TsIÉTIN (Moscow, 1936).
140. Korobkova, É. A. "An experimental investigation of the factors stimulating and depressing working capacity." Collection: Problems in the Assessment of Working Capacity and Diagnosis of Borderline States (Biomedgiz, Moscow, 1939).
141. Korobkova, É. A. "Occupational resettlement of epileptics." Sotsial'noe obespechenie, No. 9 (1940).
142. Korsakov, S. S. "The psychology of microcephaly." Voprosy filosofii i psikhologii, Book 1/20 (1894).
143. Korsakov, S. S. "Editorial comments." Voprosy filosofii i psikhologii, Book 4/24 (1894).
144. Korsakov, S. S. Course in Psychiatry (Moscow, 1901).
145. Korsakov, S. S. "Two introductory lectures." Zhurnal nevropatologii i psikhiatrii im. S. S. Korsakova, No. 1 (1952).
146. Kostandav, É. A. "Disturbances of the combined activity of the first and second signal systems in the catatonic form of schizophrenia." Trudy instituta vysshei nervnoi deyatel'nosti, Vol. 5, seriya patofiziologicheskaya (1958).
147. Kostomarova, N. M. "Qualitative characteristics of intellectual activity in patients with diffuse changes in the central nervous system as a result of head injury." Collection: Traumatic Lesions of the Central Nervous System (Moscow, 1940).
148. Kostomarova, N. M. "Methods of rehabilitation of the disabled from the Second World War with severe sequelae of brain trauma." Collection: Brain Trauma and Working Capacity (Moscow, 1940).
149. Kostomarova, N. M. "Differences in the latent periods of the reaction during differentiation of verbal stimuli by reference to logical signs." The Study of the Higher Neurodynamics in Relation to Problems in Psychology (Izd. APN RSFSR, Moscow, 1957).
150. Kostyuk, G. S. "Psychological principles." Voprosy psikhologii, No. 1 (1955).
151. Kostyuk, G. S. Problems in the psychology of intelligence." Collection: Psychological Science in the USSR, Vol. 1 (Izd. APN RSFSR, Moscow, 1959).
152. Koshkareva, K. I. "Verbal dissociation in schizophrenia and its pathophysiological basis." Proceedings of the 3rd Pavlov Conference (Tomsk, 1953).
153. Krasnogorskii, N. I. Development of Knowledge of the Physiological Activity of the Brain in Children (Leningrad, 1939).
154. Krasnogorskii, N. I. Studies of the Higher Nervous Activity of Man and Animals (Medgiz, Moscow, 1954).
155. Kraepelin, É. Textbook of Psychiatry [Russian translation], Vols. 1–2 (Moscow, 1910–1912).
156. Krol', I. A., and Granskaya, I. A. "Clinical variants of traumatic dementia." Collection: Transactions of the Ukrainian Psychoneurological Institute, Vol. 23 (Khar'kov, 1947).
157. Kublanov, Zh. L. "Experimental psychology in the clinical diagnosis of cerebral arteriosclerosis." Sovetskaya nevropatologiya, psikhiatriya i psikhogigiena, Vol. 3, No. 4 (1934).
158. Kuimov, D. T. "The clinical significance of the frontal lobes." Zhurnal nevropatologii i psikhiatrii im. S. S. Korsakova, No. 3 (1930).

159. Lebedinskii, M.S. "A psychological analysis of a case of sensory aphasia." Nevro-patologiya i psikhiatriya, Vol. 5, No. 4 (1936).
160. Lebedinskii, M.S. "The speech of the schizophrenic and aphasic." Sovetskaya psikhonevrologiya, No. 8 (1937).
161. Lebedinskii, M.S. "Speech disorders in schizophrenics." Sovetskaya psikhonevrologiya, No. 3 (1938).
162. Lebedinskii, M.S. "Dynamic characteristics of the actions of schizophrenics." Sovetskaya psikhonevrologiya, No. 1 (1940).
163. Lebedinskii, M.S. "Speech disorders in schizophrenia at various age levels." Collection: Transactions of the Ukrainian Psychoneurological Institute, Vol. 23 (Khar'kov, 1947).
164. Lebedinskii, M.S. "Types of pathological intelligence." Collection of author's abstracts (Izd. AMN SSSR, Moscow, 1948).
165. Lebedinskii, M.S. "Special features of disturbances of mental activity in lesions of the right hemisphere." Collection: Problems in Modern Psychiatry (Izd. AMN SSSR, Moscow, 1948).
166. Levy-Bruehl, L. "Primitive intelligence." The Atheist (Moscow, 1930).
167. Levitov, N.D. Pediatric and Pedagogic Psychology (Uchpedgiz, Moscow, 1958).
168. Leont'ev, A.N. The Development of Memory (Uchpedgiz, Moscow—Leningrad, 1931).
169. Leont'ev, A.N. A Sketch of the Development of the Mind (Moscow, 1947).
170. Leont'ev, A.N. "The experimental investigation of intelligence." Collection: Reports of Conferences on Psychological Problems (Izd. APN RSFSR, Moscow, 1954).
171. Leont'ev, A.N. "The nature and formation of human mental properties and processes," (paper read to the 14th International Congress on Psychology). Voprosy psikhologii, No. 1 (1955).
172. Leont'ev, A.N. "The systemic nature of mental functions." Theses of Lectures in the Faculty of Philosophy, Moscow State University (Izd. MGU, 1955).
173. Leont'ev, A.N. Problems in the Development of the Mind (Izd. APN RSFSR, Moscow, 1960).
174. Leont'ev, A.N. "Biological and social aspects of the human mind." Voprosy psikhologii, No. 6 (1960).
175. Leont'ev, A.N., and Luria, A.R. "The psychological views of L.S. Vygotskii." In book: L.S. Vygotskii, Selected Psychological Investigations (Izd. APN RSFSR, Moscow, 1956).
176. Leont'ev, A.N., and Rozanova, T.V. "Relationship between the formation of associative links and the content of the action." Sovetskaya pedagogika, No. 10 (1951).
177. Lipkina, A.I. "Analysis and synthesis in the recognition of objects by pupils of a special school." Collection: Special Features of the Perceptual Activity of Pupils at a Special School (Izd. APN RSFSR, Moscow, 1953).
178. Lubovskii, V.I. "Some special features of the higher nervous activity of oligophrenic children." Collection: Problems in the Higher Nervous Activity of the Normal and Abnormal Child, Vol. 1 (Izd. APN RSFSR, Moscow, 1956).
179. Lubovskii, V.I. "Special features of the higher nervous activity of oligophrenic children of different clinical groups." Collection: Problems in the Higher Nervous Activity of the Normal and Abnormal Child, Vol. 2 (Izd. APN RSFSR, Moscow, 1958).
180. Luria, A.R. Restoration of Brain Functions after War Injuries (Izd. AMN SSSR, Moscow, 1948).
181. Luria, A.R. Traumatic Aphasia (Izd. AMN SSSR, Moscow, 1947).
182. Luria, A.R. (editor). Problems in the Higher Nervous Activity of the Normal and Abnormal Child, Vols. 1–2 (Izd. APN RSFSR, Moscow, 1956–1958).
183. Luria, A.R. "Some problems in the study of the higher nervous activity of the normal and abnormal child." Collection: Problems in the Higher Nervous Activity of the Normal and Abnormal Child, Vol. 1 (Izd. APN RSFSR, Moscow, 1956).
184. Luria, A.R. "The regulating role of speech in the formation of active movements." Zhurnal vysshei nervnoi deyatel'nosti im. I.P. Pavlova, Vol. 6, No. 5 (1956).
185. Luria, A.R. "The study of brain lesions and the restoration of disturbed functions." Psychological Science in the USSR, Vol. II (Izd. APN RSFSR, Moscow, 1960).
186. Mansurov, N.S. "The problem of intelligence in the light of I.P. Pavlov's theories." Candidate dissertation (Moscow, 1950).
187. Martsinovskaya, E.M. "Disturbance of the regulatory role of speech in mentally retarded children." Collection: Problems in the Higher Nervous Activity of the Normal and Abnormal Child, Vol. 2 (Izd. APN RSFSR, Moscow, 1958).

188. Megrabyan, A. A. The Nature of Individual Consciousness (in Normal and Pathological Conditions), (Erevan, 1959).
189. Meerovich, R. I. "Special features of the work process in patients in a manic state." Sovetskaya nevropatologiya, psikhiatriya i psikhogigiena, Vol. 4, Nos. 9–10 (935).
190. Meerovich, R. I. "Experimental analysis of the curve of working capacity of patients with manic and depressive syndromes." Sovetskaya nevropatologiya, psikhiatriya i psikhogigiena, Vol. 4, No. 1 (1935).
191. Melekhov, D. E. "The classification of the schizophrenic type of reactions." Transactions of the Psychiatric Clinic, 1st Moscow Medical Institute, No. 4 (in memory of P. B. Gannushkina), (Medgiz, Moscow, 1934).
192. Melekhov, D. E. "The present state of the problem of working capacity in schizophrenia and the objects of such investigation." Collection: Problems in Borderline Psychiatry (Biomedgiz, Moscow—Leningrad, 1935).
193. Melekhov, D. E., and Kamenskaya, V. M. "Clinical and pathophysiological investigations of the late sequelae of closed brain injuries. Communications I–III." Zhurnal nevropatologii i psikhiatrii im. S. S. Korsakova, No. 6 (1953); No. 9 (1955); No. 10 (1957).
194. Meller, E. N. "Disturbance of the sphere of the will in schizophrenia." Nevropatologiya i psikhiatriya, Vol. 7, No. 2 (1938).
195. Menchinskaya, N. A. "The psychology of the grasping of concepts (fundamental problems and methods of investigation)." Izv. APN RSFSR, No. 28 (1950).
196. Menchinskaya, N. A. "The interrelationship of word and image in the process of the grasping of knowledge by schoolchildren." Reports of Conferences on Problems in Psychology (Izd. APN RSFSR, Moscow, 1954).
197. Menchinskaya, N. A. The Mental Development of the Child (Izd. APN RSFSR, Moscow, 1951).
198. Menchinskaya, N. A. "The Soviet psychology of education." Voprosy psikhologii, No. 5 (1957).
199. Meshcheryakov, A. I. "The participation of past experience in the formation of temporary connections in man." Voprosy psikhologii, No. 3 (1955).
200. Meshcheryakov, A. I. "Mechanisms of the processes of abstraction and generalization in mentally retarded children." Collection: Problems in the Higher Nervous Activity of the Normal and Abnormal Child, Vol. II (Izd. APN RSFSR, Moscow, 1958).
201. Mirel'zon, L. A., and Kornetov, A. I. "Disturbances of the cortical dynamics in association with incoherence of speech in patients with schizophrenia." Collection: Problems in Cerebrovascular Disorders and Schizophrenia (Odessa, 1957).
202. "The participation of reactive factors in the dynamics of the schizophrenic disturbance of intelligence." Collection: Problems in Forensic Psychiatry (Yurizdat, Moscow, 1938).
203. Myasishchev, V. N. "Working capacity and diseases of the personality." Sovetskaya nevropatologiya, psikhiatriya i psikhogigiena, Vol. 4, Nos. 9–10 (1935).
204. Myasishchev, V. N. "Personality and work of the subnormal child." In book: Mental Peculiarities of Difficult and Backward Children (Leningrad, 1936).
205. Myasishchev, V. N. "Mental functions and sets." Uchenye zapiski LGU, No. 119 (1949).
206. Myasishchev, V. N. "The problem of human attitudes and its place in psychology." Voprosy psikhologii, No. 5 (1957).
207. Myasishchev, V. N. "Principles of the experimental investigation of higher nervous activity." Uchenye zapiski LGU, No. 203/8, seriya filosofii (1955).
208. Myasishchev, V. N. "The importance of psychology to medicine." Voprosy psikhologii, No. 1 (1956).
209. Myasishchev, V. N. Personality and Neuroses (Izd. LGU, 1960).
210. Myasishchev, V. N. "Fundamental problems and the present state of the psychology of human attitudes." Collection: Psychological Science in the USSR, Vol. 2 (Izd. APN RSFSR, Moscow, 1960).
211. Nepomnyashchaya, N. I. "Some conditions of disturbance of the regulatory function of speech in mentally backward children." Collection: Problems in the Higher Nervous Activity of the Normal and Abnormal Child, Vol. I (Izd. APN RSFSR, Moscow, 1956).
212. Ovchinnikova, K. A. "Some problems in forensic psychiatric examination in cases of arteriosclerotic dementia." Problems in Forensic Psychiatry, Collection VII (Gosyurizdat, Moscow, 1957).

213. Ozeretskii, N. I. "Mental changes in hyper- and hypotension." Nevropatologiya i psikhiatriya, No. 5 (1949).
214. Ozeretskii, N. I. "Report on the Sixth Annual Conference of the International Federation for Mental Health Care." Zhurnal nevropatologii i psikhiatrii im. S. S. Korsakova, No. 5 (1954).
215. Orlovskaya, D. D. "Clinical features of the initial stages of schizophrenia in the light of I. P. Pavlov's theories." Proceedings of a Theoretical and Practical Conference Commemorating the Centenary of the Birth of S. S. Korsakov and Concerned with Current Problems in Psychiatry (Medgiz, Moscow, 1954).
216. Osipov, V. P. Textbook of Psychiatry (Gosizdat, Moscow—Leningrad, 1931).
217. Pavlov, I. P. Complete Collected Works, Vols. III–IV (Izd. AN SSSR, Moscow—Leningrad, 1951–1952).
218. Pavlov's Wednesdays, Vols. I–III (Izd. AN SSSR, Moscow—Leningrad, 1949).
219. Pavlov's Clinical Wednesdays, Vols. I–II (Izd. AN SSSR, Moscow—Leningrad, 1954–1955).
220. Pavlovskaya, L. S. The Experimental Psychological Investigation of Patients with Progressive Paralytic Dementia, Parts I–II (St. Petersburg, 1907).
221. Pavlovskaya, L. S. The Experimental Psychological Investigation of Reasoning in Mental Patients (St. Petersburg, 1909).
222. Pevzner, M. S. "The development of the encephalitic child (epidemic encephalitis)." Sovetskaya nevropatologiya, psikhiatriya i psikhogigiena, Vol. 3, No. 7 (1934).
223. Pevzner, M. S. "Structure of the intellectual defect in children and adolescents following closed brain trauma." Trudy Tsentral'nogo instituta psikhiatrii, Vol 4 (1949).
224. Pevzner, M. S. Oligophrenia (Izd. APN RSFSR, Moscow, 1960).
225. Perel'man, A. A. Schizophrenia (Tomsk, 1944).
226. Perel'man, A. A. Disorders of Intelligence (Tomsk, 1957).
227. Perel'man, A. A., Koshkareva, K. I., and Mogil'nitskii, L. T. "Special features of higher nervous activity in epileptic dementia." Proceedings of the 4th Pavlov Conference (Tomsk, 1954).
228. Perel'man, A. A., and Koshkareva, K. I. "Disturbances in the first and second signal systems in various forms and at various stages of schizophrenia." Proceedings of 4th Pavlov Conference (Tomsk, 1954).
229. Petrova, A. E. "The working capacity of patients with cerebral arteriosclerosis." Transactions of the Psychiatric Clinic of the 1st Moscow Medical Institute, No. 4 (in memory of P. B. Gannushkin), (Medgiz, Moscow, 1934).
230. Petrova, A. E., and Anikina, A. M. "The character of the working capacity in schizophrenia." Collection: Problems in Borderline Psychiatry (Biomedgiz, Moscow—Leningrad, 1935).
231. Petrova, A. E., and Anikina, A. M. "The working capacity of patients with schizophrenia with a component of cerebral arteriosclerosis." Collection: Schizophrenia and Traumatic Diseases of the Brain and Working Capacity in These Conditions (Moscow, 1936).
232. Petrova, A. E., Kononova, M. P., and Anikina, A. M. "The ability to profit from training as a differential criterion of the working capacity of patients with trauma, organic diseases, and neuroses." Collection: Schizophrenia and Traumatic Diseases of the Brain and Working Capacity in These Conditions (Moscow, 1936).
233. Petrova, A. E., and Anikina, A. M. "The role of experimental psychology in the determination of the character of the working capacity of patients with idiopathic epilepsy." Nevropatologiya i psikhiatriya, No. 5 (1936).
234. Piaget, J. Speech and Intelligence of the Child [Russian translation], (OGIZ, Moscow—Leningrad, 1932).
235. Pivovarova, V. L. "Secondary catatonia." Proceedings of an All-Union Theoretical and Practical Conference to Commemorate the Centenary of the Birth of S. S. Korsakov and Concerned with Current Problems in Psychiatry (Medgiz, Moscow, 1954).
236. Pinskii, B. I. "Special features of generalization and discrimination in the actions of oligophrenic schoolchildren." Izv. APN RSFSR, No. 57 (1954).
237. Ploticher, A. I. "Methods of investigation of conditioned speech connections in mental patients." Zhurnal vysshei nervnoi deyatel'nosti im. I. P. Pavlova, No. 6 (1955).
238. Povitskaya, R. S. "Dynamics of mental disorders in brain trauma." Nevropatologiya i psikhiatriya, Vol. 11, No. 5 (1942).

239. Povitskaya, R.S. "Traumatic dementia." Collection: Nervous and Mental Diseases of War Time (Medgiz, Moscow, 1948).
240. Polyakov, Yu. F. "Special features of slight disturbances of intelligence in schizophrenia." Collection: Problems in Schizophrenia, Psychopathy, and Reactive States (Medgiz, Moscow, 1961).
241. Polyakov, Yu. F. "Comparative characteristics of the disturbance of the dynamics of intelligence in patients with initial arteriosclerosis of the cerebral vessels and in patients with schizophrenia." Collection: Problems in Cerebrovascular Diseases, Vol. II (Medgiz, Moscow, 1961).
242. Popov, E. A. "Some pathophysiological peculiarities of schizophrenia." Proceedings of an All-Union Theoretical and Practical Conference to Commemorate the Centenary of the Birth of S.S. Korsakov and Concerned with Current Problems in Psychiatry (Medgiz, Moscow, 1954).
243. Popov, E. A. "Some special features of schizophrenic intellectual activity and its suggested pathophysiological mechanisms." Transactions of the Ukrainian Psychoneurological Institute, Vol. 24 (Khar'kov, 1949).
244. Posvyanskii, P. B. "Current problems in the diagnosis, clinical course, and treatment of progressive paresis." Doctorate dissertation (Moscow, 1952).
245. Protopopov, V. P. "Processes of abstraction and generalization in man." Vrachebnoe delo, No. 12 (1949).
246. Protopopov, V.P., and Rushkevich, E.A. Investigation of Disorders of Abstract Intelligence in Mental Patients and Their Physiological Characteristics (Kiev, 1956).
247. Ravkin, I.G. "Acute and chronic concussive states." Trudy Tsentral'nogo instituta psikhiatrii, Vol. 1 (1940).
248. Ravkin, I.G. "Clinical features and treatment of patients with schizophrenia with a chronic, unfavorable course." Collection: The Clinical Course, Pathogenesis, and Treatment of Schizophrenia (Medgiz, Moscow, 1958).
249. Raskina, R.M. "Flatness of intelligence." Zhurnal nevropatologii i psikhiatrii im. S.S. Korsakova, Book I (1927).
250. Rozenblyum, I.I. "The comparative characteristics of schizophrenia and paralytic dementia. Communication I." Sovetskaya nevropatologiya, psikhiatriya i psikhogigiena, Vol. 3, Nos. 11–12 (1934).
251. Rozenshtein, L.M. "The psychopathology of intelligence in manic-depressive psychosis and special pathological forms of mania." Zhurnal nevropatologii i psikhiatrii im. S.S. Korsakova, Book 7 (1926).
252. Rozinskii, Yu. B. Mental Changes in Frontal Lesions (Medgiz, Moscow, 1948).
253. Rossolimo, G.I. Experimental Investigation of the Psychomechanics (Izd. 1st MGU, 1928).
254. Rotshtein, G.A. Experimental Psychological Investigations of the Emotional and Volitional Sphere in Neurotics (Biomedgiz, Moscow, 1939).
255. Rotshtein, G.A. "The structural heterogeneity of the symptoms in the so-called traumatic cerebropathy." Collection: Traumatic Lesions of the Central Nervous System (Medgiz, Moscow, 1940).
256. Rokhlin, L. L. "The clinical picture of the mental disturbances in traumatic epilepsy." Collection: Transactions of the Ukrainian Psychoneurological Institute, Vol. 23 (Khar'kov, 1947).
257. Rubinshtein, S.L. Fundamentals of General Psychology, 2nd edition (Uchpedgiz, Moscow, 1946).
258. Rubinshtein, S.L. "Problems in psychological theory." Voprosy psikhologii, No. 1 (1955).
259. Rubinshtein, S.L. "I.M. Sechenov's psychological views and Soviet psychological science." Voprosy psikhologii, No. 5 (1955).
260. Rubinshtein, S.L. "Problems in the psychology of intelligence and the principle of determinism." Voprosy filosofii, No. 5 (1957).
261. Rubinshtein, S. L. Being and Consciousness (Izd. AN SSSR, Moscow, 1957).
262. Rubinshtein, S.L. Intelligence and Ways of Investigating It (Izd. AN SSSR, Moscow, 1958).
263. Rubinshtein, S. L. "The principle of determinism and the psychological theory of intelligence." Collection: Psychological Science in the USSR, Vol. 1 (Izd. APN RSFSR, Moscow, 1960).
264. Rubinshtein, S. L. Principles and Ways of Development of Psychology (Izd. AN SSSR, Moscow, 1959).

265. Rubinshtein, S. L. "The problem of faculties and questions in psychological theory." Voprosy psikhologii, No. 3 (1960).
266. Rubinshtein, S. L. (editor). The Process of Intelligence and the Principles of Analysis, Synthesis, and Generalization. Experimental Investigations (Izd. AN SSSR, Moscow, 1960).
267. Rubinshtein, S. Ya. "Assessment and restoration of working capacity after war wounds of the brain." Collection: Neurology in Wartime, Vol. 1 (Izd. AMN SSSR, Moscow, 1949).
268. Rubinshtein, S. Ya. "Restoration of working capacity in patients with war wounds of the brain." Candidate dissertation (Moscow, 1943).
269. Rubinshtein, S. Ya. "Verbal disinhibition of patients during reactive states." Manuscript (1949).
270. Rubinshtein, S. Ya. "Some schizophrenoid disturbances of intelligence of patients in reactive states." Manuscript (1950).
271. Rubinshtein, S. Ya. The Psychology of the Mentally Retarded Child (Uchpedgiz, Moscow, 1959).
272. Ruzer, E. I. "The role of the experimental psychological investigation in mental hygiene work in higher educational establishments." Sovetskaya nevropatologiya, psikhiatriya i psikhogigiena, Vol. 4, No. 2 (1935).
273. Rushkevich, E. A. "Disturbances of abstraction and generalization in schizophrenia and their pathophysiological basis." Collection: Problems in Physiology, No. 4 (Izd. AN Ukr.SSR, 1953).
274. Sagalova, S. R. "Some results of the psychological investigation of patients with cerebral arteriosclerosis." Collection: Cerebral Arteriosclerosis and Working Capacity (Biomedgiz, Moscow, 1934).
275. Simon, B. The English School and Intelligence Tests (Izd. APN RSFSR, Moscow, 1959).
276. Samarin, Yu. A. "The associative nature of mental activity." Voprosy psikhologii, No. 2 (1957).
277. Samukhin, N. V., Birenbaum, G. V., and Vygotskii, L. S. "Dementia in Pick's disease." Sovetskaya nevropatologiya, psikhiatriya i psikhogigiena, Vol. 3, No. 6 (1934).
278. Samukhin, N. V. "The structure of the organic dementias." Sovetskaya nevropatologiya, psikhiatriya i psikhogigiena, Vol. 4, Nos. 9–10 (1935).
279. Seguin, E. Training, Hygiene, and Moral Treatment of Mentally Subnormal Children (St. Petersburg, 1903).
280. Serebryakova, E. A. "Self-confidence and the conditions of its formation in schoolchildren." Candidate dissertation (Moscow, 1955).
281. Serbskii, V. P. Guide to the Study of Mental Diseases (Moscow, 1906).
282. Seletskii, V. V. "The dissociation of ideas and its significance." Zhurnal nevropatologii i psikhiatrii im. S. S. Korosakova, Book 1 (1908).
283. Seredina, M. I. "An experimental investigation of the cortical neurodynamics in epilepsy." Candidate dissertation (Moscow, 1946).
284. Seredina, M. I. "The influence of the epileptic fit on the conditioned connections of the first and second signal systems, and also on the unconditioned connections." Zhurnal vysshei nervnoi deyatel'nosti im. I. P. Pavlova, Vol. 2, No. 5 (1952).
285. Sereiskii, M. Ya. "The problem of catamnesis in the light of active treatment of the psychoses." Trudy Tsentral'nogo instituta psikhiatrii, Vol. 3 (1947).
286. Sechenov, I. M. Selected Philosophical and Psychological Works (Gospolitizdat, 1947).
287. Simson, T. P. Schizophrenia in Early Childhood (Izd. AMN SSSR, Moscow, 1948).
288. Simson, T. P. "Late sequelae of closed head injuries." Collection: Transactions of the Ukrainian Psychoneurological Institute, Vol. 23 (Khar'kov, 1947).
289. Simson, T. P. "Ways of differentiating schizophrenia from acute infectious psychoses in adolescents." Proceedings of a Theoretical and Practical Conference to Commemorate the Centenary of the Birth of S. S. Korsakov and Concerned with Current Problems in Psychiatry (Medgiz, Moscow, 1954).
290. Sluchevskii, I. F. Psychiatry, 2nd edition (Medgiz, Leningrad, 1957).
291. Skvortsov, K. A. "The syndrome of 'mentisme' (an accumulation of thoughts)." Sovetskaya psikhonevrologiya, No. 1 (1938).
292. Smirnov, A. A. "The processes of thinking during memorizing." Izv. APN RSFSR, No. 1 (1945).
293. Smirnov, A. A. "The psychology of grasping of concepts in schoolchildren." Sovetskaya pedagogika, Nos. 8–9 (1946).

294. Smirnov, A. A. "Intelligence." Chapter VIII of the book: Psychology, edited by A. A. Smirnov, A. N. Leont'ev, S. L. Rubinshtein, and B. M. Teplov (Uchpedgiz, Moscow, 1956).
295. Snezhnevskii, A. V. "Senile dementia." Nevropatologiya i psikhiatriya, No. 3 (1949).
296. Snesarev, P. E. The Theoretical Basis of the Pathological Anatomy of the Psychoses (Medgiz, Moscow, 1950).
297. Solov'eva, Z. A. "Mild intellectual disorders in schizophrenia." Sovetskaya nevropatologiya, psikhiatriya i psikhogigiena, Vol. 3, No. 5 (1934).
298. Solov'ev, I. M. (editor). Special Features of the Perceptual Activity of Pupils at Special Schools (Izd. APN RSFSR, Moscow, 1953).
299. Solov'ev, I. M. "The intelligence of mentally retarded schoolchildren when solving arithmetical problems." Collection: Special Features of the Perceptual Activity of Pupils at Special Schools (Izd. APN RSFSR, Moscow, 1953).
300. Sotsevich, G. N. "The paranoid form of schizophrenia." Proceedings of a Theoretical and Practical Conference to Commemorate the Centenary of the Birth of S. S. Korsakov and Concerned with Current Problems in Psychiatry (Medgiz, Moscow, 1954).
301. Spirkin, A. G. The Origin of Consciousness (Izd. AN SSSR, Moscow, 1960).
302. Forensic Psychiatry. A Textbook for Law Students (Gosyurizdat, Moscow, 1954).
303. Sudomir, A. K. "The dissociation of speech in schizophrenia." Sovetskaya psikhonevrologiya, Vol. 8, Nos. 4–7 (1929).
304. Sumbaev, I. S. "The psychology of schizophrenia." Sovetskaya nevropatologiya, psikhiatriya i psikhogigiena, Vol. 3, No. 4 (1934).
305. Sumbaev, I. S. "Symbolism in schizophrenia." Sovetskaya psikhonevrologiya, No. 9 (1930).
306. Sukhanov, S. A. "Paralogical intelligence." Psikhoterapiya, No. 1 (1914).
307. Sukhareva, G. E. "Difficult problems in pediatric psychiatry as a discipline based on age comparison." Nevropatologiya i psikhiatriya, Vol. 16, No. 2 (1947).
308. Sukhareva, G. E. Clinical Lectures on the Psychiatry of Childhood, Vols. I–II (Medgiz, Moscow, 1955–1960).
309. Tal'tse, M. F. "Clinical variants of oligophrenia in forensic psychiatric practice." Problems in Forensic Psychiatry, Collection VII (Gosyurizdat, Moscow, 1957).
310. Tarasov, Yu. K. "Subacute and chronic malarial psychoses." Collection: Problems in Borderline Psychiatry (Biomedgiz, Moscow–Leningrad, 1935).
311. Teplov, B. M. Psychology (Gospolitizdat, 1946).
312. Teplov, B. M. (editor). "Problems in the psychology of perception and intelligence." Izv. APN RSFSR, No. 13 (1948).
313. Teplov, B. M. (editor). "Problems in the psychology of speech and intelligence." Izv. APN RSFSR, No. 54 (1954).
314. Tikhomirov, O. K. "Verbal regulation of the movements of the mentally retarded child in conditions of conflict between verbal and direct signals." Collection: Problems in the Higher Nervous Activity of the Normal and Abnormal Child, Vol. I (Izd. APN RSFSR, Moscow, 1956).
315. Tokarskii, A. A. "Notes of the psychological laboratory of the Psychiatric Clinic, Moscow Imperial University." Voprosy filosofii i psikhologii, Books 31–35 (1896).
316. Tokarskii, A. A. "Idiocy." Voprosy filosofii i psikhologii, Book 35 (1896).
317. Traugott, N. N., and Christovich, A. S. "The test of the physiological understanding of verbal incoherence in schizophrenia." Nevropatologiya i psikhiatriya, No. 6 (1951).
318. Traugott, N. N. "Ways of studying disturbances of interaction between signal systems in clinical psychiatry." Zhurnal nevropatologii i psikhiatrii im. S. S. Korsakova, No. 6 (1956).
319. Urusova-Belozertseva, V. I. "Special features of the disturbance of intelligence in patients with frontal lobe lesions." Research for Diploma (Moscow State University, 1954).
320. Usov, A. G. "Investigation of induction relationships between signal systems." Zhurnal vysshei nervnoi deyatel'nosti im. I. P. Pavlova, No. 6 (1955).
321. Faddeeva, V. K. "An experimental study of the cortical dynamics in the manic and depressive phases of cyclothymia." Candidate dissertation (Moscow, 1946).
322. Felinskaya, N. I. "A reaction in the form of pseudodementia in schizophrenics." Collection: Problems in Forensic Psychiatry (Moscow, 1938).
323. Fol'bort, G. V. "New facts and observations on I. P. Pavlov's theory of higher nervous activity." Zhurnal vysshei nervnoi deyatel'nosti im. I. P. Pavlova, Vol. 1, No. 3 (1951).

324. Fol'bort, G. V. "Physiology of the processes of fatigue and recovery." Collection: Proceedings of a Conference of the Department of Normal Physiology of Kiev Medical Institute (Kiev, 1951).
325. Fridman, B. D. Regression of Posttraumatic Disorders (Ufa, 1942).
326. Fridman, B. D. Traumatic Lesions of the Central Nervous System (Moscow, 1946).
327. Fridman, B. D. "Clinical features and psychopathology of local cerebral syndromes in malignant hypertension." Trudy Tsentral'nogo instituta psikhiatrii, Vol. 1 (1949).
328. Khomskaya, E. D. "Pathology of the interaction between the signal systems in mentally retarded children." Collection: Problems in the Higher Nervous Activity of the Normal and Abnormal Child, Vol. I (Izd. APN RSFSR, Moscow, 1956).
329. Khvilivitskii, T. Ya. "The psychoneurotic's attitude toward work and its role in development of the work curve." Sovetskaya nevropatologiya, psikhiatriya i psikhogigiena, Vol. 4, Nos. 9–10 (1935).
330. Khoroshko, V. K. The Relationship of the Frontal Lobes of the Brain to Psychology and Psychopathology (Moscow, 1912).
331. Chamata, P. R. "Self-awareness of personality in Soviet psychology." Collection: Psychological Science in the USSR, Vol. II (Izd. APN RSFSR, Moscow, 1960).
332. Chernukha, A. A. "The experimental investigation of intellectual disorders in mild schizophrenia." Sovetskaya nevropatologiya, psikhiatriya i psikhogigiena, Vol. III, No. 5 (1934).
333. Chernukha, A. A. "Dementia in schizophrenia." Nevropatologiya i psikhiatriya, No. 4 (1938).
334. Chistovich, A. S. The Pathophysiology and Pathogenesis of Some Forms of Delirium (Novosibirsk, 1939).
335. Shevalev, E. A. "Pathological intelligence." Trudy psikhiatricheskoi kliniki Odesskogo medinstituta, No. 1 (1930).
336. Shevalev, E. A. "Analysis of the concept of dementia." Sovetskaya nevropatologiya, psikhiatriya i psikhogigiena, Vol. 4, No. 4 (1935).
337. Shevarev, P. A. "Remarks on the problem of associations." Izv. APN RSFSR, No. 80 (1957).
338. Shemyakin, F. N. "The interrelationship between concept and idea." Front nauki i tekhniki, No. 2 (1937).
339. Shemyakin, F. N. "The problem of ideas in the writings of I. M. Sechenov and I. P. Pavlov." Voprosy filosofii, No. 2 (1952).
340. Shif, Zh. I. Development of Scientific Concepts in the Schoolchild (Uchpedgiz, Moscow—Leningrad, 1935).
341. Shif, Zh. I. "Special features of the mental development of pupils at special schools." Collection: Psychological Science in the USSR, Vol. II (Izd. APN RSFSR, Moscow, 1960).
342. Shif, Zh. I. (editor). Collection: The Mental Development of Pupils at Special Schools (Izd. APN RSFSR, Moscow, 1961).
343. Shmar'yan, A. S. "Clinicopsychopathological syndromes in local brain lesions." Nevropatologiya i psikhiatriya, No. 6 (1940).
344. Shubert, A. M. "Schizophrenoid disturbances in the intellectual activity of patients with brain trauma." Problems in the Psychiatry of Wartime, Collection 4 (Moscow, 1945).
345. Shubert, A. M. "Schizophrenoid disturbances of intellectual activity in organic brain diseases." Collection: Problems in the Clinical Course and Treatment of Mental Diseases (Moscow, 1946).
346. Shubert, A. M. "Some special features of the disturbance of intellectual activity after frontal trauma." Collection: Problems in the Clinical Course and Treatment of Mental Diseases (Moscow, 1949).
347. Shubert, A. M. "Disturbances of abstraction and generalization in schizophrenia and their pathophysiological basis." Voprosy psikhologii, No. 4 (1955).
348. Shubert, A. M. "Some disturbances of perceptual activity in a traumatizing situation." Collection: Proceedings of a Conference on Psychology (Izd. APN RSFSR, Moscow, 1957).
349. Él'konin, D. B. Child Psychology (Uchpedgiz, Moscow, 1960).
350. Yudin, T. I. "Concussion." Transactions of the Ukrainian Psychoneurological Institute, Vol. XII (Tyumen', 1943).
351. Yudin, T. I. "The frontal cavity and psychoneurological syndromes associated with gunshot wounds of that area." Nevropatologiya i psikhiatriya, Vol. 14 (1945).

B. NON-RUSSIAN

352. Abderhalden, E. "Methoden der experimentellen Psychologie." Handb. biol. Arb.-
     Meth. (Berlin—Vienna, 1925).
353. Ach, N. Über die Begriffsbildung (Bamberg, 1921).
354. Acklesberg, S. B. "Vocabulary and mental deterioration in senile dementia." J.
     Abnorm. Soc. Psychol., Vol. 39, 393 (1944).
355. Allen, E. B. "Psychiatric aspects of cerebral arteriosclerosis." New Engl. J. Med.,
     Vol. 8 (1951).
356. Alzheimer, A. "Über eigenartige Krankheitsfälle des späteren Alters." Z. Neurol.,
     Vol. 4 (1911).
357. Alzheimer, A. "Die Seelenstörungen auf arteriosclerotischer Grundlage." Allg. Z.
     Psychiatr., Vol. 59, 695 (1902).
358. Anton, G. "Symptome der Stirnhirnerkrankungen." Münch. med. Wochschr., No. 27
     (1905).
359. Anzien, D. "Problèmes posés par la validation de technique projective." Bull.
     Psychol., No. 6 (1952).
360. Aschaffenburg, G. "Experimentelle Studien über Associationen." Psychologische
     Arbeiten. Edited by E. Kraepelin, Vol. 1 (Leipzig, 1896).
361. Arrudo, E., and Gerschovich, J. "Schizophrenia et schizophasia." Ann. med.-psy-
     chol., Vol. 2, No. 3 (1956).
362. Barthel, E., and Schwarz, B. "Zusammenarbeit zwischen Arzt und Psychologe in der
     Poliklinik einer psychiatrischen Klinik." Z. Psychiatr., Neurol. med. Psychol., No. 6
     (1957).
363. Baruk, H. Les Troubles Mentaux dans les Tumeurs Cérébrales (Paris, 1926).
364. Le Beau, J., and Chopy, M. "Sur les variations du lobe frontal et de certaines fonc-
     tions mentales." L'Encéphale, No. 3 (1956).
365. Beckenstein, N., and Gold, L. "Problems of the senile arteriosclerotic mental pa-
     tient (Review of 200 cases)." Psychiatr. Quart., Vol. 19 (1945).
366. Benedetti, C., Kind, H., and Mielke, F. "Forschungen zur Schizophrenielehre 1951
     bis 1955." Fortschr. Neurol., Psychiatr. Grenzgeb., No. 2/3 (1957).
367. Beringer, L. "Sprache und Denkstörungen bei Schizophrenia." Z. Neurol., Vol. 103 '
     (1927).
368. Berger, H. Trauma und Psychose (Berlin, 1915).
369. Berze, J., and Gruhle, H. W. Psychologie der Schizophrenie (Berlin, 1929).
370. Bilkiewicz, T. Psychiatria Kliniczna (Warsaw, 1957).
371. Binswanger, O. Die Epilepsie, 2nd edition (Leipzig, 1913).
372. Binswanger, L. "Daseinsanalytik und Psychiatrie." Nervenarzt (1951).
373. Birkmayer, W. Hirnverletzungen (Vienna, 1951).
374. Birnbaum, K. Der Aufbau der Psychose (Berlin, 1923).
375. Bleuler, E. Dementia praecox oder Gruppe der Schizophrenien (Leipzig, 1911).
376. Bleuler, E. Lehrbuch der Psychiatrie (Berlin, 1930).
377. Bohm, E. Lehrbuch der Rorschach. Psychodiagnostik (Berne, 1951).
378. Botwiniek, G., and Birren, J. E. "The measurement of intellectual deterioration in
     senile psychoses and psychoses with cerebral arteriosclerosis." Amer. Psycholo-
     gist, Vol. 15, 145 (1951).
379. Brieger, B. "The use of Wechsler Bellevue picture arrangement as a projective
     technique." J. Consult. Psychol., Vol. 20, 132 (1956).
380. Brower, D., and Abt, L. E. Progress in Clinical Psychology, Vol. 22 (1956).
381. Bumke, O. (editor). Handbuch der Geisteskrankheiten, Vols. I–IX (Berlin, 1928–1932)
382. Bumke, O. Lehrbuch der Geisteskrankheiten, 2nd edition (Munich, 1925).
383. Burton, A. "The use of the psychometric and projective tests in clinical psychology."
     J. Psychol., Vol. 28, 451 (1949).
384. Busemann, A. "Psychologische Untersuchungen an Hirnverletzten." Arch. Psychiatr.
     Neurol. Z. Psychiatr. Neurol., Vol. 187, No. 2 (1950).
385. Callins, A. L. "Epileptic intelligence." J. Consult. Psychol., Vol. 15, 392 (1951).
386. Claude, H. "Les psychoses paranoides." L'Encéphale, Vol. 3 (1925).
387. O'Connel, J. J., and Penrose, L. S. "Tests of psychomotor efficiency in patients treated
     with metrazol." J. Ment. Sci., Vol. 87, 183 (1941).
388. Critchley, M. The Parietal Lobes (London, 1953).
389. Delacroix, T. Le Langage et la Pensée (Paris, 1922).
390. Delay, J. Études de Psychologie Médicale (Paris, 1953).

391. Delay, J., Pichot, P., Lempérière, M., and Perse, J. "Le test de Rorschach dans l'épilépsie." L'Encéphale, Vol. 43 (1954).
392. Davis, D. R. An Introduction to Psychopathology (London, 1957).
393. Destunis, G. Einführung in die medizinische Psychologie (Berlin, 1955).
394. Domarius, E. "Zur Theorie des schizophrenen Denkens." Z. Neurol., Vol. 108 (1927).
395. Dubin, S., and Thaler, M. "The use of psychological tests on schizophrenic patients before and after shock treatment." Amer. Psychologist, Vol. 2, 283 (1947).
396. Dunker, K. Zur Psychologie des produktiven Denkens (Berlin, 1935).
397. Eysenck, H. J. "Training in clinical psychology." Amer. Psychologist, Vol. 4 (1949).
398. Eysenck, H. J. Psychology and the Foundations of Psychiatry (London, 1955).
399. Eliasberg, H., and Feuchtwanger, E. "Zur psychologischen und psychopathologischen Untersuchung und Theorie des erworbenen Schwachsinns." Z. ges. Neurol. Psychiatr., Vol. 75, 516 (1922).
400. Fairfield, L. Epilepsy (New York, 1957).
401. Feldman, V., and Cameron, D. E. "Speech in senility." Amer. J. Psychiatr., Vol. 101, 64 (1944).
402. Feuchtwanger, E. Die Funktion des Stirnhirns (Berlin, 1923).
403. Fogt, C., and Fogt, O. "Erkrankungen der Grosshirnrinde im Lichte der Topik, Pathoklise und Pathoarchitektonik." J. Psychol. Neurol, Vol. 27 (1922).
404. Frostig, J. Das schizophrene Denken (Leipzig, 1929).
405. Fuhrmann, H. Analyse des Vorstellungsmaterials bei epileptischem Schwachsinn (Giessen, 1902).
406. Goldstein, K., and Gelb, A. Psychologische Analyse hirnpathologischer Fälle (Berlin, 1920).
407. Goldstein, K. "The significance of the frontal lobes for mental performance." J. Neurol. Psychopathol., Vol. 18, No. 27 (1936).
408. Goldstein, K. Language and Its Disturbances (New York, 1952).
409. Goldstein, K. "Bemerkungen zum Problem 'Sprechen und Denken' auf Grund hirnpathologischer Erfahrungen." Acta Psychol., Vol. 10 (1956).
410. Gottschaldt, K. Der Aufbau des kindlichen Handelns (Leipzig, 1953).
411. Gruhle, H. W. Psychologie des Abnormen (Berlin, 1922).
412. Grünthal, E. "Die erworbenen Verblödungen." Forschr. Neurol., Psychiatr. Grenzgeb., July (1932).
413. Grünthal, E. Über die Erkennung der traumatischen Hirnverletzung (Berlin, 1936).
414. Hanfmann, E., and Kasanin, J. S. Conceptual Thinking in Schizophrenia (New York, 1942).
415. Harper, E. A. "Discrimination of the types of schizophrenia by the Wechsler Bellevue scale." J. Consult. Psychol., Vol. 14, 290 (1950).
416. Helm, J. "Über den Einfluss affektiver Spannungen auf das Denkhandeln." Z. Psychol., Vol. 157 (1954).
417. Hellpach, W. Klinische Psychologie, 2nd edition (Stuttgart, 1949).
418. Hoch, P. H. "Entwicklungstendenzen in der modernen amerikanischen Psychiatrie." Arch. Psychiatr. Z. Neurol., Vol. 19 (1954).
419. Hunt, W. The Clinical Psychologist (Springfield, 1956).
420. Horst, G. Über die Dummheit (Berlin, 1954).
421. Jahreise, W. "Störungen des Denkens." Handbuch der Geisteskrankheiten, edited by O. Bumke, Vol. 1 (Berlin, 1928).
422. Jaspers, K. Allgemeine Psychopathologie (Berlin, 1923).
423. Kahlbaum, K. Klinische Abhandlungen über psychische Krankheiten (Berlin, 1874).
424. Kaplan, O. J. Mental Disorders in Later Life (London, 1957).
425. Kasanin, J. S. "The disturbance of conceptual thinking in schizophrenia." Language and Thought in Schizophrenia (Berkeley—Los Angeles, 1944).
426. Katzenstein, A. "Gestalt und klinische Psychologie." Psychiatr., Neurol. med. Psychol., No. 7 (1956).
427. Katzenstein, A. "Über die Arbeit des Psychologen im Krankenhaus der Psychiatrie." Psychiatr., Neurol. med. Psychol., No. 6 (1957).
428. Kleist, K. "Die alogischen Denkstörungen." Arch. Psychol., Vol. 90 (1930).
429. Kleist, K. Hirnpathologie (Leipzig, 1939).
430. Klieneberger, O. "Hirntrauma und ihre Folgen." Monatsschr. Psychiatr. Neurol., Vol. 63 (1928).
431. Koffka, K. "Bemerkungen zur Denkpsychologie." Psychol. Forsch., Vol. 9 (1927).
432. Kraepelin, E. Psychiatrie, 8th edition (Leipzig, 1913).

433. Kretschmer, E. Der sensitive Beziehungswahn (Berlin, 1918).
434. Lagache, D. L'Unité de la Psychologie (Paris, 1949).
435. Lagache, D. "Psychologie clinique et méthode clinique."   Evolution psychiatr. (April–June, 1949).
436. Leonhard, K. Die defektschizophrenen Krankheitsbilder (Leipzig, 1936).
437. Leonhard, K. "Formen und Vorläufe der Schizophrenien." Monatsschr. Psychiatr. Neurol., Vol. 124, No. 2/3 (1952).
438. Lindworsky, J. Das schlussfolgende Denken (Freiburg, 1916).
439. Lindworsky, J. "Methoden der Denkforschung." Handbuch biol. Arb.-Meth., edited by E. Abderhalden (Berlin–Vienna, 1925).
440. Lipmann, O. Handbuch psychologischer Hilfsmittel der psychiatrischen Diagnostik (Leipzig, 1922).
441. Magnan, V. Leçons Cliniques sur les Maladies Mentales Faites à l'Asile Clinique (Paris, 1893).
442. Mayer-Gross, W. "Schizophrenie. Die Klinik." Handbuch der Geisteskrankheiten, edited by O. Bumke, Vol. 9 (Berlin, 1932).
443. McFie, J., and Piercy, M. "Intellectual impairment with localized cerebral lesions." Brain, Vol. 75, 292 (1952).
444. Meier, S. F., and Müller-Kegemann, D. "Klinischer Beitrag zum Problem des Verhältnisses von Sprache und Denken." Psychiatr., Neurol. med. Psychol., No. 9 (1957).
445. Meili, R. Lehrbuch der psychologischen Diagnostik (Berne–Stuttgart, 1955).
446. Metzger, W. Psychologie (Darmstadt, 1954).
447. Meyerhoff, H. "Das Syndrom der traumatischen Hirnleistungsschwächen im Rorschachtest." Z. Neurol., Psychiatr. med. Psychol., Vol. 61 (1950).
448. Millner, B. "Intellectual function of the temporal lobes." Psychol. Bull., Vol. 51, 42 (1954).
449. Mowbray, K. "The clinical psychologist as a human scientist." Brit. J. Med. Psychol., Vol. 27 (1954).
450. Müller-Schur, H. "Der psychopathologische Aspekt des Schizophrenie-Problems." Arch. Neurol. Psychiatr., Vol. 193 (1955).
451. O'Neil, W. M. "The relation of clinical and experimental methods in psychology." Brit. J. Med. Psychol., Vol. 26, 159 (1953).
452. Ombredane, A. L'Aphasie et l'Élaboration de la Pensée Explicite (Paris, 1951).
453. Ombredane, A. "Distinction et mise en place des aspects à la projection." Bull. Psychol., Vol. 6 (1952).
454. Petrilowitsch, N. Beiträge zu einer Struktur-Psychopathologie (Basel–New York, 1955).
455. Petrie, A. Personality and the Frontal Lobes (London, 1952).
456. Pfeifer, B. "Die psychischen Störungen nach Hirnverletzungen." Handbuch der Geisteskrankheiten, edited by O. Bumke, Vol. 7 (Berlin, 1928).
457. Pflugfelder, G. "Intellektuelle Störungen nach schweren Schadeltraumen." Monatsschr. Psychiatr. Neurol., Vol. 118 (1949).
458. Pflugfelder, G. Psychologische Untersuchungen über Bewusstseinstörungen in der Insulinkur (Basel, 1951).
459. Piaget, J. La Psychologie de l'Intelligence (Paris, 1952).
460. Pichot, P. Les Testes de Personnalité en Psychiatrie (Paris, 1956).
461. Pichot, P. Le Teste de Rorschach et la Personnalité Epiléptique (Paris, 1955).
462. Pick, A. "Beeinflussung des Denkens und der Handlung durch die Sprache." Z. Neurol. Psychiatr., Vol. 7, 38 (1917).
463. Pitrich, O. "Denkstörungen bei Hirnverletzten." Samml. psychiatr. neurol. Einzeldarstellungen (Leipzig, 1949).
464. Rashkis, H. A. "Three types of thinking disorder." J. Nerv. Ment. Dis., Vol. 106, 650 (1947).
465. Rey, A. Monographes de Psychologie Clinique (Neuchatel–Paris, 1952).
466. Rotschild, D. "Senile psychoses and psychoses with cerebral arterioscleroses." In: Mental Disorders in Later Life (Stanford–London, 1945).
467. Rotschild, D. "The clinical differentiation of senile and arteriosclerotic psychoses." Amer. J. Psychiatr., Vol. 98, No. 3 (1941).
468. Samt, P. "Epileptische Irreseinsformen." Arch. Psychiatr., Vol. 5 (1875); ibid., Vol. 6 (1876).

469. Scheld, K. F. "Die Psychologie des erworbenen Schwachsinns."   Zentr. Neurol.
     Psychiatr., Vol. 107 (1939).
470. Schilder, P. Medizinische Psychologie (Vienna, 1924).
471. Schilder, P., and Sugar, N. "Zur Lehre der schizophrenen Sprachstörungen bei
     Schizophrenen (Schizophasien)." Z. Neurol., Vol. 108, 491 (1927).
472. Schneider, C. "Über Gedankenentzug und Ratlosigkeit bei Schizophrenien." Z.
     Neurol., Vol. 78, 252 (1922).
473. Schneider, C. "Über Störungen der Sprache bei Schizophrenen." Z. Neurol., Vol. 95,
     623 (1925).
474. Schneider, C. Die Psychologie der Schizophrenen und ihre Bedeutung für die Klinik
     der Schizophrenie (Arnsdorf, 1930).
475. Schneider, K. "Wesen und Erfassung des Schizophrenen." Z. Neurol., Vol. 99, 542
     (1925).
476. Schneider, K. Probleme der klinischen Psychiatrie (Leipzig, 1932).
477. Schneider, K. Klinische Psychopathologie (Stuttgart, 1955).
478. Selz, O. Zur Psychologie des produktiven Denkens und des Irrtums (Bonn, 1922).
479. Szekely, L. "Knowledge and thinking." Acta Psychol., No. 1 (1950).
480. Sommer, R. "Die Beziehungen von Schizophrenie, Katatonie, und Epilepsie." Z.
     Neurol., Vol. 78 (1922).
481. Sonnemann, U. Existence and Therapy.   An Introduction to Phenomenological Psy-
     chology and Existential Analysis (New York, 1954).
482. Spranger, E. "Über das Verstehen in der Psychologie." Proc. Internat. Congr.
     Psychol. Groningen (Groningen, 1927).
483. Stern, F. "Arteriosclerotische Psychosen." Handbuch der Geisteskrankheiten, edited
     by O. Bumke, Vol. 8 (Berlin, 1930).
484. Sterz, G. "Störungen der Intelligenz." Handbuch der Geisteskrankheiten, edited by
     O. Bumke, Vol. 1 (Berlin, 1928).
485. Storch, A. Das archaisch primitive Erleben und Denken der Schizophrenen (Munich,
     1922).
486. Stransky, E. Über Sprachverwirrtheit (Halle, 1905).
487. Tizard, C., and Venables, P. "Reaction time of responses by schizophrenic patients,
     mental defectives, and normal adults." Amer. J. Psychiatr., Vol. 112 (1956).
488. "Die Tests in der klinischen Psychologie." Handbuch der klinischen Psychologie,
     Vol. I (1954); Vol. II (1955).
489. Wechsler, D. Manual for the Wechsler Adult Intelligence Scale (New York, 1955).
490. Wechsler, D. "Measurement and evaluation of intelligence of older persons." In: Old
     Age in the Modern World (London, 1954).
491. White, W. A. "The language of schizophrenia." Res. Nerv. Ment. Dis. Proc., Vol. 5,
     323 (1928).
492. Wilhelmi, C. "Arteriosclerotische und senile Demenz." Arch. Psychiatr., Vol. 80
     (1927).
493. Zavalloni, R. La Psychologia Clinica nello Studio del Ragazzo (Milan, 1957).